Behavioral Pharmacology

PRENTICE-HALL, INC., ENGLEWOOD CLIFFS, NEW JERSEY

Prentice-Hall Psychology Series
James J. Jenkins, editor

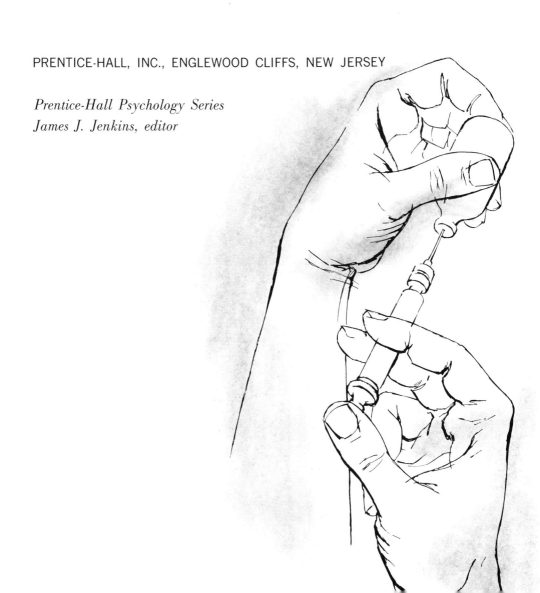

Behavioral Pharmacology

TRAVIS THOMPSON

*Departments of Psychiatry and Neurology,
Psychology and Pharmacology
University of Minnesota*

CHARLES R. SCHUSTER

*Departments of Pharmacology and Psychology
University of Michigan*

Behavioral Pharmacology
Thompson and Schuster

Library of Congress Catalog
Card Number 68–25908

Printed in the United States of America

Current Printing (last digit):

10 9 8 7 6 5 4 3 2 1

Prentice-Hall International, Inc., *London*
Prentice-Hall of Australia, Pty. Ltd., *Sydney*
Prentice-Hall of Canada, Ltd., *Toronto*
Prentice-Hall of India Private Ltd., *New Delhi*
Prentice-Hall of Japan, Inc., *Tokyo*

Foreword

It has been well over a decade since the appearance of modern tranquilizers occasioned the revival of serious scientific interest in the effects of drugs upon behavior. In the first blush of renewed enthusiasm for pharmacodynamic approaches to psychiatric problems, a host of new "psychopharmacology" laboratories sprang up in industry, government, and the universities. With very few exceptions, the professional and technical personnel who managed and staffed these laboratories were psychologists chiefly interested in the experimental analysis of behavior and concerned with pharmacological agents primarily as variables that might enhance such behavioral research. In addition, the challenge of developing laboratory analogues of human behavioral aberrations against which the efficacy of potentially useful therapeutic drugs could be tested also held some obvious appeal. The intrinsic interest in and knowledge about drugs, however, could be safely estimated as minimal, at least among the vast majority of early psychopharmacologists.

Fortunately, a fervent dedication to pharmacology was not a prerequisite for the exploration and exploitation of the tremendous behavior-analysis potential in the screening and evaluation of the so-called psychotropic drugs. Ample pharmacological support was to be found in most of the settings nurturing the new laboratories; and the need for some way to assess the behavioral effects of thousands of compounds already collecting dust on the chemist's shelf far outweighed any requirement for pharmacological sophistication. Ironically, however, few of the psychopharmacology laboratories of a decade ago devoted much effort to the "screening" problem per se, although both the pharmacological and psychological literature rapidly swelled with reports of interesting if somewhat isolated drug effects upon behavior. Presumably, the methods and techniques required for the bigger, long term job ahead would emerge from these developmental efforts. But little, if any, systematic ordering of this rapidly burgeoning body of psychopharmacological knowledge could be discerned during those early days.

In an effort to keep the lines of communication open, a host of symposia, conferences, and international meetings (including the First International Congress of Neuropsychopharmacology held in Rome in 1958) provided landmarks in the early growth and development of this new field of scientific endeavor. Organizations were formed and took shape, each satisfying the needs of particular professional segments of the field. These ranged in scope from the Collegium Internationale Neuropsychopharmacologicum, and the American College of Neuropsychopharmacology, to the somewhat more modest Behavioral Pharmacology Society. New journals and periodicals inevitably appeared. Two representative publications, *Psychopharmacologia* and the *Journal of Neuropharmacology*, are devoted almost exclusively to the accommodation of an expanding literature in this field, and such a development quite naturally forecasts an era of textbook writing.

One of the steps in the development of a new branch of science—the formation of an intradisciplinary association—seems to have been of particular importance in laying the groundwork for this book. The Behavioral Pharmacology Society, in any event, represents one of the first organized efforts by a relatively small group of professionals to maintain a recurrent forum for the exchange of information in the area of psychopharmacology. In the spring of 1957, within a year or two of the appearance of the first behavioral pharmacology laboratories in a few selected drug houses and universities, a group made up mostly of psychologists (although Peter Dews of the Harvard Medical School Pharmacology Department was in attendance) gathered in Philadelphia to constitute the charter membership of this productive, viable, and stimulating organization. It is perhaps no accident that of the twenty or so who attended, the overwhelming majority evinced a strong interest in the experimental analysis of behavior and in operant methodology. It will not be hard to discern the roots of the present volume in the basic conceptual framework espoused by this group.

Thompson and Schuster have undertaken here the task of organizing and systematizing the fundamental assumptions, technologies, and data relationships upon which a scientific behavioral pharmacology must be based. This book is a concrete example of how rapidly behavioral pharmacology is progressing beyond the uncritical acceptance of interesting demonstrations involving "drug effects upon behavior." The systematic ordering of data, involving parametric analysis of functional relationships, is now a recognized requirement for the practice of this new science. The present volume clearly bears the hallmark of a growing sophistication. Indeed, the dilettantes of the early psychopharmacology research era are giving way to a hard core of interdisciplinary scientists preparing for the difficult but rewarding task of systematically investigating the many complicated interrelationships that characterize the drug-behavior area.

Another important emphasis in this book is the unique contribution of the experimental analysis of behavior, with its emerging technological developments, to the elucidation of drug-behavior interactions. In particular, the application of operant-conditioning techniques is appropriately represented as contributing significantly and uniquely to the reliability, sensitivity, comprehensiveness, and precision of drug-behavior evaluations. Convincing support is also provided for the position that the behavioral methods involved are not to be viewed as gimmicks for training animals to do cute tricks, but as the systematic outgrowth of principles derived from extensive observation of the behavior of organisms interacting with a changing environment. Clearly, to the extent that this message alone is effectively communicated, the authors have performed nobly in the service of their profession.

In *Behavioral Pharmacology*, both the pharmacologist and the psychologist will find a useful selection of materials presented in clear and readable form. Despite the somewhat independent course of scientific development that has characterized the two disciplines, their paths into the future would now seem inevitably intertwined. This volume bears eloquent testimony to the emerging promise of this most recent wedding of scientific disciplines. The authors, moreover, provide a clear statement of the objectives to be attained. Their intimate association with problems, methods, criteria, results, and interpretations in psychology and pharmacology makes this exposition a major step in bridging the conceptual and methodological gap between two laboratory and clinical disciplines.

J. V. BRADY, PH.D.
Neuropsychiatry Department
Walter Reed Army Institute
of Research

Preface

Behavioral pharmacology represents the wedding of two scientific disciplines, psychology and pharmacology. As is true in any marriage, the two partners, while sharing many common conceptions and goals, must settle certain differences before a harmonious working relation can be established. This has certainly been the case with the new field of behavioral pharmacology. It would be misleading to suggest that a unified discipline concerned with the behavioral actions of drugs has already evolved; however, it would be equally misleading to overlook the interests shared by the two parent disciplines, and to ignore the fact that psychology and pharmacology are moving increasingly closer together (though their contiguity varies considerably from one area to another, depending on one's vantage point).

In order to gain perspective and to understand the basic concepts of behavioral pharmacology, the aims and principles of the parent disciplines must be systematically analyzed. They must be juxtaposed and examined carefully. This book delineates the basic structures of psychology and pharmacology, and explores areas of compatibility. A great many fundamental conceptual problems remain unresolved, and empirical questions relating one set of variables to the other are unanswered. However, the authors hope that the analysis presented here may help readers formulate their own experimental solutions to some of these problems.

Our choice of the term *behavioral pharmacology* as opposed to *psychopharmacology* reflects our biases and the scope of this book. Since the principles and experiments to be described deal with observable behavioral changes, the term *behavioral pharmacology*, which does not imply neural or mental events, seemed preferable. Further, we are dealing with behavioral pharmacology as a basic biological science. Our coverage is restricted to behavioral observations made under controlled experimental conditions. Although clinical experience with drugs that modify behavior has suggested many valuable areas of experimentation, no attempt has been made to review the clinical literature.

Our purpose in writing this book was to provide a systematic introduction to the principles and techniques of experimental psychology and the principles of pharmacology as they are applied in behavioral pharmacology. To this end, the book has been divided into five parts: Section 1 is an introduction to basic behavioral pharmacology; Section 2 discusses the fundamental principles of pharmacology; Section 3 covers fundamental principles and techniques of experimental psychology; Section 4 deals with the application of the principles and techniques of psychology and pharmacology to the special problems of behavioral pharmacology; and Section 5 consists of appendixes devoted to practical information and techniques.

It is assumed that the reader is acquainted primarily with either psychology or pharmacology and has little training in the other discipline, but it is hoped that the information provided in the first three sections will give the student enough background in the area he knows least to allow him to read critically the final sections on behavioral pharmacology. However, minimal familiarity with organic chemistry and physiology will be necessary before these discussions can be meaningful.

Although we have stressed fundamental principles, we intend this book to be a practical aid to students who wish to carry out experiments in behavioral pharmacology. We have therefore appended a list of procedures for finding both the source and form of drugs for experimental use, methods of calculating drug dosages, and methods of drug administration. Also included in an appendix is a description of the more widely used types of commercially available behavioral research equipment.

Readers familiar with the behavioral sciences will recognize our great indebtedness to Professor B. F. Skinner for our fundamental concepts in psychology. We would also like to express our gratitude to the many pioneer investigators in behavioral pharmacology whose work and writings have molded our thinking. We are particularly indebted to Dr. Joseph V. Brady who contributed greatly to the authors' basic conceptions of the analysis of behavioral actions of drugs.

We are also indebted to Dr. F. E. Shideman for his very thorough editing of Chapters 2 and 3, and to Dr. Gordon Heistad for his constructive suggestions regarding the prediction of drug actions in humans (Chapter 8). The authors are particularly grateful for Dr. John Falk's invaluable comments, which significantly altered the manuscript. The thoughtful comments and suggestions of students in the Psychopharmacology Training Program at the University of Minnesota were helpful and greatly appreciated. The readability of the manuscript is due in large part to the editorial assistance of Thurlene Shechtman, library and art work by Grace Emley, and its meticulous preparation by Carolyn Flynn and Diane Kunde. Finally, we would like to thank Professor J. Jenkins, the editor of this series.

TRAVIS THOMPSON
CHARLES R. SCHUSTER

Contents

Section IV

Behavioral Pharmacology

1

Behavioral Pharmacology as a Basic Science

Although drugs that affect behavior have been widely used by mankind for thousands of years, the science of *behavioral pharmacology* is a recent development. One major reason for the delay in its evolution is that only recently have scientists recognized that behavior is a phenomenon amenable to study by the methods of the natural sciences. The demonstrated precision and sensitivity of certain laboratory techniques, developed for the experimental analysis of behavior, has led to their application in several of the social and biological sciences. Behavioral pharmacology represents only one of the many outgrowths of a rapidly developing science of behavior.

DEFINITION OF BEHAVIORAL PHARMACOLOGY

Behavioral pharmacology is a branch of biological science that uses the tools and concepts of experimental psychology and pharmacology to explore the behavioral actions of drugs. The tools of experimental psychology can,

1

for present purposes, be characterized by the phrase "behavioral control techniques." The principal "tools" of pharmacology are drugs. Thus, whether one is interested in controlling behavior to delineate a drug's action or in using drugs to analyze behavioral processes, the analysis falls into the realm of behavioral pharmacology.

For present purposes a drug is tentatively defined as any chemical substance affecting a biological system. Behavior is provisionally defined as effector activity of an organism observable by other organisms.

Historically the study of the effects of drugs on unlearned reflexes has been the province of neuropharmacologists and physiologists, while behavioral pharmacology has been primarily concerned with learned or conditioned responses. We must recognize that this is an arbitrary division of labor and that a full description of a drug's behavioral effects would include drug-correlated changes in both the learned and unlearned responses of the organism.

SCOPE AND PURPOSE OF THIS BOOK

This text deals exclusively with the experimental aspects of behavioral pharmacology. There is no attempt to incorporate the extensive literature on clinical observations of behaviorally active drugs. In a field as complex and as young as the one dealing with drug-behavior interactions, clinical observations serve primarily to suggest experiments. We do not intend to deprecate clinical research with behaviorally active drugs, but rather to point out that the goals of the basic scientist and the clinician differ. The clinician uses behaviorally active drugs to produce beneficial changes in his patients' behavior; the behavioral pharmacologist is not only interested in observing behavioral changes produced by drugs but in analyzing the mechanisms of the drugs' effect. Although, as noted, clinical observations serve primarily to suggest profitable areas of experimentation, the experimental data on drug-behavior interactions may aid the clinician in understanding both his successes and failures in drug therapy.

You will meet in this text many diverse subjects, from fish to men. The problem of generalizing from experimental findings in different species is one that must be dealt with empirically rather than from an armchair. It is certain that behavioral differences between species exist and that drug-behavior interactions will differ in different animal species. It is equally certain that experimental techniques applicable to human and infrahuman subjects are now available and that, ultimately, a comparative behavioral pharmacology will elucidate precisely the similarities and differences in the behavioral responses of different species to drugs. Our main concern at present is the reliability of experimental results, regardless of the species of the subject.

Another restriction in this text's coverage should be noted: As is implied by the title, we are interested in the *behavioral* effects of drugs. Currently, extensive research is being directed toward understanding the physiological and biochemical changes in the nervous system associated with drug administration; and a comprehensive correlation of a drug's biochemical, physiological, and behavioral effects may eventually be possible. At this stage in the development of neuropharmacology and behavioral pharmacology, we are not in a position to demonstrate empirically very many meaningful relations of a drug's effect at these three levels. This separation will vanish only when there is more experimental information about drug-environment interaction as well as about the neural loci and biochemical mechanisms of pharmacological agents that influence the behavior in question.

The general purpose of this book is to bridge the conceptual and methodological gaps confronting the student of pharmacology or psychology as he attempts to conduct or understand experiments in behavioral pharmacology. Succeeding sections present the fundamental principles of pharmacology, the principles and techniques of experimental behavioral control, and the application of these principles and techniques in behavioral pharmacology.

If communication between students of psychology and pharmacology is improved by this book, the authors will have been successful. Although few can ever absorb enough knowledge to be expert in more than one area of science, if one is able to ask meaningful questions of colleagues in other disciplines, he can often avoid experimental pitfalls. It is toward the attainment of this objective that this text has been written.

The research literature in behavioral pharmacology is vast. Of the thousands of papers and books concerned with behavioral actions of drugs, we have only referred to a small percentage that effectively illustrate our points. A great many other papers, of course, are equally interesting and valuable. However, attempting to formulate principles and research tactics in behavioral pharmacology, we have found it necessary to be highly selective. Readers wishing detailed literature analyses can refer to any of several excellent reviews (Brady, 1957; Dews and Morse, 1961; Cook and Kelleher, 1963; Gollub and Brady, 1965).

GOALS OF BEHAVIORAL PHARMACOLOGY

As is true of most scientific enterprises, behavioral pharmacology has goals both in applied and pure science. The diversity of goals is further multiplied by the fact that investigators in this field may be either psychologists or pharmacologists. Ultimately, of course, the aim of both pure science and applied science is to understand completely the effects of drugs on behavior; but this common goal is as yet distant. In the meantime, it is helpful to take a look at the more immediate goals of different investigators:

1. The use of behavioral observation to "screen" new chemical compounds in order to determine their potential usefulness in medical practice.

2. The use of refined behavioral techniques for the experimental analysis of the mechanisms of a drug's effect.

3. The use of drugs as a means or tool for the analysis of complex behavioral processes.

We will now deal more fully with each of these goals and the problems associated with each.

Behavioral Observations for Screening New Chemical Compounds

The major impetus behind the recent development of behavioral pharmacology was the introduction of the "tranquilizing" agents, chlorpromazine and reserpine, into medical practice. The success of these drugs in ameliorating destructive and assaultive behavior in institutionalized psychotics stimulated both the government and private pharmaceutical manufacturers to ferret out other behaviorally active drugs. New testing procedures at the infrahuman level were needed to determine which of the thousands of compounds produced yearly by the pharmaceutical chemists might possess clinically desirable behavioral activity. For obvious practical reasons, a new chemical compound can receive only limited testing; thus the behavioral observations that will be the criteria for choosing a compound that warrants further testing in humans must also be limited. The problems of validating animal drug-testing procedures to predict clinically desirable behavioral changes in humans are discussed in Chapter 8. Here it suffices to say that this need for behavioral testing procedures was largely responsible for the rapid establishment of behavioral pharmacology laboratories in industrial pharmaceutical companies and in universities.

As indicated above, the goals of procedures for screening drugs are practical. Principally, screening processes are used to predict whether a chemical compound will produce desirable behavioral changes in humans at dosage levels not injurious to health. It is unnecessary (and rare) to understand completely the behavioral mechanism of the drug's action in the test situation. Further, it is not necessary that a testing procedure in any obvious way resemble the type of human behavior to be modified. For example, mescaline produces violent scratching at the site of subcutaneous injection in mice, while chlorpromazine antagonizes or blocks mescaline in producing this scratching behavior—we would have a very powerful but simple screening test if it could be shown that all drugs that antagonize mescaline-induced scratching resemble chlorpromazine in their behavioral action in humans. Unfortunately, such a simple test seldom proves to be a valid predictor of a drug's behavioral effects in man. The point is, however, that for the short-range goals of drug testing, the only criterion for selecting a behavioral test is its validity as a predictor of drug action at the human level. Some of the less obvious shortcomings and pitfalls of drug-screening procedures are discussed in Chapter 8.

The Use of Behavioral Techniques for a Refined Analysis and Description of a Drug's Activity

This is the area of major emphasis of this book. It is our contention that only when behavioral pharmacologists have a sound empirical base can they intelligently go about the job of developing better drug-screening procedures. In other words, only from pure-science investigations of drug-behavior interactions will come precise specification of what portion of a drug's activity spectrum produces clinically desirable behavioral effects.

Changes at a variety of functional biological levels must be observed if the action of any chemical compound administered to a living organism is to be described fully. For example, analysis of a compound's CNS activity can be done in various ways. Biochemical procedures can determine changes in brain chemistry following drug administration; neurophysiological techniques (e.g., electroencephalograms, depth electrode recording and stimulation, etc.), are equally useful in analyzing and describing a drug's effect on the nervous system. Similarly, the organism's observable behavior can be used as a means of describing and analyzing a drug's effect. Ultimately, we hope to be able to specify covariations among a drug's biochemical, neurophysiological, and behavioral effects; because of the biochemical and neurophysiological complexities involved, however, this is a far distant goal.

It is also important to realize that orderly functional relations between drugs and behavior can and have been obtained and that this kind of analysis can be as important as various types of microanalysis. Unfortunately, the behavioral effects of drugs have been gravely oversimplified by the specious practice of labeling drugs "tranquilizers," "psychic energizers," etc.; and the simplicity falsely suggested by these terms has added little to the discipline of behavioral pharmacology. The behavior of even the simplest living organism is the result of a highly complex interaction between the organism and its controlling environment. As nearly all drugs have multifarious actions on an organism, one cannot expect that analysis of drug-behavior interactions will be a simple or short task. Fortunately, methods for the experimental analysis of behavior are rapidly emerging, and their application to many problems in behavioral pharmacology is feasible.

To recapitulate, let us ask: What are the goals of the pure science of behavioral pharmacology? They are, first, to devise the most parsimonious techniques of behavioral control in the investigation of drugs; and second, to use these behavioral control techniques to investigate the mechanisms of drug action. A corollary of the latter goal is to establish a meaningful functional classification of pharmacological agents. Eventually, we hope to perceive structure-function relations that will provide for the construction of drugs having specific behavioral activity. It is from such findings that basic principles of drug action will flow. However, a great deal of work remains to be done before we can determine whether the latter goal is attainable.

Drugs as a Means of Analyzing Complex Behavioral Problems

This application has received the least attention in behavioral pharmacology. Drugs are accepted "tools" in physiological investigations, but the use of drugs for investigating behavioral phenomena is currently a potential rather than an established method. We can only suggest here examples of behavioral problems in which drugs might prove to be valuable investigative agents:

1. The role of internal autonomic responses in the acquisition and maintenance of aversively controlled behavior.
2. The role of stimuli from the various visceral organs in the control and regulation of behavior.
3. Self-administration of drugs for controlling one's own behavior.

The grave limitation in this area of investigation is that the currently available drugs have such a wide spectrum of behavioral activity; however, as drugs with greater specificity come to hand, it may yet prove to be a fertile field for the behavioral pharmacologist.

Lest the reader proceed beyond this chapter anticipating the development of a "new synthesis" of basic behavioral science and pharmacology, he should be forewarned. We present no "new synthesis." The theories and constructs of the two disciplines will *not* be shown to mesh like the gears of a well-oiled clock. Indeed, it will become apparent not only that the two disciplines are incongruous in many areas, but that such great gaps separate them that the possibility of effectively engaging their working parts in the foreseeable future remains remote. Thus, the reader should not proceed expecting to find significant *synthesis;* he may, however, find our *analysis* of value.

The first step is to lay bare the principles, the basic data, and the aims of the two disciplines. The approach is descriptive and analytic, emphasizing research methods and tactics. In those few areas of knowledge where descriptions of physiological and behavioral events appear to be converging, we have attempted to explore the basic principles to the limits of the data. To many readers the remaining chasm separating the two domains may be ominous and intolerable. The inherent pleasure of filling in the interstices in men's knowledge will lead them to construct theories to bridge the unknown;

but the research tactic developed here is based on recognition and tolerance of the unknown. This is perhaps the most difficult aspect of descriptive science and is no doubt responsible for the limited popularity of the method. The overwhelming advantage of the descriptive approach lies in the empirical soundness of the entire structure of scientific knowledge, from the microstructural foundation to the molar behavioral superstructure. By considered design, the succeeding chapters pursue the descriptive approach to the analysis of the interactions of chemical substances with environmental variables controlling behavior.

2

Principles of Drug Action

THE AIMS OF PHARMACOLOGY

The administration of drugs to relieve pain, ward off evil spirits, heal the sick, and grow hair on bald men's heads long preceded the development of a science of drugs. Treatment of the sick with chemicals and animal and vegetable substances has been recognized for many centuries as a proper activity for physicians. *Therapeutics,* as this practice has been called, until recently held precedence over scientific investigation of the mechanisms by which drugs act. The range of practical applications for drugs is overwhelming, yet our understanding of their basic mechanisms of action is still limited. It is becoming increasingly clear, however, that the continued improvement of therapeutic application demands an understanding of these mechanisms. This direction in the evolution of pharmacology was prophesied by Paul Ehrlich, whose aim was to find a specific drug for the treatment of a specific disease. We know today that realization of this goal must come in the distant future, if at all; but, if phamacologists are ever able to construct a specific compound for the treatment of a specific disorder, their success will necessarily be a result of the development of a basic science of the principles of drug action.

As basic scientists approaching a new domain, we can best begin by asking simple questions. The simplest question to ask about an observed drug's effect is: How does it work?, or, in academic jargon, what is its mechanism of action? The simplicity of the question belies the complexity of the problem, for this *is* the basic question of pharmacology. Before pursuing answers, it might be wise to reflect on its implications. What will comprise an acceptable answer? Or, when is *a* mechanism of action, *the* mechanism of action?

Implicit in this dual question is the assumption of all science that there exists some set of variables to be measured and that these vary as a consequence of changes in some other set of variables. In pharmacology the variables to be measured are often called the *responses* of a biological system. Such responses can be a change in the structure of the hemoglobin molecule, a depletion of certain neurohormones, a change in heart rate, or an increased rate of running in a T-maze. In other words, in pharmacological language a "response" is a change that can be measured in some aspect of an organism; and the independent variables that produce such responses are usually drugs. Thus, intravenously administered epinephrine will produce a pressor response; curare, a response of striate muscle relaxation; and amphetamine, a response of increased spontaneous motor activity in a "jiggle-cage."

Returning to our question, we find that it also assumes that responses produced by a drug should be describable in terms of some more basic set of phenomena or principles. A change in blood pressure may be explained as the result of alterations in the distribution of body fluids, cardiac enzyme deactivation, etc.; and changes in muscular tonus attributed to change in conduction between nerves and muscles. Thus, one set of observations is usually described in terms of changes at another biological level.

When little is known about a drug, the proposed explanations usually involve concepts at a relatively gross physiological level; but as information is accumulated, explanations become progressively fine-grained and refer to biochemical and biophysical events. At any given time, analysis at the level immediately available is usually believed to provide a satisfactory account of *the* mechanism of action of a drug; and all previously adequate levels of descriptions are thought of as only partial specifications of the total mechanism of action. Clearly, then, "mechanism of action," in the sense of scientific explanation, can refer to description on a variety of levels, ranging from statements about the gross movements of an entire organism to discussions of physical-chemical reactions. The defining characteristic of such mechanisms is that they *refer to a verifiable description of a drug effect that can be shown to covary uniquely with the measured action ("response"), and this relation can be subsumed under a more general class of relations.* The level of description chosen is determined by our knowledge and technology and by the individual scientist's aesthetic preference for one level over another.

Once a drug's mechanism of action has been delineated at a given level, or events at one level related to those at an adjacent level, the role of related variables in altering the drug's effects can be explored. Thus, it may be fully as important to know that the relative amount of fatty tissue in the body will alter the action of a fat-soluble barbiturate as it is to be able to specify all the steps in the drug's mechanism of action.

In the millennium, when the mechanisms of action are known and all relevant variables have been explored, the ultimate aim of pharmacology will have been realized and general laws describing the interactions of chemical substances with living organisms will have been established. In the meantime, approximate descriptions and low level laws will have to suffice.

AN HISTORICAL INTRODUCTION

From the beginning of recorded history, man has recognized that chemical and natural vegetable substances administered to humans and other animals alter their health. However, only recently has order been imposed on the mixture of folklore, mythology, and witchcraft that made up the mysterious body of knowledge called therapeutics. Indeed, *pharmacology, the science concerned with the actions of chemicals on biological systems,* is really only 150 years old. While the early history of pharmacology contains many entertaining episodes, only after 1800 did a science of pharmacology come into being. A study of this period will provide the student of behavioral pharmacology with insights into basic differences in the aims and orientation of the pharmacologist and the psychologist, and will enable him to appreciate the rationales behind them.

Although the first recorded compendium of medicinal agents, the *Papyrus Ebers,* dates from approximately 1552 b.c., scientific pharmacology was still in its infancy 3,300 years later; and only at the end of the eighteenth century had discoveries in the fields of anatomy and physiology made a science of drugs possible. As might be expected, the earliest pharmacologists were anatomists and physiologists who used drugs to study phenomena of more central interest to them.

François Magendie was an anatomist who was primarily concerned with studying sensory and motor pathways to and from the spinal cord. In the course of his experiments, Magendie discovered, in 1817, that strychnine-induced convulsions were mediated via the spinal cord. Claude Bernard (1813–78), a student of Magendie, made numerous discoveries in the areas of physiology and drug action. Particularly important for the history of pharmacology was his discovery, in 1856, that the action of curare is localized at the neuromuscular junction. This information paved the way for other investigators who sought to establish specific loci of drug action. Oswald Schmiedeberg (1838–1921) took pharmacological research one step further by demonstrating that organs could be isolated from the organism in order to investigate the site of drug action.

That drugs react with specific sites in the organism was, as the preceding examples suggest, one of the prevailing concepts of nineteenth-century pharmacology. Between the middle of the nineteenth and the first decade of the twentieth century, a major concept was evolved, one that shaped the future development of pharmacology. The fact that certain chemical configurations are more likely than others to act on tissue was first demonstrated by Crum-Brown and Fraser in 1868; and they are credited with conducting the first "structure-activity" experiment. This notion was resurrected near the turn of the century by Fischer (1894), who asserted that chemicals had configurations similar to geometrical shapes and that they combined with portions of tissue that had complementary geometrical configurations. This came to be known as the "lock-and-key" theory of drug action. In 1905, Langley proposed that a specific portion of the myoneural junction, called a "receptive substance," was the site of action of drugs such as curare and nicotine.

Fischer's schematic metaphor and Langley's posited "receptive substance" were then synthesized and assimilated into the more comprehensive theory of chemotherapeutics by Paul Ehrlich. In 1907 Ehrlich observed that various dyes and immunological agents possessed selective affinity for different tissues and that there appeared to be some relation between the composition of molecular side chains and this differential affinity. As a result, he speculated that a chemical introduced into the body becomes attached to portions of protoplasm. Ehrlich called the "combining group of the protoplasmic molecule to which the introduced group is anchored" the *receptor*. The receptor theories profoundly altered the course of pharmacology and have dominated the explanatory foundation of drug action to the present time.

A. J. Clark (1885–1941) organized the diffuse array of information making up the body of contemporary pharmacology, and synthesized it with Ehrlich's contribution. His aim was "to determine how far the actions produced by drugs on cells can be explained by the known laws of physical chemistry" (1937). This he accomplished in his book, *The Action of Drugs on Cells* (1933), in which he distilled the basic principles of modern quantitative pharmacology. "Quantitative pharmacology," Clark said, "is founded on the assumptions that drugs act by entering into a chemical relation with certain receptors in the cells and that there is some simple relation between the amount of drug fixed by these receptors and the action produced." Clark's expanded receptor theory is the cornerstone of pharmacology today, despite the fact that no specific receptor has ever been isolated. As we delve into the early literature of "psychopharmacology," we will see that the notion of receptor sites in the nervous system has played an important role in the way pharmacologists have conceptualized the actions of behaviorally active drugs.

Specific historical references to the pharmacology of behaviorally active drugs are very limited. The first systematic experiments investigating the subjective effects of drugs administered to man were conducted by Kraepelin in 1892. Perhaps more important conceptually was *A Treatise on the Chemical Constitution of the Brain* (1884) by Thudichum, in which a chemical explanation of schizophrenia was proposed. Thudichum went so far as to generalize that "many forms of insanity are unquestionably the external manifestations of the effects upon the brain substance of poisons fermented within the body, just as mental aberrations accompanying chronic alcoholic intoxication are the accumulated effects of a relatively simple poison fermented out of the body." Conducted during the same period (1884–87), Sigmund Freud's experiments on the behavioral actions of cocaine presaged many twentieth-century findings concerning the self-administration of cocaine.

In 1897, Arthur Heffter described his subjective experiences after ingesting mescal buttons. He concluded that mescaline was the ingredient responsible for visual sensations associated with ingestion of mescal (peyote) cactus. Some years later, in 1938, the Swiss pharmacologists Stoll and Hofmann isolated the common nucleus of the ergot alkaloids and synthesized d-lysergic acid diethylamide (LSD-25). When Hofmann was subsequently involved in further investigations with LSD-25, he accidentally ingested a small quantity of the drug. In this serendipitous fashion, the marked hallucinogenic effects of this lysergic acid derivative were discovered.

I. P. Pavlov, one of the most important figures in the history of psychology also contributed significantly to the development of a science dealing with behaviorally active drugs. When the famous Russian physiologist was professor of pharmacology at the Military Academy in St. Petersburg (1890–95), he instructed students in principles of pharmacology based on laboratory investigations with animals. His own and his students' investigations were designed to delineate the physiological mode of action of drugs within the central nervous system. Pavlov argued as follows:

> It is obvious that the reflex is the most important and more frequent manifestation of nervous activity throughout the life of a complex organism. The reflex helps to establish both a continuous, correct and accurately balanced interaction between the individual parts of the body as a whole to its environment. Reflexes are initiated by stimulation of peripheral terminals of centripetal nerves. These terminals are distributed throughout all organs and tissues, and we must regard them as being extremely variable in form, specific in function, resembling the nerve terminals of sense organs, and adapted for selective stimulation by me-

chanical, physical or chemical means. The amount of work done by them determines at any given moment the degree and pattern of activity in various parts of the body. (1894).

Clearly, Pavlov conceived of chemical receptors in the nervous system that could be studied by the analysis of reflexes. He assumed that changes in reflexes produced by drugs mirror selective stimulation or inhibition of chemical terminals in the nervous system. This assumption is very much like Clark's hypothesis that drugs produce their effects by entering into chemical combination with specific receptors in cells. Both men's inferences were based on the conviction that one should be able to specify the link between a known chemical introduced into the body and subsequent changes in the functioning of cells or groups of cells or of the entire organism. In the absence of direct information clarifying the exact nature of receptors or of Pavlov's reflex-stimulator or reflex-inhibitor areas, investigators committed to these theories should be aware that they are hypothetical constructs and use them accordingly (MacCorquodale and Meehl, 1948). Like all widely accepted hypothetical constructs, their very strengths can comprise their weaknesses. Thus, the tremendous explanatory power of the receptor theory may be a function of its broadness. One should avoid expanding the concept into a vague, all-encompassing model that purports to explain everything but, in the last analysis, is not subject to empirical test.

Pavlov's account of the action of drugs on the nervous system reveals more clearly that the receptor theory as used in pharmacology is very closely related to the physiological definition of sensory receptors. However, the two concepts are too often used interchangeably, with regrettable consequences. In pharmacological writing, we find that, instead of the term "receptor" referring to the site where a drug molecule combines with a cell, it is often used to denote a transducer capable of "stimulation" or "depression"; the apparent conceptual distance between stimulation or depression of a single cell to behavioral stimulation or depression is then all too short. Appealing as the analogy may be, and easy as it is to slip from one meaning of a term to another, it must be realized that "receptor" is only a working model, not a matter of empirical fact.

An alternative way of dealing with receptor theory has been suggested by Ariens (1964). Since receptors are a *functional entity* in the model for drug action, Ariens has proposed to concentrate on the relation of the known structure of the drug molecule to the resulting pharmacological action. An analogous approach is widely used in psychology when theoretical constructs are not available for direct investigation. The term "intervening variable" has been applied to such functional entities to distinguish them from constructs that suggest properties over and above those immediately observable (MacCorquodale and Meehl, 1948).

Localization of Site of Drug Action

Among the aspects of drug research most confusing to nonpharmacologists are the various experimental procedures designed to delineate the site of drug action. Why should one be interested in the ability of a drug to block convulsions elicited by electrical stimulation of the brain? Of what relevance is the drug-produced reduction of the pressor response elicited by intravenous administration of epinephrine? While the rationale for such lines of research may be abundantly clear to most pharmacologists, psychologists are usually unaware of the fundamental premises on which they are based. Yet these premises are basic to an understanding of a large portion of pharmacologic research, and should be examined before proceeding.

Drugs may act (1) directly at the site of administration, (2) by indirect reflex action, (3) by reaching a specific concentration in certain organs or tissues, or (4) by reaching a specific concentration in particular cells or cell fractions. Specific research procedures are designed to determine which of these levels of action is necessary for the observed effect.

The grossest localization refers to local action as opposed to generalized or systemic effects. A drug may act directly at the site of administration (e.g., a local anesthetic); or it may be generally active throughout the body in tissues of a particular type (e.g., a smooth muscle relaxant). Local drug effects are seldom important in behavioral pharmacology. It is the analysis of systemic drug actions that occupies the larger portion of pharmacologists' efforts, requiring further discussion.

Historically, surgical intervention, electrical stimulation, and chemical "blocking agents" have been used to localize systemic drug actions. Claude Bernard interrupted circulation to one leg of a frog, but left innervation intact. A curare solution was injected into the frog. Stimulation of the nerve leading to the leg that was prevented from exposure to the drug produced the usual contraction, whereas the leg with intact circulation did not respond to stimulation. Stimulating the muscle of either leg directly, however, elicited contraction, leading Bernard to conclude that the action of curare must be localized at the neuromuscular junction. Similar combinations of surgical and physiological techniques are among the commonest procedures employed in localizing the site of drug action.

The irreversible effects of surgical removal of tissue can be circumvented by temporarily interrupting function by using drugs that block normal processes. Such compounds are called "blocking agents" and will be discussed further in Chapter 4. If after blocking a specific normal function, a test drug continues to produce its effect the investigator can conclude that the chemically interrupted function is not a necessary condition for the action of the test drug. Blocking agents can be used to assist in localizing the site of drug action by a process of elimination.

In recent years, increasing attention has been given to biochemical mechanisms and procedures for localizing drug actions. The concentrations of a drug or its metabolites can be estimated in various organs and tissues, and some indication of distribution through various tissues obtained. Subsequently, enzyme systems active in these tissues can be isolated in functional condition and subjected to reasonable concentrations of the test drugs. Among the most widely used techniques today is the administration of radioactively labeled isotopes of normal atomic constituents of the drug. These radioactively "tagged" molecules can be followed, for their presence in various tissues and cellular fractions is readily ascertainable. Combinations of isotopic techniques with spectrophotometric methods—particularly useful in analysis of very small quantities of cell fractions—can provide leads to the precise locus of biochemical action.

While the above distribution techniques are valuable for specific lines of investigation, their validity may suffer from the possibility that distribution may not correlate with site of action. For example, many drugs are found in high concentrations in the liver, not because the liver is the site of action, but because it is the locus of many biotransformations. Thus, distribution studies suggest sites of action that, along with other information, can provide strong circumstantial evidence for a specific locus of action.

The Dose-Response Relationship

An observation fundamental to all quantitative pharmacology is that an orderly relation exists between the quantity of drug administered and the magnitude of its effect. The quantity of drug required to produce a given effect is called the *dose*. The relation between the dose and the magnitude is called the *dose-response* or dose-effect relationship.

Two basic forms of this relationship have been observed—the graded and the quantal. In the *graded* dose-effect relationship, it is assumed that cells or portions of cells are differentially sensitive to the drug. The curve relating dose and magnitude of a graded effect is a hyperbola (Fig. 2.1). The all-or-none (*quantal*) dose-effect relationship is assumed to reflect a responding biological system that responds either maximally or not at all. Quantal responses are usually described by a sigmoid curve, if plotted cumulatively, as in Fig. 2.2. However, noncumulative quantal dose-effect distributions are skewed. Careful examination can often show that quantal effects of drug dosage are log-normally distributed. Therefore, dose-response curves are frequently plotted by the logarithm of the dose rather than by the dose itself.

By plotting the measured quantal effect in terms of the percentage of subjects exhibiting the effect (e.g., anesthesia) as a function of dosage,

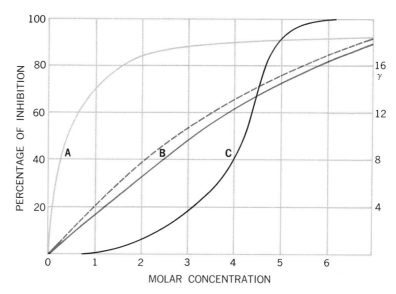

Fig. 2.1 Three forms of dose-response curves of drugs acting on isolated frog hearts. A. Hyperbolic. B. Linear. C. Sigmoid. (Clark, 1933, p. 140, Fig. 31)

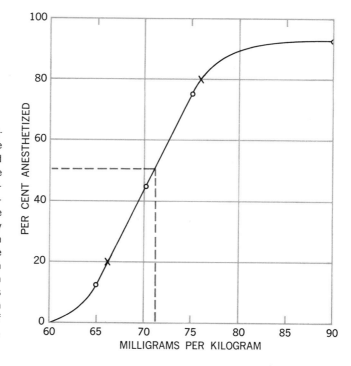

Fig. 2.2 Characteristic sigmoid dose-response curve. The quantal response is expressed as the percentage of mice anesthetized by the intraperitoneal administration of cycloheptenylethyl barbiturate. The ED-50 can be estimated by drawing a horizontal line from the 50 per cent point to the smooth curve, and running a second line intersecting with this point to the abscissa. Thus half the mice would have been anesthetized by a dose of 71 mg/kg. (Marsh, 1950, p. 20, Fig. 4)

the distribution of intersubject variation in drug response can be obtained (Fig. 2.2). The dotted line separating the top half of the distribution of cases from the bottom half (50 per cent anesthetized) indicates the *median effective dose* (ED-50). In this case, 71 mg. per kilogram of body weight intraperitoneally of sodium cycloheptenylethyl barbiturate anesthetized 50 per cent of the subjects. If the measured response is the number of deaths resulting from administration of the drug, the dosage separating the top half of the distribution of cases from the bottom half is called the *median lethal dose* (LD-50). A convention for expressing the margin of safety in dosage, based on the ratio of LD-50/ED-50, is called the *therapeutic index*. The larger the therapeutic index, the greater the margin of safety.

The significance of dose-response curves becomes more apparent in the study of the actions of a compound with complex effects. Although the respiratory depressant actions of morphine are well-known, the relation between the dosage of morphine and the degree of depression is not entirely clear. If one were to arbitrarily select a dose of morphine and measure the degree of respiratory depression one hour later, one might conclude that morphine had no effect, a profoundly depressing effect, or an inconsistent effect, depending on the dose administered. Even more confusing is the fact that doses differing by a factor of 50 may produce equal degrees of depression. Findings of this nature might lead one to the erroneous conclusion that no orderly relation exists between morphine dosage and degree of respiratory depression. Figure 2.3 reveals that the apparent disorder arises from the fact that the degree of respiratory depression bears a U-shaped relation to morphine dosage. Thus, 1 mg. per kilogram of body weight intravenously can produce the same degree of depression as 50 mg. per kilogram of body weight intravenously (Miller, Gilfoil, and Shideman, 1955). Similar nonlinear effects are common with behaviorally active drugs and must be considered carefully in designing drug-behavior research.

In addition to making sense out of nonlinear functions, one can glean other information essential to selecting appropriate doses of a drug, or permitting comparisons of results obtained using two or more drugs, from dose-response curves. Figure 2.4 presents dose-response curves for two drugs (A and B) on the same response. Drug A has a very steep curve, indicating that small variations in dose from the ED-50 will produce very large changes in the measured effect. Drug B, with the same ED-50, has a rather gradual dose-response curve, indicating that relatively large changes in dose will be necessary to produce a sizeable response. If a dosage of Drug A is given equal to Drug B's ED-25, one would expect to see virtually no effect of the drug. On the other hand, administering a dosage of Drug A equal to Drug B's ED-75 would produce a very profound effect.

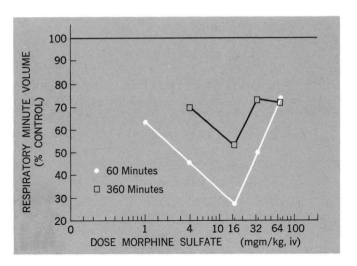

Fig. 2.3 A V-shaped dose-response relationship. The effect of intravenously administered morphine sulfate on respiratory minute volume. Note that it is possible to obtain the same percentages of reduction in respiratory minute volume with dosages varying by a factor of fifty. (Miller, Gilfoil, and Shideman, 1955, p. 356, Fig. 7)

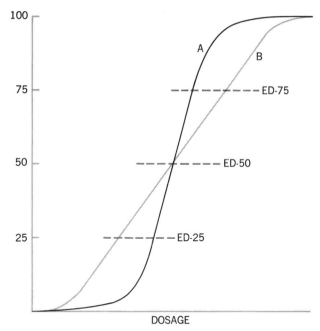

Fig. 2.4 Dose-effect curves for two drugs with the same ED-50 but differing slopes. While a dosage of drug A equal to drug B's ED-25 would have very little effect, a dosage of drug A equal to drug B's ED-75 would have a profound effect.

Types of Drug Action

When pharmacology evolved beyond an art of applying remedies, one of the first facts the new science faced was that drugs cannot change the physiological function of tissue, but can only alter the degree of functioning of various cells. It is generally acknowledged today that the basic action of drugs is to increase or decrease the degree of activity in cells, but not to alter the kind of activity. When a particular function of particular types of cells is increased, these cells are said to be *stimulated;* when that functioning is decreased, they are said to be *depressed.* Another effect on cellular function has been attributed to drugs, namely, irritation. The term "drug irritation" refers to alterations in nutrition, growth, or morphology of tissue (Krantz and Carr, 1958). While some authors treat irritation as a separate type of drug action, such effects can, for all practical purposes, be subsumed under the foregoing categories without altering the meaning of the terms "stimulation" or "depression."

Dosage Forms

A drug *dosage form* is the physical state in which a drug is administered. Drug dosage forms range from exotic lamellae and aesthetically exciting aerosols to less glamorous doughy poultices applied to the skin. While many of these forms are no doubt interesting to the clinician, they are of little direct value in basic infrahuman research. Readers specifically interested in such matters are referred to the introductory chapters of any of several medical pharmacology textbooks for a description of the more unusual preparations (e.g., Drill, 1958; Krantz and Carr, 1958; Goodman and Gilman, 1965). Basic information regarding the dosage forms most commonly used in research with infrahuman subjects will be provided here.

The substance in which a drug is dissolved or suspended is called the *vehicle.* Vehicles vary according to the physical properties of the drug, the route of administration, and the specific site of application. An oil vehicle would not be used for drugs to be introduced directly into a vein, for example. Nor would a drug that is insoluble in water be administered in a water vehicle (unless a suspension is prepared, e.g., tragacanth). The most widely used vehicles in research are distilled water, isotonic saline, various oils, and suspending substances.

There are four types of preparations of particular interest for the present purposes: aqueous solutions, oil solutions, alcoholic solutions, and aqueous suspensions. In general, *solutions* are preparations of a drug dissolved in a vehicle. The most widely used solutions are aqueous (either distilled water or saline°). When a solution is prepared by a pharmaceutical manufacturer in a sterile form specifically for injection, it is called an *injection*. When a drug will not readily dissolve in water or oil within a reasonable temperature range, it is often placed in a *suspension*. A gum or other viscid substance is used to surround the drug particles and maintain them in a relatively homogeneous phase. Such preparations are usually administered orally or intramuscularly. Occasionally, orally or subcutaneously administered drugs are prepared in an alcohol solution (e.g., tincture of opium) because the alcohol vehicle disappears very rapidly, leaving only the active compound.

Routes of Administration

The pathway by which a drug is introduced into an organism is called the *route of administration*. The more commonly used routes are: (1) oral (peroral, abbreviated P.O.) and (2) parenteral (any route outside the alimentary tract, usually understood to mean subcutaneous, intravenous, intramuscular, or intrasternal injections). Other routes are important in general pharmacology but play a small role in behavioral research with drugs.

Drugs given to humans are most commonly administered orally, however this method is less frequently used for laboratory animals. A drug is administered by swallowing or through a tube inserted through the nose or mouth. The oral route is used in basic research primarily because it facilitates the determination of absorption rates and of whether any of the drug is destroyed in the gastrointestinal tract, and because it allows us to conduct studies parallel to those carried out with humans.

Because of the difficulty of restraining large animals (e.g., monkeys), oral administration is of greater practical value in small subjects (mice, rats). One method of administering drugs orally to rats and mice entails forcing the jaws open with the forefinger and thumb of the left hand while a rubber catheter connected to a burette containing the drug solution is held in the right hand. The tube is inserted into the animal's esophagus, and the valve of the burette is opened, allowing the drug to flow by gravity directly into the stomach. Since mice and rats cannot vomit, this is a satisfactory method for introducing drugs without danger of loss of the drug.

The term *parenteral administration* is usually limited to the introduction of drugs by mechanical crossing of skin or membrane barriers so that the drug is directly introduced into the desired site of application. Since none of the drug can be lost by vomiting, or destroyed by gastrointestinal fluids, the dosage is more certain in parenteral administration. In addition, the rate of distribution to the site of action is usually more rapid.

° Unless specified otherwise, "saline" refers to a solution of sodium chloride in distilled water that is isosmotic with red blood cell plasma.

Parenteral administration usually involves the inserting of a hollow needle into the desired site, then emptying the contents of a reservoir containing the drug through the needle. Commercially available glass or plastic syringes with various types of interchangeable needles certainly provide the most common and convenient methods of parenteral administration. Several kinds of syringes and needles are discussed in Appendix I.

There are many routes for parenteral administration, but the ones most widely used in infrahuman research are the subcutaneous, intramuscular, intraperitoneal, and intravenous routes. Figure 2.5 illustrates subcutaneous, intramuscular, and intravenous, as well as intradermal administration, the last of which is used for local anesthesia and tests for sensitivity to pollen extracts.

In *subcutaneous* (S.C.) or hypodermic injections the tip of the needle is inserted immediately under the skin where a nonirritating solution is expelled. *Intramuscular* (I.M.) injections are accomplished by inserting the needle deep into a muscle and expelling a solution or suspension. Oil suspensions may be injected intramuscularly, providing the possibility of in-

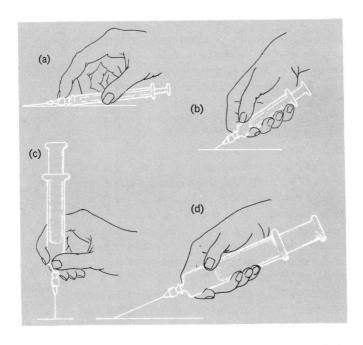

Fig. 2.5 Needle injections. Note position of needle in each injection. (a) Intradermal. (b) Subcutaneous. (c) Intramuscular. (d) Intravenous. (Wright and Montag, 1949, p. 93, Fig. 27)

troducing a long-acting "oil depot." While intramuscular administration is frequently used with dogs, monkeys, and larger animals, subcutaneous administration can be used for both large and small animals. *Intraperitoneal* (I.P.) administration is perhaps the most commonly used route in rats. The needle is inserted directly into the peritoneal cavity, providing for rapid drug absorption. *Intravenous* (I.V.) administration is used when immediate action and maximal certainty of dosage are required. The tip and shaft of the needle are inserted into the lumen of a vein, and the drug is directly expelled into the vein. Only aqueous solutions, which will not damage blood and its constituents, or produce local vascular irritation may be used. Intravenous administration requires greater skill than any of the other routes; however, the advantage of far greater experimental control provided by this method usually outweighs the fact that additional training is required for the administration of drugs by this route.

Absorption and Distribution

The amount of drug reaching the site of action per unit of time determines the effect produced. Once a drug has been introduced into an organism, it is absorbed and distributed to the site of action. The amount of drug reaching the site of action is primarily dependent on the amount administered, its physical condition, the character of the membranes the drug must pass, and the route that it must take to get from the site of administration to the site of action. The time taken to get from the site of administration to the site of action is determined by the rate of absorption.

The absorption rate, in turn, is primarily determined by the route of administration, the physical properties of the drug preparation, and the rate of administration. These are the manipulatable factors that determine how rapidly a drug reaches the site of action. The absolute absorption rate can be expressed in terms of the change in concentration of the drug at the site of application over time. Figure 2.6 illustrates how theoretical absorption and excretion curves produce the concentration curve of the amount of drug at the site of action. This theoretical curve is modified by a set of variables, not all of which are readily controllable. The absolute rate of drug absorption from the site of administration can be considered a physiochemical relation between the drug and the transporting medium. The transporting medium (blood) is the primary factor regulating the absolute absorption rate. Other factors that, in combination with circulation determine absorption rate, are solubility of the drug, its concentration, and the nature of the immediate absorbing surface.

Drugs tend to move from sites of high concentration to areas of lower drug concentration. However, movement of a drug from the site of admin-

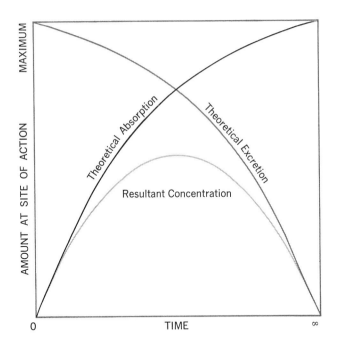

Fig. 2.6 Theoretical absorption and excretion curves, yielding a curve of concentration at the site of action. Although symmetrical curves of this type are theoretically possible, almost all decay curves are hyperbolic and bear little resemblance to the absorption curves. Similarly, the resultant curve of the actual amount reaching the site of action is never symmetrical and is modified by numerous factors, as discussed in the text. (Marsh, 1950, p. 82, Fig. 13)

istration along a concentration gradient very seldom limits absorption rate. Most frequently, the amount of blood flowing through tissue determines how rapidly a drug will be absorbed. Therefore, anything that modifies circulation—exercise, temperature, presence of other drugs—also alters rate of absorption. Obviously, in intravenous administration, circulation is not an absorption-limiting factor, and blood levels of a drug reach their maximal concentration immediately. Figure 2.7 presents the comparative durations of action curves for intramuscular, intravenous, subcutaneous, and oral routes of administration, in which serum concentrations were determined for various periods following administration. Clearly, intramuscular administration most closely approximates intravenous administration, while oral administration and subcutaneous routes, though very slow, maintain serum drug levels for a longer period. Although intraperitoneal administration is associated with a duration curve similar to that obtained with the intramuscular route, it provides a slower but longer lasting peak drug concentration.

Fig. 2.7 Routes of administration and serum concentrations of penicillin. Three milligrams of penicillin G per kilogram of body weight were administered at various times to one individual, and the amounts of penicillin activity in the serum determined at time intervals. It is readily apparent that certain routes of administration greatly influence uptake and also elimination. Much drug is wasted by some routes, and more frequent administration of the drug is necessary if effective blood levels are to be maintained. (Marsh, 1950, p. 85, Fig. 14)

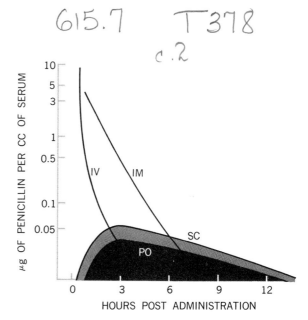

Distribution

When the drug concentration in the blood equals the concentration at the site of administration, absorption is said to be complete. This does not, however, imply that the drug has been equally distributed to all tissues of the body. As indicated earlier, Ehrlich and others recognized that drugs are differentially distributed throughout the body. The factors determining differential distribution are poorly understood, but some variables are known to be important. Drug molecules vary greatly in size, from methanol, with a molecular weight of 32, to some of the biological macromolecules with molecular weights of up to 4×10^7 (Bernal, 1958). It would be astounding if such variability in size were not reflected in differential distribution.

The solubility properties of the drug comprise another factor known to alter distribution. For example, thiobarbiturates are very soluble in fat, and therefore tend to be rapidly distributed in adipose tissue. Other compounds tend to have affinities for proteins of blood plasma, not on the basis of their solubility but because of their protein-binding properties. Finally, distribution to tissues depends on the presence and concentrations of the same or similar drugs in those tissues. Addition of the same drug or of its antagonists may lead to no increase in concentration in given tissues if receptor sites for that drug are already saturated.

Fate

Following absorption, a drug may undergo transformation in the body and be ultimately excreted either unchanged or as a biotransformation product. The biotransformations that a drug undergoes and the mechanism of its excretion are referred to as the *fate* of a drug. Figure 2.6 presented the theoretical excretion curve, revealing the assumption that the mechanisms of drug excretion are diametrically opposite to those of absorption. As a matter of fact, the routes of excretion are very seldom the simple inverse of those of absorption. It is worthwhile to consider briefly the most common routes of excretion: the kidney, the lungs, the skin, the bile duct, and the intestines.

Volatile agents, such as the anesthetic gases and alcohol, are excreted across the pulmonary membrane. We are all aware that sodium chloride is excreted in part across the skin; however, few other compounds of significance are found on the skin surface. Organic arsenicals are among the drugs excreted across the bile duct; and certain agents like quinine, as well as some sterols, are excreted in the feces. The vast majority of drugs are excreted by the kidneys. Because of the central role of the kidneys in removing drugs from the body, proper functioning of these organs is of extreme importance in drug research. Renal damage may increase a drug's duration of action; it even may have lethal consequences at a dosage that would otherwise be well within a tolerable range.

Some drugs, such as the inhalant anesthetics, are excreted from the body in unchanged forms. Most drugs, however, undergo some chemical changes prior to excretion. The transformation of a drug with a specific biological action to an inactive form, or to a form with different effects, is called biotransformation.° Biotransformations are of four basic types: oxidation, reduction, hydrolysis, and conjugation.

There is a group of oxidative enzymes present in liver microsomes capable of oxidizing a number of drugs. Careful examination of these enzyme systems has revealed that they should properly be considered hydroxylases that catalyze the direct incorporation of molecular oxygen into substrates. An example of such a system is the following general deamination reaction:

$$R—CH_2—CH(NH_2)—CH_3 \xrightarrow{OH} RCH_2—CO—CH_3 + NH_3$$

Several other enzyme systems also found in liver microsomes are capable of carrying out drug reduction reactions. The following type of hydrogenation is performed by flavoprotein reductases:

$$R—CH{=}CH—COOH \longrightarrow R—CH_2—CH_2—COOH$$

The hydrolases are generally distributed throughout body fluids and in various cellular fractions. They are of two general types, the esterases and the amidases. Acetylcholine and certain local anesthetics are rapidly hydrolized by such enzyme systems.

° Unfortunately, the term "detoxification" has been widely used to refer to such changes, although at times the product is more toxic than the initial agent. The widely used term *biotransformation*, suggested by Brodie and Axelrod (1949), has been adopted here.

Many compounds undergo conjugation to form products with less or different effects than the original active agent. These include glucaronide and ethereal sulfate formation, acetylations, mercaptan transformations, and a variety of other synthetic transformations (Holland, Klein, and Briggs, 1964).

The significance of these transformations will become more obvious when we discuss some of the actions of the behaviorally active drugs. In anticipation, it might be pointed out that one of the more commonly accepted hypotheses about the neurochemical mechanism of action of many drugs used in psychiatry is that they alter an enzyme system that oxidizes certain naturally occurring brain monoamines. Thus, a crucial link in establishing the mechanism of action of such behaviorally active drugs is the delineation of their role in transformation of these amines to inactive forms.

Multiple Administrations of the Same Drug

In research, where several replications of a procedure on the same animal are desirable, the investigator would like to be certain that there is no interaction between successive administrations of the same drug. At times, it is found that the dose required to produce the same effect must be increased on successive administrations. When this occurs, it is said that *tolerance* has developed. Multiple administrations of the narcotic analgesics and barbiturates are particularly likely to lead to the development of tolerance. Certain other chemically related drugs can, when administered in place of the original drug, produce a very similar response; at times, they can substitute for the original drug. Usually, as tolerance develops to the original drug, tolerance also develops to substitute drugs so that successively higher doses of such drugs are also required to produce the original effect. Under these conditions, it is said that *cross tolerance* has developed.

If discontinuing a drug to which an animal has developed considerable tolerance precipitates a characteristic syndrome of illness (often including vomiting, convulsions, and even death), the animal has become *physically dependent* on the drug. If an animal reliably self-administers the drug if provided with the opportunity, the term *behavioral dependence* applies. Thus, an organism that is physically dependent may be behaviorally dependent as well, though the converse is not necessarily true. Humans who exhibit behavioral dependence without physical dependence are said to be *habituated* to the drug.

Another problem arises when readministration of the same drug occurs before the effects of the previous dose have disappeared. When a drug has not been entirely excreted or has not undergone complete transformation before a second dose is administered, *cumulation* results. Such factors as the presence of the necessary enzymes to carry out the transformation reaction, the normal functioning of the excretory mechanism (e.g., excretion by the

kidney), or storage can affect the likelihood of cumulation. Under these conditions, the concentration of the drug in various tissues and fluid compart-
ments progressively increases. In general, if a drug is administered repeatedly,
a portion is transformed and excreted, but a certain amount remains. Cumulation rate depends on the interval between administrations and the dose. It
can be shown by derivation that the maximal level to which a drug will accumulate on repeated administrations, if expressed in multiples of the level
following the first dose, is equal to one divided by the fraction of the original
dose that has disappeared at the time of readministration (Wells, 1958).
Hence, in general:

$$y = \frac{1}{x}$$

where y equals multiples of the original level, and x equals the fraction disappeared. For example, if readministration occurs when half of the original
dose is gone, eventually the drug will accumulate in the body until it reaches
a level twice the original dose. A typical cumulative effect is illustrated in
Fig. 2.8, where data from five administrations of the same dose of a drug
are presented. While partial recovery occurs following each dosing, the level
following the last administration is well above that seen on the first injection.

Obviously, a major consideration in gauging cumulative effects is interadministration interval. By spacing successive administrations sufficiently far
apart, it is usually possible to avoid cumulation. However, the disappearance
of the active compound or its metabolites does not necessarily indicate that
a drug effect may still not exist. For example, the drug may cause morpho-
logical or biochemical changes in cells which may far outlast the presence of
the active agent. In these cases, cumulative effects are not defined by the
presence or absence of the drug but by the changes in the measured drug
effect.

The *storage* of drugs, or the specific affinity of drugs for certain "inactive" tissues in the body, may create an unexpected cumulative effect. Thio-

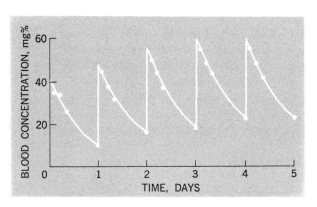

Fig. 2.8 The cumulation of the
blood concentration of atrolactamide
with time when the drug was read-
ministered to a dog at 24-hour intervals. Note that on the fourth administration an essentially steady state
has been achieved. (Wells, 1958; in:
Drill [Ed.], 1958, p. 12, Figs. 1–9)

pental, for example, diffuses from the bloodstream to the central nervous system, where it appears to produce its anesthetic effect. Simultaneously, the drug is incorporated into adipose tissue, for which it has a very high affinity. If relatively low doses of Thiopental are administered, the drug rapidly diffuses from the brain to fatty tissue, terminating anesthesia. If, however, repeated doses of Thiopental are given, the drug saturates the body's fat stores and an inordinately long state of anesthesia may ensue, since the drug no longer tends to diffuse from the brain to fatty tissues. If the dosage is high enough, death may result (Shideman, 1958).

Presence of Other Drugs

Other drugs present at the time an active chemical is introduced can enhance the effect of the active drug, diminish its effects, or in no way alter the effect of the active agent. Therapeutically, the latter relation is usually desired (e.g., when giving two drugs for different therapeutic purposes simultaneously), although occasionally it is necessary to diminish the effects of toxic doses, or to enhance the effect of inadequate doses, of one drug by giving another drug. One drug may enhance the effect of another in three ways: by potentiation, by synergism, or by summation. In *potentiation,* the magnitude of effect in two combined agents is greater than the sum of their individual effects. Two drugs said to be *synergistic* produce an effect greater than that produced by either alone but not greater than the sum of the two single effects. Drugs that *summate,* as the term implies, merely add their individual effects to produce a total effect.

When one compound diminishes the effect of another, it is said to *antagonize* it. The antagonist may accomplish this by producing an opposite physiological action by some entirely different mechanism; or it may merely neutralize the effect of the active compound by combining with it chemically (e.g., chelating agents).

One of the most interesting types of antagonism with respect to understanding mechanisms of drug action is competition for receptor sites. Ehrlich was one of the first to recognize competitive antagonism, and many investigators after him have emphasized the significance of this mechanism for receptor theory (Ariens, 1964; Holland, Klein, and Briggs, 1964). Clark (1937) found the general quantitative relation between the dose of an antagonist and the effect produced to be hyperbolic. Figure 2.9 illustrates competitive antagonism by an antihistaminic agent on histamine-induced hypotension.

Factors That Modify Drug Action

A wide array of factors that are not readily manipulatable modify drug action. They are not manipulatable in the sense that a given environment and subject may be imposed on the experimenter rather than selected by

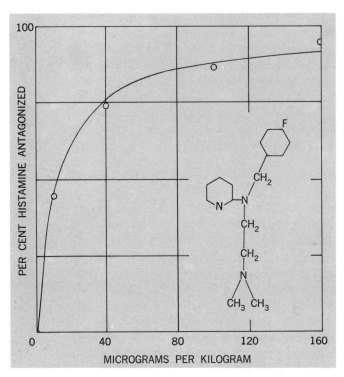

Fig. 2.9 Competitive inhibition of histamine-induced hypotension in dogs. An anesthetized dog is given graded doses of histamine intravenously, and the falls in blood pressure recorded. Ten micrograms of antihistaminic per kilogram is injected and the histamine administration repeated. Further doses of antihistaminic are injected until the response to histamine is almost entirely inhibited. Within wide limits, the actual amount of histamine given before and after the antihistaminic is unimportant since the ratio of effective to antagonized histamine will remain the same. Such a constant ratio between the active agent and the antagonist is a primary criterion of competitive antagonism. (Marsh, 1950, p. 62, Fig. 12)

him. A maxim in clinical work with drugs is that the very old and the very young patient present special problems. Young animals are often more sensitive to the effects of drugs than are adults. Similarly, older animals may be hypersensitive to some drugs and have very little sensitivity to others. Only rarely are these variables explored experimentally; they are usually controlled by selecting populations of the same adult age range.

The sex of the subject may also determine drug effects. Females often require relatively more barbiturate anesthetic than males. And there is ample evidence to indicate that genetic factors may influence drug action, with some strains of animals being highly responsive to a given drug while others are virtually insensitive. A catchall category of *idiosyncrasies and hypersensitivities* refers to unexpected toxic or allergic responses to a dose which has proven safe with other members of the same species.

The surrounding environmental conditions certainly alter drug actions, as will be discussed at length in later chapters. The ambient temperature is capable of altering drug action through changes in circulation, and by altering body temperature, which controls the rate of chemical transformation and combinations.

The subject's body weight is often listed as an unmanipulatable variable controlling drug action, although body weight, as we use the term here, is often manipulated. Drugs cannot be administered to all animals in the same absolute quantities without respect to their body weight. Thus, a rat weighing 100 gm. cannot tolerate the same dosage as an animal weighing 300 gm. Indeed, failure to take such a weight differential into consideration could well have lethal consequences. In order to compensate for differences in body weight, drug dosages are usually calculated and expressed in terms of number of grams or milligrams of drug per unit of the animal's weight. Thus, if we found that 3 mg. of sodium pentobarbital anesthetized the 100 gm. rat in the previous example, we might expect the 300 gm. rat to be anesthetized by 9 gm. of pentobarbital. From this, we might conclude that the dosage necessary to anesthetize this particular type of rat under these conditions is 30 mg. of pentobarbital per kilogram of body weight (expressed as 30 mg/kg). This is called the body weight method of expressing drug dosages.

3

Behaviorally Active Drugs

THE THEORY OF NEUROHUMORAL TRANSMISSION

Pharmacologists generally believe that the brain is the primary site of action of most behaviorally active drugs; and this assumption determines, to a great extent, experimental approaches to the analysis of a drug's mechanism of action. As a matter of fact, there is a good deal of evidence that many behaviorally active compounds do exert considerable influence over brain functions. Though the specific mechanisms are largely unknown, knowledge of peripheral neurohumoral transmitter mechanisms suggests that at least some behaviorally active drugs accomplish their effects by altering such transmission. While the foregoing assumption is widely accepted, it is essential that the reader understand that drugs acting outside the central nervous system can profoundly alter behavior, as well. This consideration is especially important since virtually all behaviorally active drugs exert both peripheral and central effects.

Drugs may cause changes in striate muscle tonus, blood pressure, glandular secretions, smooth muscle activity; any such changes could be reflected in altered behavior. Any drug capable of producing such effects could, in principle, be classified as *behaviorally active*. Thus, one might consider certain antibiotics, anticholinergics, antihistamines, peripheral muscle relaxants, and the like in the category of behaviorally active drugs. However, in an effort to be consistent with most of the literature, we will reserve the term "behaviorally active" for compounds thought to produce their behavioral effects through direct central actions, rather than indirect peripheral actions. Such central actions, as indicated above, are thought to be determined at least in part by modified neural transmission. To understand the subsequent discussion of types of centrally acting drugs, it will first be necessary to review knowledge and theories about neurohumoral transmission.

Most of the evidence regarding humoral transmission has been gathered in experiments that use peripheral nervous tissue. It is therefore not clear if the same processes operate in the central nervous system; it seems likely, however, that similar, if not identical, events take place there (McLennan, 1963). It is known that outside the central nervous system, a space exists between the terminal part of an axon and an adjacent cell. Such a space or *junction* is either a *synapse* (space between two nerve cells) or a *neuroeffector junction* (space between a nerve cell and a muscle or gland cell). Stimulation of a prejunction nerve cell may propagate an action potential, and a response in an adjacent, associated neuron, muscle fiber, or gland cell.

During the nineteenth century, numerous investigators demonstrated that the injection of adrenal gland extracts produces effector cell responses that closely resemble those produced by the stimulation of sympathetic pre-effector cells. Other investigators found that acetylcholine injections produce responses characteristic of those produced by the stimulation of parasympathetic fibers. These findings led them to introduce new terms to designate such substances: *sympathomimetic*, referring to agents whose actions mimic the effects of sympathetic nerve stimulation; and *parasympathomimetic*, referring to agents whose actions mimic parasympathetic nerve stimulation.

In further experiments, Dale (1914) found that the actions of acetylcholine produce mixed effects. Smooth muscle contractions elicited by acetylcholine are antagonized by atropine, but not by curare; skeletal muscle contractions elicited by acetylcholine are antagonized by curare but not by atropine. Dale therefore assumed that two types of receptors for acetylcholine are found in different effectors and that one type is antagonized by atropine and the other by curare. The receptor called *muscarinic* is antagonized by atropine, and produces effects similar to those caused by muscarine injection; that is, it produces postganglionic parasympathetic actions on the heart, glands, and smooth muscles. The other receptor, called *nicotinic*, is antagonized by curare and gets its name because it produces effects like those following nicotine injection—sympathetic ganglionic stimulation, and skeletal muscle stimulation.

A great many later experiments supported the notion that chemical substances, such as acetylcholine, mediate the activation of postsynaptic cells, but there was no conclusive evidence for this until 1921, when Otto Loewi performed the crucial experiment. He perfused fluid obtained from one frog heart through a second frog heart. The original (donor) heart was innervated by an intact vagus nerve (Fig. 3.1). Stimulation of the vagus nerve of the donor heart produced diminution in its own rate; but, more important,

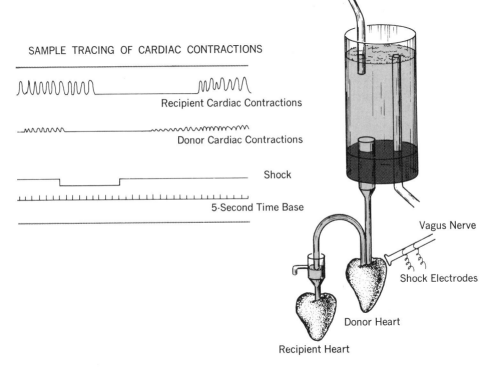

SAMPLE TRACING OF CARDIAC CONTRACTIONS

Recipient Cardiac Contractions

Donor Cardiac Contractions

Shock

5-Second Time Base

Vagus Nerve

Shock Electrodes

Donor Heart

Recipient Heart

Fig. 3.1 Bain's modification of the Loewi experiment demonstrating the production of acetylcholine following stimulation of the vagus nerve to the frog's heart. The donor heart is perfused with a balanced salt solution, which then passes to an isolated recipient heart. The vagus fibers of the donor heart are electrically stimulated, producing an immediate arresting of contractions by the donor, with slowing and more gradual arrest of the recipient heart. Arrest of the recipient heart is due to acetylcholine in the perfusate from the donor heart. (After Bain, 1932)

it also caused a diminution in the rate of the second heart while that organ was being perfused by the fluid from the stimulated heart. Stimulation of the vagus therefore released a substance, that produced effects like vagal stimulation, from the first heart into the perfusing fluid. Subsequent research has shown that the substance appearing in the perfusate was acetylcholine.

The notion that two basically different mechanisms mediate nerve junction transmission evolved from these early findings. One mechanism involved an acetylcholine-like effect, and therefore was called *cholinergic*. The other was called *adrenergic* because it involved an epinephrine-like effect. On this basis, the fibers of the autonomic nervous system may be classified functionally as cholinergic or adrenergic. Since fibers innervating skeletal muscles also liberate acetylcholine, these are described as cholinergic as well.

There are considerably fewer subtypes of adrenergic nerve fibers than of cholinergic nerve fibers. Adrenergic fibers generally consist of sympathetic postganglionic fibers (with the exception of nerves to sweat glands and certain vessels). Sympathetic nerve fibers synapse in ganglia along the spinal cord (the sympathetic trunk), then continue to the effector organ. Transmission from the preganglionic axon to the postganglionic cell in the sympathetic trunk is mediated by acetylcholine, while transmission from the postganglionic fiber to the effector is adrenergic (Fig. 3.2).

Cholinergic fibers are more complex. As indicated above, all preganglionic transmission, whether sympathetic or parasympathetic, is cholinergic. All postganglionic parasympathetic fibers (viz., to smooth muscles and glands), certain postganglionic sympathetic fibers (viz., to sweat glands and some blood vessels), and all fibers innervating skeletal muscles are cholinergic. Finally, the preganglionic fibers terminating in the adrenal medulla are cholinergic. The relations of the various types of fibers to their neurotransmitters are summarized in Fig. 3.2.

It is widely believed that chemical substances liberated by presynaptic fibers in the central nervous system mediate transmission of nerve impulses in the central nervous system. Whether the neurohumors active in the central nervous system are the same as those found peripherally is unknown. Distribution studies, however, indicate that significant quantities of epinephrine, norepinephrine, and serotonin (to be discussed shortly) occur in certain areas of the brain. When certain drugs with demonstrated behavioral actions are administered to a living organism, the concentration of these monoamines in the brain may be altered. Thus, it seems that there may be a relation between the brain concentration of epinephrine, norepinephrine, and serotonin and the behavioral actions of certain drugs.

On the basis of this line of reasoning, intensive investigation of brain monoamines and behaviorally active drugs has been undertaken, and it has been found that epinephrine, norepinephrine, and 5-hydroxytryptamine (serotonin) are similarly distributed in the brain, each occurring in higher concentrations in areas associated with central autonomic regulation.

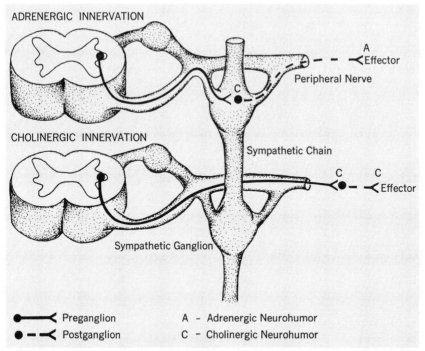

ADRENERGIC INNERVATION

CHOLINERGIC INNERVATION

A
Effector

Peripheral Nerve

C

Sympathetic Chain

C   C
Effector

Sympathetic Ganglion

●━━< Preganglion   A - Adrenergic Neurohumor
●- -< Postganglion   C - Cholinergic Neurohumor

Fig. 3.2 Sections of the spinal cord illustrating adrenergic and cholinergic innervation. Adrenergic innervation involves a cholinergic mediator substance in the sympathetic ganglion and an adrenergic mediator at the effector. Cholinergic innervation involves cholinergic mediators both at the ganglia and effector junctions. (Drawn by authors)

GROSS OBSERVATION AND DRUG ACTION

The foregoing discussions of neurohumoral transmission and of the concepts of stimulation and depression as they are used to categorize the actions of drugs on various types of cells, might lead one to surmise that a similar descriptive scheme could be applied to the behavioral actions of drugs. Traditionally, some such dichotomous classification has been applied to the relatively simple reflex behaviors described by pharmacologists; the criterion used in selecting behaviors for investigation has been the degree to which such behaviors are believed to reveal increased or decreased neural activity.

Skill in discriminating drug-induced changes in behavior can be a very important part of effective pharmacological research on behavior. Some behavioral changes induced by a drug may not be immediately measurable with a given procedure, but if the experimenter recognizes the presence of signs beyond his testing procedure's sensitivity, he may be able to alter his experimental technique to take account of such behavioral effects. Recognition of certain signs may also provide a basis for further investigation of physiological or biochemical mechanisms of a drug's action. Finally, for certain predictive purposes (e.g., addiction liability), ratings of specific sets of signs may prove adequate in themselves with certain types of drugs (Irwin, 1954).

Unfortunately, the exclusive use of direct observation tends to be associated with unwarranted assumptions about mechanisms of drug action and the "psychological effects" of a drug. A cursory examination of the clinical literature reveals the many pitfalls associated with such methods. A further limitation of direct observation involves the sensitivity and reliability of the human observer. A human observer simply is no more capable of transducing certain types of behavioral information than he is able to measure blood pressure directly. Nor can the human observer maintain equal sensitivity and reliability 24 hours a day for months at a time. Thus, while direct observation is an important part of drug-behavior research, it is equally essential that its limitations be recognized.

In attempting to determine, by direct observation, the drug that an experimental animal has received, the skilled observer first categorizes the sensory, skeletal muscle, and autonomic signs. These effects are then matched with those produced by various classes of drugs until the observed effects match the actions produced by a known drug. Where the symptoms are relatively clear-cut, the number of drugs that could produce such effects is limited. However, the signs are usually not so simple. Under some conditions, an array of compounds is capable of producing some or many of the effects observed; diagnosis then approximates educated guessing. Indeed, the nonspecificity of drug action makes classification extremely difficult.

In the case of behaviorally active drugs, classification is a particularly knotty problem. We would like to present an optimistic picture, even though we do feel that the solution to problems of classifying behaviorally active drugs lies in the accumulation of more data. Until a consistent vocabulary for describing and categorizing such drugs is established, the reader faced with a disparate literature will need some framework in which to operate; we hope that the following section will provide him with a workable frame of reference.

CLASSIFICATION OF DRUGS

It seems logical that the classification of drugs should have preceded the development of a science of drugs, much as the classification of plants and animals preceded the development of botany and zoology. As a matter of fact, drugs *have* been classified, reclassified, and reclassified again. Early taxonomic schemes were based either on therapeutic application or natural origin.

As biochemistry and pharmaceutical chemistry developed, some investigators felt that therapeutic schemes were less than satisfactory and suggested a radical shift to purely chemical classification. Under such a system, drugs that are chemically similar, differing perhaps in a methyl or hydroxyl group, would belong to the same class. The chemical scheme has also proved unsatisfactory not only because it is of little value to therapeutic application, but because compounds in the same class may have entirely different biochemical and physiological mechanisms of action.

Accordingly, a third general approach, based on anatomical or physiological site of action, emerged. This is the basic system used in most medical pharmacology texts today, although none can maintain an entirely consistent taxonomic scheme. For example, certain fluid therapies, cytotoxic drugs, and behaviorally active drugs pose special classificatory problems. However, wherever possible, drugs are classified according to site or mechanism of action.

While the currently used taxonomic schemes are applicable to most drugs, the student who must make scientific sense out of classificatory schemes for behaviorally active drugs may find himself in a quandary. The fact that an antihistamine, a sedative-hypnotic, a central adrenergic agent, and an ergot derivative all belong to a class of "behaviorally active" drugs may lead him to conclude that chaos reigns where he expected to find order. The disorder in drug classification stems from our very limited understanding of the basic physiological, biochemical, and behavioral mechanisms of drug action.

A way of temporarily circumventing the problem is to ignore classification per se and to examine directly those drugs with known behavioral effects in order to determine whether they share other properties. The result of such an enterprise would be an approximate list of drugs or groups of drugs with certain common characteristics. A great many gaps would exist to be filled in as data are made available. We have compiled such a list below and present it, not as an empirically derived classification scheme, but as a guide to the major groups of drugs of behavioral interest.°

Since drugs are, for the most part, the independent variables manipulated in pharmacology, this partial list will serve as an introduction to the kinds of chemical manipulations most frequently performed in behavioral research with drugs. The terms we have used to describe these drugs have been drawn from various authors and therefore reflect no single viewpoint. At the same time, we have attempted to select descriptive terms that represent a consensus for a given drug or group of drugs.

° This partial list of drugs includes not only behaviorally active drugs, but other compounds that are (1) prototypes within a group, (2) important for an understanding of actions of other drugs, or (3) in certain cases, agents which should be distinguished from drugs with predominant behavioral effects. We have tried to exclude behavioral information from the descriptions of the properties of these drugs, since this will be partly covered in later chapters. Further, we feel that the data are inadequate for making generalizations regarding the "predominant" behavioral actions of most of the drugs on this list and that it would be gratuitous to do so.

A PARTIAL LIST OF DRUGS OF BEHAVIORAL INTEREST

Sympathomimetic Agents: Substances that produce physiological responses similar to those produced by the sympathetic adrenergic nerves are called *sympathomimetic agents.* These physiological responses include cutaneous vasoconstriction and skeletal muscle vasodilatation, cardiac acceleration, pupillary dilatation (mydriasis), nictitating-membrane contraction, intestinal relaxation, pilomotor contraction, and glycogenolysis. Pharmacologically, all agents in this class are related to the natural prototype, *epinephrine.* As indicated earlier, epinephrine (Adrenalin or Suprarenin) and levarterenol (noradrenaline or norepinephrine) are naturally occurring compounds that are involved in adrenergic neuroeffector transmission.

Epinephrine   Levarterenol (norepinephrine)

It is commonly assumed that the actions of natural adrenergic agents are mediated by a specific adrenergic receptor. While the exact nature of the receptor is unknown, it appears to belong to an effector cell that is innervated by an adrenergic nerve. Some effector cells that respond to adrenergic action are stimulated by epinephrine; others are inhibited by it. If epinephrine were the only adrenergic agent, it would be sufficient to state that there are two receptors, one excitatory and the other inhibitory. However, when we consider related natural and synthetic adrenergic agents, it is apparent that some more complex relation must exist. It has been proposed that there are at least two types of adrenergic receptors, designated for convenience *alpha* and *beta.* The alpha receptor is primarily concerned with excitatory responses and is most sensitive to epinephrine (two to ten times more so than to levarterenol). The beta receptor is associated with inhibitory responses (with the exception of the heart) and is most sensitive to isopropyl-arterenol, another adrenergic agent.

Epinephrine is usually administered subcutaneously or intramuscularly, while levarterenol is usually administered intravenously. The rate of absorption can be diminished by epinephrine's local vasoconstrictor action, which effectively retards blood flow. The duration of action following intravenous administration of moderate doses is very short (two to three minutes). Epinephrine and levarterenol are inactivated predominantly by two enzymes. One of these, monoamine oxidase (Ahlquist, 1958), effects oxidative deamination; the other, catechol-O-methyltransferase, brings about O-methylation of the benzene ring.

A second major group of sympathomimetic amines, the *amphetamines,* is of particular interest to behavioral pharmacologists. Amphetamine is structurally related to epinephrine; but it differs from epinephrine in ways that seem to be partly responsible for its resistance to enzymatic destruction in the body. As a result, amphetamine can be administered orally while epinephrine cannot. Owing to the presence of an asymmetric carbon atom in its molecule, amphetamine can exist in two pure forms and the racemic mixture. The dextrorotatory form, *d*-amphetamine (Dexedrine), is approximately twice as potent as the racemic form (amphetamine), while the levorotatory form (Benzedrine) is the least potent of the three. As a result, most of the physiological effects of epinephrine administration can also be evoked with amphetamine.

$$CH_2-\overset{\overset{\displaystyle CH_3}{|}}{CH}-NH_2$$

Amphetamine

One of the most pronounced effects of amphetamine appears to be on the central nervous system, where it accelerates and desynchronizes the electroencephalogram and facilitates monosynaptic and polysynaptic transmission in the spinal cord. In laboratory animals, low and moderate doses produce increased spontaneous motor activity as measured in jiggle cages or photoelectric cell activity chambers. Humans report insomnia and subjective feelings of euphoria, and exhibit generally increased motor activity. These symptoms are usually attributed to "central nervous system stimulation," although the exact relation between effects on the central nervous system and these behavioral phenomena remains unclear (Dews and Morse, 1961).

The behavioral properties of amphetamine are discussed at length in a later chapter. While amphetamine's pharmacological effects are similar to those of epinephrine, it appears to have a somewhat different mechanism. Whereas epinephrine acts directly on the effectors, amphetamine may exert its sympathomimetic effect through release of norepinephrine from storage sites in the adrenergic nerve terminals (Trendelenburg, 1963).

Parasympathomimetic Agents: Drugs that activate effector cells innervated by fibers of the craniosacral and somatic efferent nerves are called *parasympathomimetic.* The prototype for all drugs of this group is *acetylcholine.* While acetylcholine is effective in relatively low concentrations at receptor sites, it is rapidly destroyed by the enzyme acetylcholine esterase. Since only small amounts of the drug reach the receptor sites, acetylcholine is very difficult to deal with in *in vivo* experiments. Because of this property, acetylcholine is of little therapeutic value, although it is widely used in basic research.

The effects of acetylcholine on the heart are particularly striking, as these mimic vagal stimulation. Low and moderate doses produce weakening of atrial contraction, slowing of heart rate, and disturbances of atrioventricular conduction. Eventually, as high doses are reached, complete atrioventricular block ensues and fibrillation results. The gastrointestinal tract is also sensitive to acetylcholine, especially the intact myoneural structure of the intestine, where acetycholine produces contractions in smooth muscles. Isolated gut is responsive to acetylcholine as well, but far less so than it is *in vivo*.

$$H_3C-\overset{\overset{\displaystyle O}{\|}}{C}-O-CH_2-CH_2-\overset{+}{N}\overset{\nearrow CH_3}{\underset{\searrow CH_3}{-CH_3}}$$

Acetylcholine

While it is generally thought that gastric secretions are controlled by acetylcholine, firm proof has thus far eluded researchers. Acetylcholine esterase metabolizes the drug so rapidly that it is extremely difficult to obtain increased gastric secretions with the drug alone. If anticholinesterase drugs are given to block the enzyme prior to acetylcholine administration, marked hydrochloric acid secretion results (Riker, 1958).

Though it is widely believed that acetylcholine plays a very important role in central nervous system functions; relatively little attention has been given to its effects on the mechanisms of action of behaviorally active drugs. Topically applied to certain areas of the cerebral cortex, the drug produces activation patterns; certain areas beneath the floor of the fourth ventricle (those that control respiratory functions, vomiting, and cardiovascular functions) are also responsive to local application. Some investigators have suggested that acetylcholine mediates synaptic transmission in the central nervous system, or that it controls interneuronal excitation as suggested by Nachmansohn and coworkers (1950, 1951).

One of the most interesting pharmacological actions of acetylcholine is at the motor end-plate of striate muscles. The trimethyl ammonium end of the molecule is believed to play a central role in receptor combination and in effector excitation. It is now thought that the strong ionic charge of the cationic end of the molecule endows it with a particular affinity for the motor end-plate. Following the combination of the cationic end of the molecule with receptors in the end-plate, the end-plate is depolarized and contraction of the muscle fiber ensues. This excitatory function is normally limited in duration, with residual acetylcholine being metabolized by the esterase. If, for some reason, the concentration of acetylcholine is excessive, or if an esterase-blocking agent is present, there is an excessive discharge of the membrane potential followed by loss of muscular function. This is the mechanism of depolarizing paralysis possessed by certain drugs (e.g., succinylcholine).

Other related compounds that may be of behavioral interest are muscarine, choline, and methacholine. *Muscarine,* an alkaloid isolated from the mushroom *Amanita muscaria,* was used in early studies of pharmacological activation of the parasympathetic nervous system. Indeed, as was noted earlier, muscarine was the prototype for drugs that act on smooth muscles, glands, and any other organs directly innervated by postganglionic cholinergic nerves. It produces gastrointestinal spasms, hypotension, miosis, bradycardia, and other evidences of parasympathetic stimulation. Unlike acetylcholine, muscarine does not activate autonomic ganglion cells or motor end-plates of skeletal muscles.

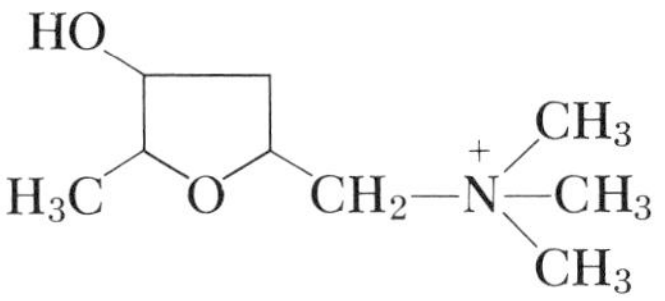

$$HO-CH_2CH_2-N^+(CH_3)_3$$

Muscarine

Choline, the parent compound from which acetylcholine is derived, is also of some interest. Choline is capable of producing all the effects of acetylcholine, but only in concentrations from 1,000 to 100,000 times as great as those required for comparable effects with the latter compound. Thus, although the trimethylammonium structure common to the two compounds is believed to be necessary for cholinergic activity, it obviously does not account for the difference in potency. It appears that the esterification of the alcoholic end of the molecule is necessary for this increase in activity; and it is believed that esterification also enhances receptor combination.

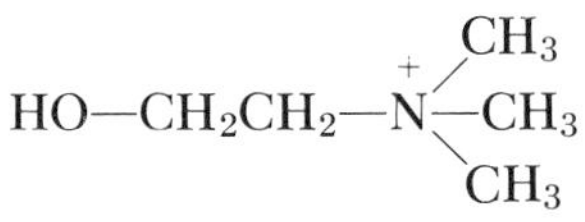

$$HO-CH_2CH_2-N^+(CH_3)_3$$

Choline

Methacholine (acetyl-B-methylcholine) differs from acetylcholine in that it possesses a methyl group on the carbon beta to the ammonium center. Methacholine was originally developed for the reduction of tachycardia and hypertension. In general, it produces effects very much like those produced by acetylcholine, but it is much longer-acting and less susceptible to esterase metabolism. Methacholine increases gastrointestinal tone and, unlike acetylcholine, induces copious gastric secretion. In overdose, it causes nausea, vomiting, and diarrhea. Untoward actions include bronchoconstriction and bladder constriction (sometimes causing involuntary urination). Methacholine is poorly absorbed orally and, because of the danger of cardiovascular collapse with intravenous or intramuscular injection, it is usually administered subcutaneously.

Parasympathetic Depressants: A *blocking agent* is a compound that antagonizes the action of another drug, or nerve stimulation at neuronal junctions. Several families of drugs are used therapeutically because they are capable of blocking the actions of natural adrenergic or cholinergic agents. We are concerned here with agents called *parasympathetic depressants* because they belong to a drug group particularly effective in blocking cholinergic postganglionic excitation. All older members of this class of drugs were originally isolated from several plants—*Atropa belladonna* (deadly nightshade), *Hyoscyamus niger* (black henbane), *Datura stramonium* (jimsonweed). The active components of these plants are *l*-hyoscyamine, *dl*-hyoscyamine, or *l*-scopolamine. The most widely used compounds today, those that have been investigated in behavioral research, are atropine (*dl*-hyoscyamine) and scopolamine.

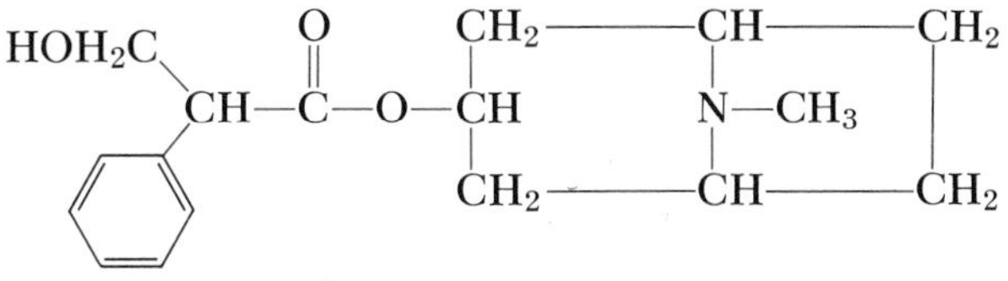

Atropine

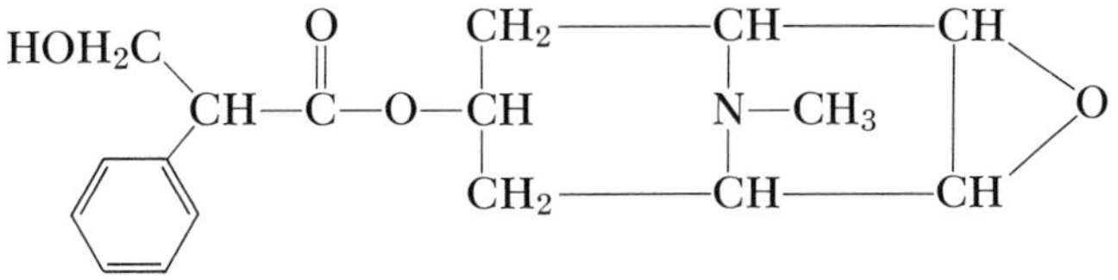

Scopolamine

Although some vagal action of CNS origin is exerted on the heart by both atropine and scopolamine, they certainly do not mimic the action of acetylcholine. As a matter of fact, atropine has effects opposite to those of acetylcholine on most organ systems. The temporary decrease in heart rate associated with moderate doses of atropine is followed by a prolonged elevation. Atropine produces dilatation of small peripheral vessels, which gives a flushed appearance to the skin. The central nervous system effects of atropine and scopolamine at therapeutic dosages are not impressive. There may be mild respiratory stimulation; and chronic administration of relatively high doses has been associated with hallucinations and disorientation (atropine toxicity).

In general, the belladonna alkaloids (atropine and scopolamine) reduce intestinal tone, motility, and secretions. Salivary and respiratory secretions are markedly reduced as well, with resultant dryness of the mouth, nose, and throat. Since the radial muscle fibers of the iris of the eye and the muscles regulating lens thickness are innervated by cholinergic fibers, it is not surprising that atropine and scopolamine produce mydriasis, and poor accommodation of the lens.

Atropine is usually administered subcutaneously or orally, although other routes can be used. The effects of atropine can be observed for as long as four to six hours, depending on the dosage and route of administration. Atropine and scopolamine appear to be competitive inhibitors of acetylcholine at muscarinic receptor sites. It is thought that atropine combines reversibly with receptor groups on effector cells, thus preventing acetylcholine from exerting its normal function.

Agents Acting on Ganglia: Transmission of impulses from preganglionic to postganglionic nerve cells is thought to be mediated by acetylcholine, whether the nerves are sympathetic or parasympathetic. A variety of agents is capable of either enhancing or blocking ganglionic transmission. One type of action may involve initial stimulation of the postganglionic membrane, much as acetylcholine stimulates the motor end-plate, followed by complete depolarization of the postganglionic membrane at higher doses. The consequences are, thus, initial stimulation of effectors, i.e., postganglionic nerve cells or an analogous structure, followed by complete blockade. *Nicotine* is a drug that acts in this way.

Nicotine

Nicotine, the principal alkaloid of tobacco leaves, has mixed ganglionic stimulant-blocking effects as well as direct effects on the central nervous system and the motor end-plate. In humans it is usually self-administered via the lungs as tobacco smoke, but in experimental animals it can be administered either orally or parenterally. It causes peripheral vasoconstriction, with associated rise in heart rate and blood pressure. In moderate dosages, nicotine produces an array of gastrointestinal effects, generally characterized as parasympathetic stimulant actions. Most of these effects are attributable to ganglionic stimulant effects (described earlier as nicotinic). As dosage increases, progressive postganglionic depolarization occurs, and ganglionic blockade results. As a consequence, acetylcholine released by further volleys of preganglionic nerve impulses is incapable of exciting postganglionic nerves. At this level, marked changes in gross motor activity are obvious. The symptom of striate muscle twitching is also present, owing to action at the motor end-plate. Eventually, central neural stimulation is sufficient to induce convulsions with associated cardiovascular collapse and respiratory arrest. Behaviorally, the most interesting effects of nicotine are the increased motor activity associated with certain dosages and the prolonged self-administration of the drug by humans in the form of cigarettes and cigars, and pipe and chewing tobacco.

A second group of ganglion-blocking drugs acts by preventing acetylcholine from combining with postsynaptic receptors. The exact mechanism of this inhibition is not clear, although there is a strong suggestion that it is a competitive inhibition. *Tetraethylammonium*, a very fast-acting ganglion-blocking agent, has been used for its hypotensive effects. It causes pupillary dilatation, dryness of the mouth, decreased gastric secretions, decreased gastrointestinal motility, tachycardia, hypotension, peripheral vasodilatation, and urinary retention.

Because tetraethylammonium is poorly absorbed from the gastrointestinal tract, it is usually administered intravenously. It produces its peak effect in two to three minutes, and is rapidly excreted, with half the dose appearing in the urine within 30 minutes. The primary dangers associated with its administration are cardiovascular collapse and respiratory failure. The functionally related compound, hexamethonium, has effects very similar to those of tetraethylammonium, but is longer-acting.

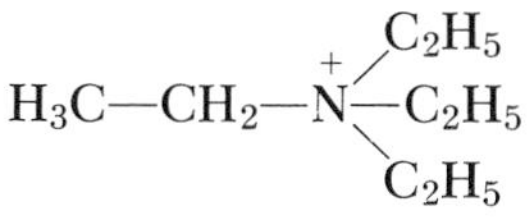

$$H_3C—CH_2—\overset{+}{N}\overset{\diagup C_2H_5}{\underset{\diagdown C_2H_5}{—C_2H_5}}$$

Tetraethylammonium

Neuromuscular Blocking Agents: There are various drugs, called *neuromuscular blocking agents*, that cause striate muscle paralysis by competitively antagonizing the action of acetylcholine at the motor end-plate. The best known member of this group is *curare*, originally used by South American Indians to paralyze wild game. The crude material is obtained from the resins and gums of the vine of *Chondodendron tomentosum*. This gum contains several alkaloids capable of paralyzing striate muscles; however, the only compound available in commercially significant quantities is *d*-tubocurarine. As can be seen in the diagram below, *d*-tubocurarine is a very complex compound containing two quaternary ammonium groups. It is available as a chloride with moderate water solubility, low lipid solubility, and high alcohol solubility. Curare's mechanism of action was first suggested by Claude

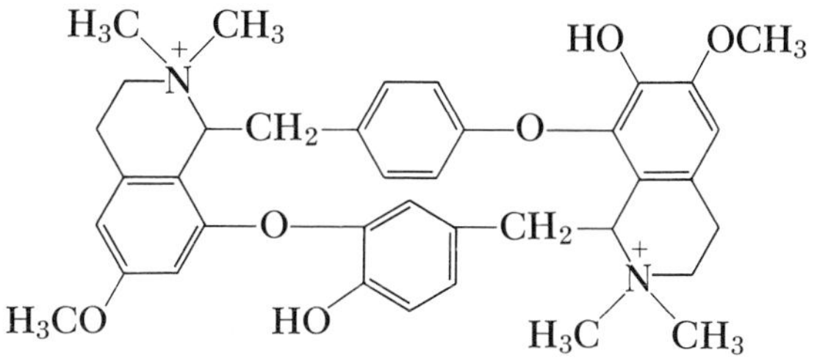

d-tubocurarine

Bernard, who demonstrated that stimulation of the motor nerves of curare-treated animals did not cause muscle contraction, but that direct stimulation of the muscle was adequate to cause contraction. These data indicated that some blocking action at the myoneural junction interferes with stimulation of the motor end-plate. It now appears that *d*-tubocurarine competes with acetylcholine, also a quaternary ammonium compound, for receptor sites in the motor end-plate.

Another group of myoneural blocking agents acts by mimicking the effect of acetylcholine at the myoneural junction. The consequence is that the response of the muscle declines with continued stimulation until complete "depolarization" has taken place. Decamethonium and succinylcholine (Anectine) act in this fashion.

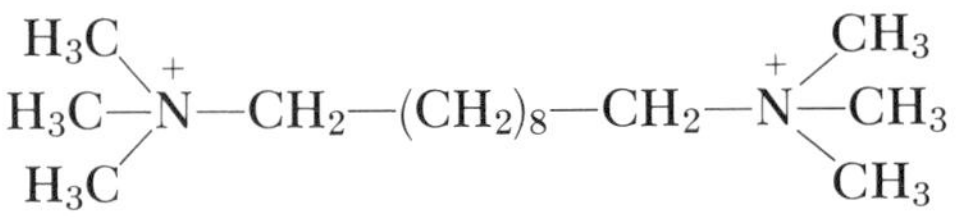

$$H_3C-\overset{H_3C}{\underset{H_3C}{\overset{+}{N}}}-CH_2-(CH_2)_8-CH_2-\overset{+}{N}\overset{CH_3}{\underset{CH_3}{\overset{CH_3}{}}}$$

Decamethonium

$$\begin{array}{c} CH_2-\overset{\overset{O}{\|}}{C}O-CH_2CH_2-N\overset{CH_3}{\underset{CH_3}{\overset{CH_3}{}}} \\ | \\ CH_2-CO-CH_2CH_2-N\overset{CH_3}{\underset{CH_3}{\overset{CH_3}{}}} \\ \overset{\|}{O} \end{array}$$

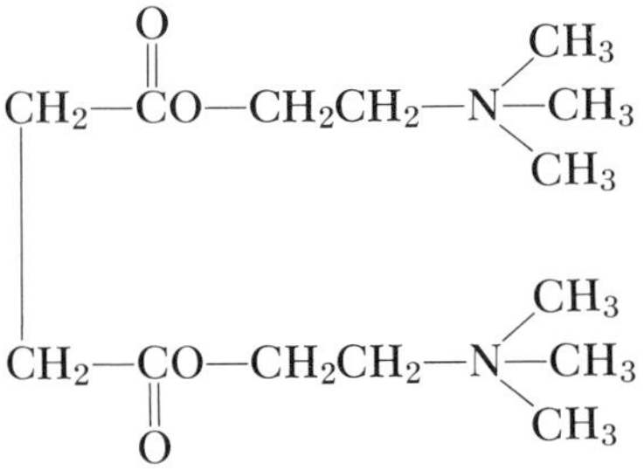

Succinylcholine

Systemic effects of curariform drugs include rapid fall in blood pressure, tachycardia, loss of striate muscle control at low doses, and striate muscle paralysis at higher doses. As a consequence of such paralysis, respiration is impaired or ceases entirely. The curariform drugs are poorly absorbed from the gastrointestinal tract and are therefore administered parenterally. During surgical anesthesia, these drugs are usually administered intravenously, although they can be introduced by other parenteral routes. *d*-tubocurarine is bound; it undergoes transformation in striate muscles and in the liver, and is excreted by the kidneys. When administered intravenously, half the drug disappears from the plasma in 10 to 15 minutes. Succinylcholine chloride is an extremely short-acting compound, with an average dose producing muscular relaxation for only two to four minutes. Decamethonium bromide reaches its peak effect in four to eight minutes, depending on the dose, with complete return of muscular strength in approximately 20 minutes (McIntyre, 1958).

Skeletal Muscle Relaxants (Propanediols): Unlike the myoneural blocking agents, the propanediols produce selective depression of subcortical and spinal polysynaptic transmission with little or no effect at the myoneural junction. The most prominent effect of the propanediols is skeletal muscle relaxation without paralysis or unconsciousness. The first drug of this type to be used therapeutically was mephenesin. It has been used as an adjunct in general anesthesia; to reduce the severity of seizures experienced by psychiatric patients receiving electroshock; to produce relaxation of muscle tone in acute spasms; and, more recently, to produce a feeling of relaxation in highly anxious patients. The latter application foreshadowed the development of one of the more widely used behaviorally active drugs, meprobamate.

$$H_2-C-OH$$
$$H-C-OH$$
$$H_2-C-O-$$
$$H_3C$$

Mephenesin carbamate

$$H_2-C-O-CONH_2$$
$$H_7C_3-C-CH_3$$
$$H_2-C-O-CONH_2$$

Meprobamate

Meprobamate shares some of the properties of mephenesin, particularly the ability to depress polysynaptic reflexes. Unlike mephensin, however, meprobamate seems to have marked effects on the cortex and thalamus at dosages that produce relatively little muscular relaxation. A number of early reports suggested that meprobamate altered the behavior of psychiatric patients, particularly anxious neurotic persons. Because its behavioral effects are relatively mild as compared with barbiturates and some of the more potent behaviorally active compounds, many psychiatrists and general practitioners relied heavily on meprobamate for the outpatient treatment of neurotics and patients with chronic somatic complaints. Subsequent reports indicate, however, that meprobamate has a moderate addiction liability (that is, patients who have made chronic use of high doses of the drug will experience an abstinence syndrome if it is discontinued). It should not, therefore, be used indiscriminately for chronic treatment (Lemere, 1956).

Basic behavioral studies with meprobamate reveal no pronounced effects at dosages that do not produce significant impairment of movement. Thus, while meprobamate appeared for some time to possess unique behavioral properties, the weight of current evidence suggests that such traits were more a product of wishful thinking than a matter of fact (Laties and Weiss, 1958).

Meprobamate is relatively insoluble in water and is therefore usually administered orally in a suspension or in tablet form to humans. The principal behavioral effects of the drug in humans disappear after four to six hours. A small portion of the drug is excreted unchanged in the urine, but the majority of it appears to be metabolized either in a conjugated form or in another fashion, presently undetermined.

Another muscle relaxant, not properly included in the same group with the propanediols, is chlordiazepoxide (Kadenbach and Lührs, 1961). This compound has been used in psychiatric practice to treat anxiety because it "relaxes" the patient without producing marked ataxia. It has muscle relaxant effects similar to those of the propanediols, some anticonvulsant actions, and mild analgesic effects. Its mechanism of action is unknown. Like meprobamate, chlordiazepoxide has addiction liability, producing in humans a withdrawal syndrome within seven to eight days following cessation of a high dosage (Hollister, Motzenbecker, and Degan, 1961).

Narcotic Analgesics: Of all the drugs employed in medicine, certain of the opium alkaloids and their derivatives have the longest and most celebrated history. Opium was mentioned in the writings of the Sumerians, who lived in Mesopotamia from about 5000 to 4000 B.C. (Terry and Pellens, 1928). It has been described in nearly every compendium of medicinal agents down through the ages, and remains today the source of some of the most valuable drugs used in medical practice. Opium is the dried exudate of the poppy plant, *Papaver somniferum;* and it has over 20 different alkaloids. Of these compounds, only three are of major practical value: morphine, codeine, and papaverine.

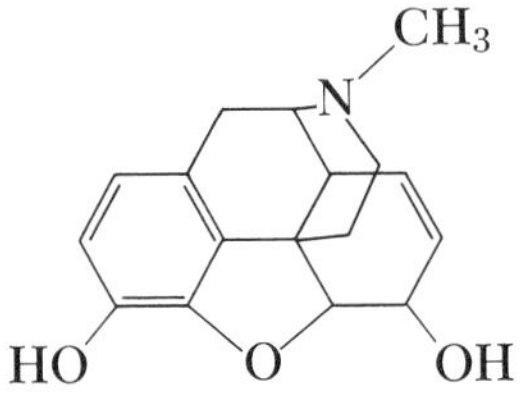

Morphine

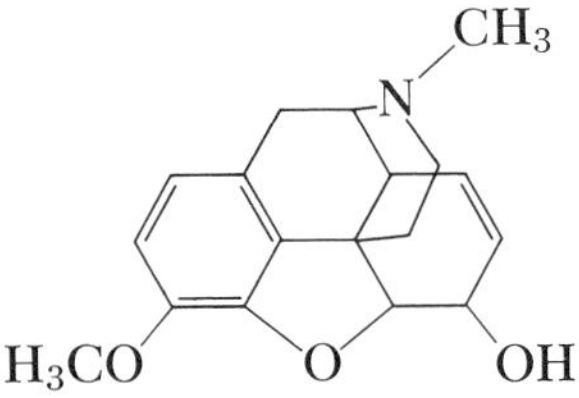

Codeine

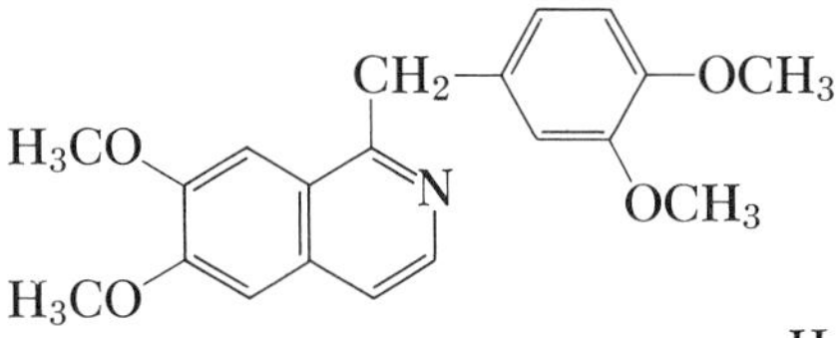

Papaverine

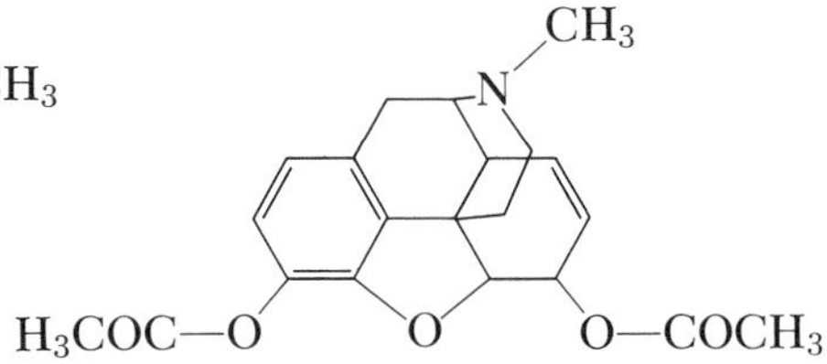

Diacetylmorphine
(Heroin)

The primary therapeutic application of morphine is the relief of pain. While morphine has been extensively explored, and most investigators agree that the site of its analgesic action is in the central nervous system, its specific mechanism remains unknown. Morphine relieves all types of pain but is more effective against continuous dull pain than intermittent sharp pain. Maximal analgesic effect occurs 20 minutes after intravenous administration, and within 60 to 90 minutes if the drug is given subcutaneously. Morphine's two-component action on the nervous system has been termed "biphasic." Morphine administered to humans tends to produce an early "stimulant" phase characterized by strychnine-like spinal stimulation, medullary vomiting center stimulation, bradycardia, and miosis. Subsequently, cerebral cortex depression (analgesic effect, narcosis), hypothalamus and brainstem depression, respiratory depression (medullary), cough reflex depression, and depression of the medullary vomiting center occur.

Codeine differs from morphine in several respects. It has only about one-fifth morphine's analgesic potency; however, it is very effective in depressing the cough reflex. As compared with morphine, the addiction liability of codeine is very low. For this reason, codeine is considered safer for use as a cough medicine than are other opiates.

Diacetylmorphine (heroin) has approximately five times the analgesic potency of morphine and is relatively short-acting (two to three hours). It is no longer listed in the *United States Pharmacopoeia*. Several other derivatives of morphine are similarly effective analgesics, with varying sedative and cough-suppressing properties. The most widely used of such drugs are dihydromorphinone (Dilaudid) and methyldihydromorphinone (Metopon).

Another morphine derivative worthy of consideration is nalorphine hydrochloride (Nalline). Nalorphine is of particular therapeutic value as an antagonist of morphine. Law enforcement agencies have used it as a tool for the detection of morphine addiction in humans because it induces signs and symptoms of acute abstinence in the morphine-dependent subject. Such use is dangerous, however, because nalorphine-induced withdrawal can be very severe; it may bring on convulsions and even respiratory and cardiovascular collapse. Nalorphine is, nevertheless, a valuable drug for treating the respiratory depression produced by morphine-type compounds. It is also valuable as a research tool for analyzing the mechanisms of action of morphine.

N-allylnormorphine (Nalorphine)

The last morphine derivative of interest in the present context is apomorphine. Apomorphine differs from all other members of its group in that its preponderant effect is the stimulation of medullary vomiting. Thus it is used to induce vomiting following acute poisoning when the stomach still contains some of the toxic material. Vomiting occurs five to ten minutes after subcutaneous administration.

Apomorphine

Another group of opiate analgesics includes the drugs most widely used for the relief of pain. Meperidine (Demerol) and methadone are preferred over morphine for analgesic therapy because they possess relatively less addiction liability than that agent. Methadone is analgesically as effective as morphine but only one tenth as potent. Since the effects of these compounds on the various organ systems are similar in most respects to those of morphine, we will not dwell on them. Let it suffice to say that analgesic effects presumed to be mediated via the cerebral cortex and midbrain are obtained at dosages that produce relatively few reports of subjective euphoria. As with the naturally occurring opiates, the depressive effects on respiration of meperidine and methadone can be antagonized by nalorphine.

Meperidine   Methadone

We have repeatedly referred to the "addiction liability" of natural and synthetic analgesics without specifying just what is meant by this term. Drug addiction is a complex and little understood problem in humans, and therefore much of the terminology involved in its description is not applicable to experimental animals. The definition of addiction set forth by the World Health Organization° emphasizes damage to the individual and society and

° "Drug addiction is a state of periodic or chronic intoxication, detrimental to the individual and to society, produced by the repeated consumption of a drug (natural or synthetic). Its characteristics include: (1) An overpowering desire or need (compulsion) to continue taking the drug and to obtain it by any means. (2) A tendency to increase the dose. (3) A psychic (psychological) and sometimes a physical dependence on the effects of the drug." (World Health Organization, 1950)

is clearly beyond the scope of drug addiction research with animals. However, if we examine the process carefully, we need not make evaluative statements in order to define addiction liability.

An experimental animal that has the opportunity to self-administer a drug repeatedly can be tested for addiction. If the animal (1) exhibits a characteristic physical *abstinence syndrome* (vomiting, tremors, convulsions, etc.) when the opportunity to self-administer the drug is withdrawn, (2) continues to self-administer the drug when the opportunity is again provided, and (3) increases the dosage over successive self-administrations, we can say the animal is *addicted.* This encompasses two defining syndromes: (1) a physical abstinence syndrome, and (2) a behavioral syndrome of self-administration characterized by the tendency to increase the dosage of the drug.

Numerous clinical writers have distinguished addiction from habituation in human drug abuse. The human who is habituated will readily self-administer the drug if it is available; but he has little tendency to increase dosage, and exhibits no physical abstinence syndrome on withdrawal of the drug. Another term applied to this category of drug dependence is *psychic dependence.* This term suggests that the process is mental as opposed to physical and therefore not measurable. The choice of terminology is unfortunate, as will be pointed out in the chapter that deals in detail with a program of research on drug dependence.

Many theories have been proposed regarding the mechanism of drug dependence, the development of tolerance to opiates, and the abstinence syndrome; however, the actual processes involved remain subject to conjecture. The best evidence suggests that adaptation to the continued presence of these drugs in the central nervous system involves biochemical changes, especially changes concerned with energy release mechanisms (Krueger, Eddy, Sumwalt, 1941; Tatum and Seevers, 1931; Wikler, 1953).

Sedatives and Hypnotics: The first drugs used for management of psychiatric patients were anesthetics and drugs that produced sleeplike states. These compounds acted by generally depressing cerebral excitation. The two classes of compounds that have been distinguished according to the degree of cerebral and behavioral depression produced are hypnotics and sedatives. Capable of producing anesthesia at high doses, *hypnotic* (or soporific) drugs administered in lower doses cause drowsiness, reduced motor activity, and reduced responsiveness to the environment; if even lower doses are given, *sedation* results. In sedation, the central nervous system's threshold for irritability is elevated, but the sleeplike drowsiness associated with the hypnotic state is not induced.

Among the first sedative-hypnotics employed were the *bromides.* Bromides cause central nervous system depression associated with motor incoordination, slurred speech, and confusion; a syndrome of intoxication follows chronic bromide administration. While these compounds have been shown to depress the motor cortex, their specific mechanism of action is not known.

The bromides are usually administered orally and are rapidly absorbed from the gastrointestinal tract. Bromides are poorly distributed across many membranes, including nerve cell membranes. Their effects may not be immediate, but may build up slowly. Though excretion begins quickly after administration, it progresses extremely slowly, with traces of the bromide detected in the urine as long as 20 days after ingestion of a single dose. This unusually slow rate of excretion may account in part for the tendency of a single dose to produce a hangover effect.

Chloral hydrate and *paraldehyde* used to be employed in many hospitals for the management of atavistic psychiatric patients. These compounds can depress the central nervous system sufficiently to produce anesthesia. Their therapeutic index is so small, however, that they are seldom used for this purpose today. In humans, these compounds are administered orally or rectally to produce drowsiness and insensitivity to stimuli. At therapeutic dosages (1 to 2 gm. in humans), the duration of sleep or drowsiness is about five hours, with little hangover effect. As a result, these drugs have replaced the bromides for most sedative purposes. Their mechanism of action is unknown.

Chloral Hydrate   Paraldehyde

Unlike the aforementioned compounds, the *barbiturates* are used both as anesthetics and sedative-hypnotics. All the barbiturates are derivatives of barbituric acid and are classified according to their durations of action: long, intermediate, short, and ultrashort. The potency and duration of action are determined, in part, by the characteristics of the alkyl side chains. An increase in the length of the side chains increases the potency and decreases the duration of action. Substitution of a branched chain for a straight chain produces a shorter duration of action, unsaturated short chains being more active than saturated short chains. The barbiturates with an ultrashort duration of action commonly have sulfur in place of oxygen on position two. Figure 3.3 presents examples of the various types of barbiturates classified by structure and duration of action.

Numerous hypotheses have been proposed to explain the cerebral depressing action of the barbiturates, but many loose ends remain unaccounted for. Barbiturates have very little effect on the gastrointestinal tract and only alter striate muscle activity at very high doses. Effects on the kidney are indirect, because the barbiturates produce hypotension secondary to cardiovascular depression, which in turn results in suppression of urine formation. The consequence is prolongation of drug action.

Barbiturates may be administered by all routes and vary in rate of ab-

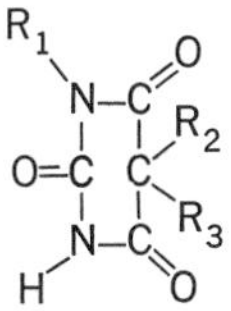

BARBITURIC ACID NUCLEUS

Barbiturate	R_1	R_2	R_3	Duration of Action
Barbital	H—	C_2H_5—	C_2H_5—	Long
Phenobarbital	H—	C_2H_5—	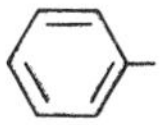 (phenyl)	Long

Amobarbital	H—	C_2H_5—	CH_3—CH—CH_2—CH_2—
			        |
			      CH_3
				Intermediate

Pentobarbital	H—	C_2H_5—	CH_3—CH_2—CH_2—CH—
			             |
			           CH_3
				Intermediate

Secobarbital	H—	CH_2=CH—CH_2—	CH_3—CH_2—CH_2—CH—
			             |
			           CH_3
				Short

Hexobarbital	CH_3—	CH_3—	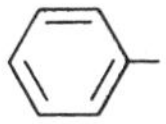 (phenyl)	Ultrashort

Fig. 3.3 Duration of action and chemical structure of barbiturates. Representative long, intermediate, short, and ultrashort acting barbiturates with corresponding modifications of R_1, R_2, and R_3 radicals. (Shideman, 1958; in: Drill [Ed.] 1958)

sorption according to the particular compound administered, the site of administration, and the nature of the experimental subject. The attainment of maximal blood concentration following oral administration varies from four to 18 hours, depending on the drug administered. Following intravenous administration, equilibrium between blood and various tissues is rapidly established, with different barbiturates possessing varying tissue affinities. Thiopental is very soluble in lipid tissue, while barbital is minimally soluble (only 5 per cent). The ultrashort action of the thiobarbiturates appears to be due to their extremely high solubility in body fats rather than to rapid metabolism or excretion. With the exception of barbital, barbiturates undergo transformation before excretion. They may be oxidized, lose N-alkyl radicals, undergo desulfuration, or be hydrolyzed (the barbiturate ring). As might be surmised, the longer-acting barbiturates are more slowly metabolized than the short-acting compounds. Barbiturates are excreted almost entirely by the kidneys. The process is extremely slow, making repeated administration of the same dose of the same drug a questionable procedure unless accumulation is taken into consideration (Shideman, 1958).

Tolerance to barbiturates develops slowly but ultimately leads to physical dependence. On discontinuation of high doses, an abstinence syndrome of longer duration than opiate abstinence syndromes ensues. Seven to ten days of illness following barbiturate withdrawal is common, and the condition is frequently characterized by grand mal convulsions, hyperthermia, delirium and, occasionally, death. Barbiturates are used more freely than opiates in medical practice, yet in certain respects, barbiturate dependence is more dangerous and damaging to the organism than opiate dependence. (Isbell, *et. al.*, 1950).

Phenothiazine Derivatives: Most of the drugs discussed up to this point have been known to psychiatrists, pharmacologists, and psychologists for many years; however, for a long time there was little interest in the behavioral actions of these compounds. Not until the 1950's, and the clinical introduction of the first "tranquilizing" drugs, did the behavioral actions of drugs arouse wide notice. The first major compound introduced was chlorpromazine (1954), although the closely related drug promazine had been developed for different purposes 10 years earlier (Gilman and Shirley, 1944). The most remarkable action of chlorpromazine is its ability to reduce the frequency of aggressive, agitated outbursts in seriously ill psychotics, with relatively less of the ataxia, skeletal muscle incoordination, and drowsiness associated with the bromides, chloral hydrate, paraldehyde, and the barbiturates. It was this apparent specificity of behavioral action that generated tremendous interest in the pharmacological manipulation of behavior. Indeed, for several years, chlorpromazine and other phenothiazine derivatives were the primary concern of researchers in the new field of "psychopharmacology." Because the phenothiazines have played a major role in the development of a science dealing with the interaction of drugs and behavior, we will discuss chlorpromazine and its relatives in some detail.

The parent compound of this group, phenothiazine, was used as a vermifuge and anthelmintic for many years. Because of the frequency of blood dyscrasias and liver damage associated with its use, however, humans are no longer treated with it (Berger, 1960). Following the discovery of the behavioral action of chlorpromazine, pharmaceutical chemists synthesized many other phenothiazine derivatives. Those that survived initial toxicity screening have been classified into three subcategories, all of which possess behavioral actions; these categories are the piperazine propyl series, the dimethylaminopropyl series, and the methylpiperidyl series. These subgroups vary from the phenothiazine nucleus at the number-two and number-ten positions, as indicated in Fig. 3.4.

Chlorpromazine is used here as the prototype of phenothiazine compounds, since the others differ from chlorpromazine primarily in the degree to which various effects are produced. Chlorpromazine is a dimethylaminopropyl phenothiazine that possesses a chloride radical on the number-two carbon. It has been assumed that chlorpromazine, like most behaviorally active drugs, has a primary site of action in the central nervous system. Chlorpromazine has been found to have little effect on monosynaptic or polysynaptic reflex arcs in the spinal cord, further, it appears to produce little "generalized" central nervous system depression. It has therefore been suggested that this agent causes specific modulation of reticular formation transmission. If so, this would produce the characteristic sleeplike electroencephalogram patterns and account for some of the behavioral effects encountered (Funderburk, King, and Unna, 1953; DeMaar and Martin, 1956). The chemoreceptor trigger zone in the medulla is depressed by chlorpromazine, thus inhibiting vomiting (Cook and Toner, 1954; Galviano and Wang, 1955). Central thermoregulation is altered so that body temperature tends to fluctuate with room temperature (Courvoisier, *et al.*, 1953; Dawson and Hiestand, 1955).

The absorption and distribution of chlorpromazine varies considerably with species and ambient temperature; it occurs rapidly, however, following either oral or parenteral administration. For example, maximal concentration of the drug in the lungs and kidneys of mice was obtained 48 hours after administration when the animals were maintained in a room at 18°C, and six hours after administration when the room temperature was 28°C. (Kok, 1955). Tissue distribution varies with species, with the highest concentrations found in the lungs of rabbits (Kok, 1955) and the brains of dogs (Salzman and Brodie, 1956). Within 72 hours after intravenous administration, 1.25 per cent (Salzman and Brodie, 1956) to 8 per cent (Lehmann and Hanrahan, 1954) of the total amount administered can be recovered in the urine as unchanged drug. Another 12 per cent is excreted as chlorpromazine sulfoxide, and at least two other metabolites can be distinguished in the urine (Salzman, Moran, and Brodie, 1955). It is thought that most of the biotransformation takes place in the liver, which is a common site of toxicity in humans receiving the drug (Cares and Buckman, 1961), although the site of metabolism is not necessarily related to the observed hepatotoxicity.

There is extensive evidence that chlorpromazine and the other phenothiazine derivatives diminish unconditioned spontaneous motor activity, e.g., as measured in a jiggle cage or photoelectric cell activity chamber. The effects of a given dose on conditioned responses of various types are not at all simple; the evidence that effects depend to a considerable extent on the animal's past history and its current circumstances is discussed at length later.

A. *Phenothiazine Group*
   a. *Dimethyl-Amino-Propyl Subgroup*

	STRUCTURE	CHEMICAL NAME	GENERIC NAME	TRADE NAME
1.		10-(3-dimethylamino-N-propyl) phenothiazine	*Promazine*	Sparine
2.		2-chloro-10-(3'-dimethylamino-N-propyl) phenothiazine	*Chlorpromazine*	Thorazine
3.		10-(3-dimethylaminopropyl)-2-(trifluoromethyl) phenothiazine	*Triflupromazine*	Vesprin
4.		2-Methoxy-10-(3'-dimethylamino propyl) phenothiazine	*Methoxypromazine*	Tentone

b. *Piperazine-Propyl Subgroup*

	STRUCTURE	CHEMICAL NAME	GENERIC NAME	TRADE NAME
1.		2-chloro-10-[3-(1-methyl-4-piperazinyl)-propyl]-phenothiazine	*Prochlorperozine*	Compozine
2.		10-[3-(1-Methyl-4-piperazinyl propyl]-2-trifluoromethyl-phenothiazine	*Trifluoperazine*	Stelazine
3.		1-(2-hydroxyethyl)-4-[3-(2-chloro-10-phenothiazyl)-propyl]-piperazine	*Perphenazine*	Trilafon

STRUCTURE	CHEMICAL NAME	GENERIC NAME	TRADE NAME

4.

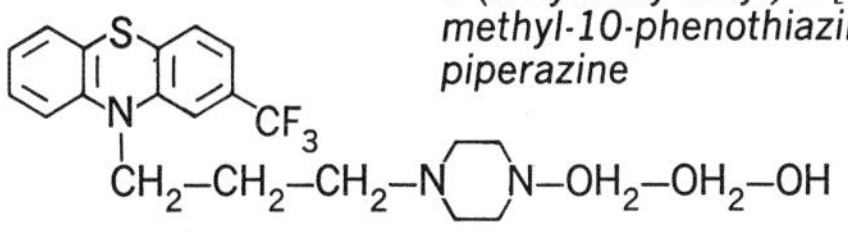

1-(2-hydroxy-ethyl)-4-[3-(2-trifluoro-methyl-10-phenothiazinyl)-propyl]-piperazine — *Fluphenazine* — Prolixin Permitil

CH₂—CH₂—CH₂—N‿N—OH₂—OH₂—OH (CF₃)

5.

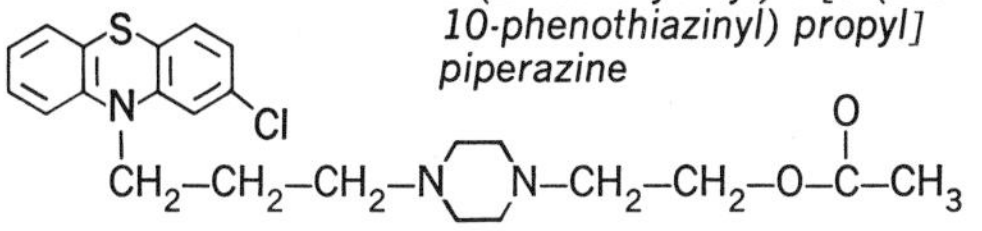

1-(2-Acetoxyethyl)-4-[3-(2-chloro-10-phenothiazinyl) propyl] piperazine — *Thiopropazate* — Dartal

$$CH_2-CH_2-CH_2-N\text{‿}N-CH_2-CH_2-O-\overset{\overset{\displaystyle O}{||}}{C}-CH_3$$

6.

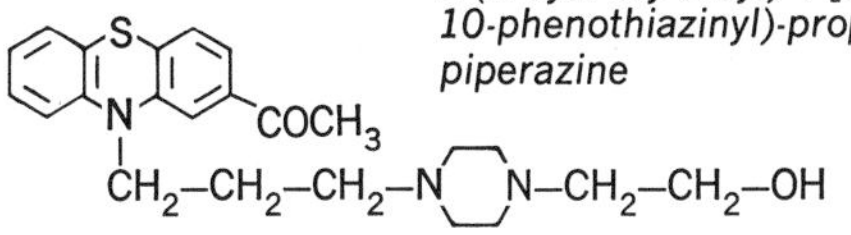

1-(2-hydroxy-ethyl)-4-[3-(2-acetyl-10-phenothiazinyl)-propyl]-piperazine — *Acetophenazine* — Tindal

CH₂—CH₂—CH₂—N‿N—CH₂—CH₂—OH (COCH₃)

7.

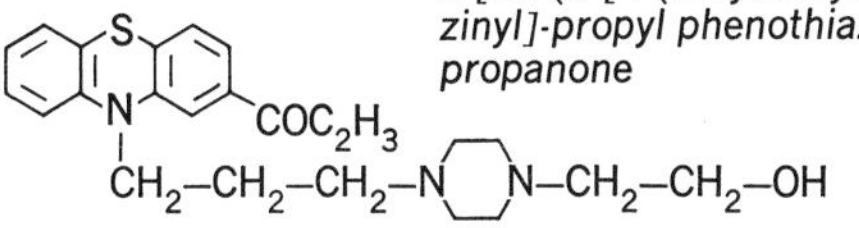

1-[10-(3-[4-(2-hydroxyethyl)-1-pipero-zinyl]-propyl phenothiazine-2-yl]-1-propanone — *Corphenazine* — Proketazine

CH₂—CH₂—CH₂—N‿N—CH₂—CH₂—OH (COC₂H₃)

MAJOR TRANQUILIZERS—3

c. Methyl-Piperidyl Subgroup

STRUCTURE	CHEMICAL NAME	GENERIC NAME	TRADE NAME

1.

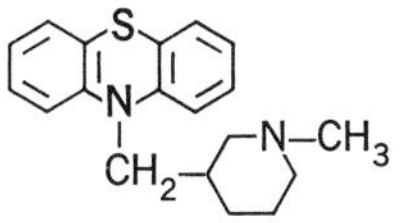

N-(1-methyl-3-piperidyl methyl) phenothiazine — *Mepazine* — Pacatal

2.

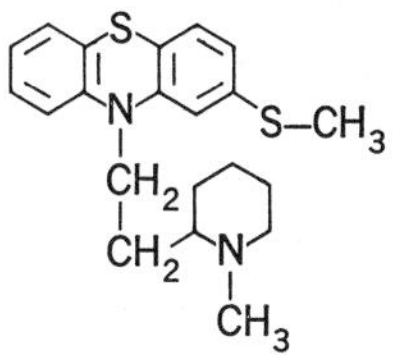

2-Methylmercapto-10-[2 (N-methyl-2-piperidyl) ethyl] phenothiazine — *Thioridazine* — Mellaril

Fig. 3.4 Classification of phenothiazine derivatives, used clinically as "major tranquilizers." The three chemical subclasses are distinguished on the basis of the side chain attached to the amino group as follows: (a) dimethyl-amino-propyl phenothiazines. (b) Piperazine-propyl phenothiazines. (c) Methyl piperidyl phenothiazines. (Benson and Schiele, 1962, pp. 12–14, Figs. 3a, 3b, 3c)

Visual inspection of animals treated with moderate doses of chlorpromazine reveals that very aggressive animals are less aggressive, hyperactive animals are less active, difficult-to-handle animals are somewhat more docile, etc. These effects are different from those produced by the barbiturates, where comparable degrees of "taming" or reduction in skeletal-motor activity would be associated with profound ataxia, stupor, and hypnosis. At the same time, it is by no means proven that these effects are not confounded by other drug effects, e.g., hypotension, muscular weakness, and that the observer does not assume that a generally less-active animal has been made specifically tamer. These are but a few unsolved problems involved in evaluating the behavioral effects of the phenothiazines.

Rauwolfia Alkaloids: Aside from the phenothiazine derivatives, the Rauwolfia alkaloids have made the greatest impact on the development of a basic science of drugs and behavior. *Rauwolfia serpentina* is a woody plant that has been used in India for centuries for a variety of therapeutic purposes. Of the various compounds contained in its root, *reserpine* appears to be the most behaviorally active.

Like the phenothiazines, reserpine has been associated clinically with descriptive terms like "calming effect," "reduction of tensions," and "diminished hostile-aggressive behavior" (Bein, 1956).

Reserpine

Reserpine was first isolated from *Rauwolfia serpentina* in 1952, and was synthesized in 1956. As can be seen from the diagram of its chemical structure, reserpine bears a slight resemblance in at least part of its molecule to the neurohumor 5-hydroxytryptamine. Reserpine causes hypotension that ranges from very slight diminution of blood pressure to large baric drops in hypertensive patients. Reserpine usually increases gastrointestinal secretions and motility; but its autonomic effects are limited primarily to gastrointestinal and cardiovascular responses, although it does produce generally increased tonic parasympathetic activity and decreased tonic sympathetic activity (Bein, Gross, Tripod, and Meier, 1953).

Reserpine has had decreasing clinical use as a behavioral depressant in recent years and is now primarily interesting as a research tool. When the drug is administered intravenously, very little effect can be seen for 20 to

40 minutes. The acute effects of sedation, hypotension, etc., then observed are quite different from those that appear after five to ten days of reserpine administration.

After rats have received intraperitoneal doses for several days, the initial diminution of spontaneous motor activity is lessened, and the animals appear very much as they did before receiving any drug. Over this period, however, reserpine will have significantly altered neurohormonal levels (specifically norepinephrine, epinephrine, and 5-hydroxytryptamine). Thus reserpine's initial effect is markedly to diminish brain concentrations of these endogenous agents. After several successive days of reserpine treatment, however, the brain levels of these substances again increase, reaching maximal levels in seven to ten days. If reserpine is discontinued, the neurohormonal levels return to normal over a seven-to-ten-day period.

Studies of brain concentrations of reserpine indicate that the drug has been metabolized and excreted long before the hormonal depletion has disappeared. Thus, reserpine has a gradual onset of action that causes a neurohormonal depletion that outlasts the presence of the drug itself in the organism. This suggests that reserpine may activate the release of other endogenous substances. In any event, there is indication that some degree of covariation exists between the brain concentrations of the aforementioned amines, which are depleted by reserpine, and the behavioral actions of the drug. This thesis has been most actively pursued by Brodie and coworkers (Brodie and Shore, 1957).

It should be apparent that the hypothesis that amine concentrations in the brain control behavior (particularly "emotional-abnormal" behavior) has significantly influenced the direction of much neurochemical-psychopharmacological research. Information about the pathways by which these amines are synthesized, their distribution and storage, and their biotransformations is of basic importance to understanding the actions of behaviorally active drugs like reserpine. We therefore find that current intensive investigations are based on the assumption that these mechanisms are indeed *the* mechanisms of action of the behaviorally active drugs.

Unfortunately, the evidence is not as clear as one would like it to be. For example, brain concentrations of the monoamines do not seem to vary systematically with phenothiazine administration; yet these drugs produce profound alterations in behavior. Similarly, investigations of the dibenzazepine compounds reveal that there is little or no relation between their behavioral effects and brain concentrations or amines. Thus, while certain very strong evidence suggests a covariation between the behavioral actions of a drug and the brain levels of naturally occurring neurohumors, the generality of the relationship has not been clearly established.

Dibenzazepine: The dibenzazepine compounds are structurally similar to the phenothiazine derivatives, and have similar behavioral actions. They are reported to act as sedative agents in animals and normal humans, but as antidepressant agents in individuals with certain psychiatric depressive conditions. The differences between the effects of low and high doses of the most widely used dibenzazepine, *imipramine*, are very marked. Low doses cause increased blood pressure and increased gastrointestinal motility, and facilitate the pharyngeal ciliary beat in the frog (cholinergic), while opposite effects are obtained with high doses (Osbourn and Sigg, 1960).

Imipramine

The behavioral depressant actions of imipramine have been studied with respect to brain levels of 5-hydroxytryptamine, epinephrine, and norepinephrine; the interaction of imipramine with reserpine-induced depletion of these monoamines has also been investigated. Imipramine has no tendency to deplete brain monoamines, although it does antagonize the central nervous system actions and the behavioral depressant actions of reserpine. Imipramine was initially believed to reduce the behavioral depressive effects of reserpine by maintaining normal monoamine levels in the brain; however, careful examinations of animals treated with both drugs have revealed no signs of behavioral depression, although the degree of monoamine depletion was comparable to that in control subjects not pretreated with imipramine (Sulser, Watts, and Brodie, 1962). Thus, the mechanism of action of the dibenzazepines remains unknown.

Xanthines: One of the most commonly consumed nonprescription drugs in the United States is caffeine. Caffeine, like theobromine and theophylline, is a naturally occurring drug with an xanthine nucleus. These drugs have the ability to produce central nervous system stimulation, with predominant effects on the cerebral cortex. Our discussion is limited to caffeine, since it is the most interesting xanthine for behavioral purposes. In any event, the other xanthines differ primarily in their relative intensities of action.

Caffeine is capable of increasing excitability in all parts of the central nervous system, with the cerebral cortex and medullary centers exhibiting particular sensitivity to it. Large doses may produce muscle twitches and lead eventually to clonic and tonic spasms. The mechanism of this stimulant effect on the central nervous system is unknown. It is believed, however, that certain metabolic enzymes may be inhibited by caffeine and that such inhibition may result in the accumulation of acetylcholine (Gemmill, 1958). Stimulation of the medulla by caffeine administration produces respiratory acceleration, but the practical value of this effect is questionable. Though in mild respiratory depression (e.g., that caused by barbiturate overdosage), the depth of respiration may be increased, profound respiratory depression is unaffected by caffeine.

Smooth muscles (e.g., bronchioles, blood vessels, intestines) are directly depressed by caffeine, while gastric secretions are increased. It is often assumed that caffeine also increases cardiac output, but this is not usually the

Caffeine

case with therapeutic doses. Caffeine can directly stimulate the heart *in vitro,* but vagal regulation via the medulla usually overcomes any stimulant action in the intact animal. Blood pressure is little affected, if at all.

Caffeine is rapidly absorbed, either orally or intramuscularly. Following intravenous administration, 12 to 22 per cent disappears from the blood each hour, and is rapidly metabolized (Axelrod and Reichenthal, 1953). There appears to be no propensity for accumulation. Mild toxic effects include tremors, vomiting, heightened spontaneous motor activity, and tachycardia. Very large overdoses or rapid intravenous administration can cause muscle twitches, convulsions, respiratory collapse, hypotension, and cardiac fibrillation.

Diphenylmethane Derivatives: Several compounds possessing atropine-like anticholinergic actions appear to have some behavioral depressant actions as well. Because of the anticholinergic side effects, they have not gained widespread therapeutic use; as a consequence, relatively little is known about them. Their effects in experimental animals can range from diminution of spontaneous motor activity to the production of manic excitement. They do not antagonize amphetamine, nor do they potentiate barbiturates. In general, neither the basic pharmacology nor the behavioral properties of this class has been clearly delineated. Examples of such drugs are benactyzine, azacyclonol, and hydroxyzine.

Monoamine Oxidase Inhibitors: The effects of brain monoamines on behavior have not been finally determined, but enough evidence implicates them in the effects of behaviorally active drugs to necessitate careful consideration of this class of endogenous agents. Indeed, as was noted above with reference to reserpine and related drugs, depletion of these amines is at times associated with behavioral depression. Similarly, blocking the metabolic inactivation of 5-hydroxytryptamine, epinephrine, and norepinephrine is thought by some investigators to be associated with an antidepressive effect in human patients. The mechanism of this blocking action is not clearly understood; but it is thought to involve either conjugation with the inactivating enzyme to form a stable substrate, or the blockade of enzyme synthesis. In order to understand the proposed mechanisms, we must reconsider the synthesis and metabolism of the monoamines.

It has been known since 1928 that liver homogenates contain an enzyme that oxidizes tyramine. Later studies, revealing that epinephrine, norepinephrine, and serotonin are also oxidized by enzymes present in liver homogenates, have introduced the notion of a nonspecific monoamine oxidase enzyme.

The discovery that a relation exists between behavioral change and the inhibition of monoamine oxidase was accidental. It was found that tuberculous patients treated with iproniazid exhibited elevated mood. Independent studies with iproniazid revealed that it selectively inhibits monoamine oxidase. These findings suggested that psychiatric depression might be the result of monoamine depletion, and that monoamine restoration by inhibition of monoamine oxidase might constitute a new treatment for depression (Bosworth, 1960). Unfortunately, iproniazid was found to be toxic and to produce a relatively high incidence of jaundice. This led to the development of numerous other hydrazine compounds that retain monoamine-oxidase-inhibiting action but exhibit varying degrees of toxicity.

Like reserpine, the monoamine oxidase inhibitors are characterized by delayed action; their behavioral effects, too, outlast the presence of the drug in the body. In experimental animals, spontaneous motor activity is increased after five days of iproniazid administration (Blaschko and Chrusciel, 1960; Brown, 1960). The behavioral depressant action of reserpine is also antagonized by this drug. It appears, then, that reserpine and iproniazid exert their effects at least in part by regulating the brain levels of monoamines. Thus, in the light of other information, it appears that brain monoamine concentration may influence behavior, although other variables, or other metabolites, are also involved.

Drugs Producing Sensory Distortion: Various compounds, ranging from toxins like lead and organophosphate insecticides to mescaline and lysergic acid diethylamide, are known to produce sensory distortions. These may be visual, auditory, or tactile, or they may be complex distortions involving both temporal and spatial factors. Discovery of a naturally occurring compound that produces many such sensory alterations and relatively few debilitating effects leads to widespread self-administration of the drug by humans. Historically, in many parts of the world, self-administration of such drugs has occurred as part of religious practices or accepted socio-cultural activities; but as a rule, self-administration has been socially and legally prohibited in Western culture. As is so often the case, these constraints have been associated with increased self-administration of the prohibited compounds. Thus, the conditions leading to self-administration of sensory-distorting drugs seem to be primarily social, while the behavioral effects of such drugs appear to depend both on direct changes in the nervous system and on environmental factors.

The *cannabinol drugs* are usually inhaled as smoke or drunk as a tea, both of which are made from the dried leaves of either *Cannabis sativa* or *Cannabis sativa* var. *indica*. In this country the product is called marijuana and is illegal. The characteristic effects reported in humans are distortions of time, heightened sensitivity to colored stimuli, and, at times, hallucinations. To a significant degree, the euphoric effect of marijuana seems to be a function of a sympathetic social environment. The synthetic marijuana derivative synhexyl is said to produce approximately the same effects and has been demonstrated to alter behavior involving temporal discrimination in experimental animals (Ferster and Skinner, 1957). Cannabinols do not produce physical dependence.

Members of another family of sense-distorting drugs are structurally related to serotonin by their possession of an *indolethylamine* moiety.

Indolethylamine Moiety   Lysergic Acid Diethylamide

When Hofmann (1943) discovered that the ergot derivative lysergic acid diethylamide (LSD-25) produced profound sensory distortion, hallucinations, and other unpleasant side effects (vomiting and tachycardia), a good deal of interest was generated in it as a possible "model" psychosis drug, especially since hallucinatory effects induced seemed to resemble psychotic hallucinations. Subsequent investigations have suggested that hallucinatory action may be about all that LSD-25 effects have in common with psychosis. However, in its ability to antagonize almost completely the effects of 5-hydroxytryptamine, LSD-25 may be related to other behaviorally active drugs. High concentrations of LSD-25 have been shown to impair transmission of nerve impulses through the lateral geniculate body, suggesting the possible site of the drug's sensory distortion. Tolerance to the behavioral effects of LSD-25 develops very rapidly (e.g., after three successive daily administrations). Many animal subjects exhibit increased spontaneous motor activity while under its influence, as they do with most other drugs that stimulate the central nervous system.

There are undoubtedly many naturally occurring sense-distorting compounds similar to LSD-25. Bufotenine, psilocybin, harmine, and yohimbine are a few of the many compounds with mixed stimulant and depressant effects, capable of producing hallucinations and other sensory distortions. In no case is the mechanism of action understood, either pharmacologically or behaviorally. Whether these compounds will prove to be of major significance in behavioral pharmacology remains to be seen.

Unfortunately, it is very difficult to obtain adequate experimental information about the behavioral actions of these drugs, since their subjective effects seem to be particularly dependent on a sympathetic social environment. It has been suggested by those who use such drugs for religious purposes that favorable subjective effects are destroyed by a neutral, objective environment. This observation, coupled with the fact that it is not really possible to create an entirely sympathetic environment in a well-controlled laboratory setting, suggests that the conditions under which drugs might produce appropriate sensory experiences may be incompatible with scientific experimentation.

4

Principles of the Experimental Analysis of Behavior

The days of powdered unicorn horn are gone, and pharmacologists may view their prescientific predecessors with some measure of self-satisfaction; psychologists, unfortunately, have less reason for complacency. While pharmacology has evolved into a relatively sophisticated biological science, psychology has remained, until recently, in a more primitive scientific state. Historically, nonobservable phenomena and hypothetical entities have preoccupied psychologists. Conations and cognitions, ids and needs, engrams and nerve cell assemblies have been invoked in hypothetical explanation of behavioral events; and these ubiquitous but ever-evasive constructs have occupied the mainstream of psychological thought since psychology was first abortively expelled from the womb of philosophy.

As in pharmacology, the development of objective methods of observation in the new discipline of psychology preceded the establishment of a scientific approach to the study of behavior. However, before systematic observation was even possible, the question of what to observe had to be settled. Even I. P. Pavlov's remarkable experiments on the salivary reflex relegated behavioral data to a secondary role. Although Pavlov had developed the most precise techniques for behavioral control, he viewed them solely as tools with which to study the then unmeasurable actions of the central nervous system. It wasn't until 1913 that *behavior* was seriously suggested as subject suitable for scientific investigation. John B. Watson's *Behaviorism* led psychologists to adopt behavior as the subject matter of their science rather than opting, as they had in the past, for nonobservable internal events and processes. This emphasis on the observable actions of organisms not only made possible a science of behavior, it also marked the beginning of the experimental analysis of behavior.

Watson's revolutionary view of behavior brought scientific psychology through its infancy. Like most truly new movements, behaviorism generated extreme antagonism as well as avid support. For some, the traditional "inner man" was at stake, while others protested the rejection of internal physiological processes in favor of external behavioral events. Although the initial impact of behaviorism waned, it was revived 25 years later by a new group of behaviorists, whose spokesmen were Clark L. Hull and Burrhus F. Skinner. While Hull (1943) seemed to be primarily concerned with a theoretical analysis of behavior, Skinner (1938) directed his attention to an atheoretical-descriptive approach. During the years between 1940 and 1960, votaries of both theorists analyzed behavioral events at the level of observation; in their concern with the logical relations between experimental operations and observation, they resembled the modern physicists who analyzed physical phenomena operationally (Bridgman, 1927). In recent years, there has been increasing interest in a purely descriptive science of behavior, much as Skinner proposed in 1938.

In this book the approach to the analysis of behavior is largely in the tradition of the behaviorism of Watson and the descriptive behaviorism of Skinner. It is well, therefore, to begin this discussion with a set of definitions based on the fundamental concepts of these two scientists.

BASIC TERMINOLOGY

The term "behavior," which Watson introduced to the realm of scientific inquiry, is cardinal. When the layman speaks of behavior, he refers in a general way to whatever an organism is doing. More accurately, one might say that behavior is "what [one organism] is observed by another organism to be doing" (Skinner, 1938). But even this cautious definition of behavior is too vague to be scientifically useful.

To avoid conceptual fuzziness, scientific observations must be specified both spatially and temporally; e.g., an action potential is described in terms of distance traveled along an axon per unit of time. Similarly, *behavior is defined as the movement of an organism or its parts within a spatial and temporal frame of reference, as observed by other organisms* (the dog moved from compartment A to compartment B [a distance of 14 feet] in 9.2 seconds). This definition is at a level of physical description susceptible of confirmation by any number of observers. No reference is made to events, either mental or physiological, that are not immediately observable. This is the domain with which descriptive behaviorism deals; and it is a domain to be further described as we specify the operations by which given classes of behavior are observed, and discuss the functional relations among various classes of operations and behaviors.

Much of behavior seems to vary with certain aspects of an organism's environment. When it can be shown that a given *part* of behavior can be manipulated at will by modifying *a specific aspect* of the organism's surroundings, then the environment legitimately enters into a description of behavior. Such an aspect of the environment, or the modification of such an aspect, is called a *stimulus;* the correlated part of behavior is called a *response* (Skinner, 1938). Neither term may be defined without the other. These interdependent concepts, neither of which can stand alone, together form the basic unit of behavioral analysis.

Now it must be carefully noted that the terms *reflex* and *conditioned reflex*—but not reflex arc—*refer to the covariation between a given stimulus and a given response.* A blow to the patellar tendon is followed by a leg kick. The stimulus is a blow to the patellar tendon; the response a leg kick. The relation between the two is called the patellar reflex. This says nothing whatever by way of "explanation" at a neurological level.

Specifying the series of neurons activated, the sites of synapses, etc., would constitute a description of the *reflex arc.* Many laws about the *reflex* can be established without knowing anything about the *reflex arc.* In a sense then, *reflex* and *reflex arc* are independent concepts. Investigators frequently study one with no concern whatever about the other. The neurophysiologist may ask for a description of the biophysical events at the first synapse in a three-neuron reflex arc. The psychologist may ask about the relation of the interval between stimulus presentations to the magnitude of the response. Both may be interesting questions leading to worthwhile empirical contributions, but they are essentially independent. Though the two investigators may eventually arrive at common questions, such congruity need not be immediately apparent. Failure of behaviorists and neurophysiologists to arrive at questions of common interest in no way invalidates questions of either orientation. They are simply different questions.

Stimulus-response relations like the one described above are the units of behavioral analysis, while the reflex arc is a unit of physiological analysis. We will discuss this distinction further, but it is essential that the two concepts be distinguished from the outset.

A CLASSIFICATION OF BEHAVIOR

All behavior can be viewed in terms of the covariation of certain aspects of the environment with components of behavior. Some stimuli can be shown to be associated with certain changes in behavior at their first conjunction. For example, a newborn infant will turn its head in the direction of a nipple touched against its cheek the first time the stimulus is presented. To this type of behavior (which occurs intact on the first presentation of the stimulus) we apply the term *unconditioned*.

There are other stimuli that, while initially ineffective in eliciting a given response, come to elicit that response after repeated presentation in conjunction with a second stimulus. The same infant will not salivate when the smell of roasting turkey is presented, no matter how long he has gone without milk; however, some years and many Thanksgiving dinners later, the smell of roasting turkey will elicit profuse salivation. This type of behavior is called *conditioned*.

The simplest types of unconditioned behavior are seldom studied by psychologists, but are more frequently studied by physiologists and neuropharmacologists. These are the relatively simple reflexes—eye blink, knee jerk, Babinski reflex. Most reflexes of this class are of interest because they reveal specific clinical neurological signs that distinguish normal from abnormal functioning. Many of the behavioral measures used in classical pharmacological techniques employ behaviors of this type. They are relatively fixed, involve the same muscle topographies, have narrowly defined latencies and response durations, and are elicited by highly specific stimuli. It is important to note that this type of behavior is *elicited* by environmental stimuli and has moreover, an involuntary character that is almost entirely dependent on the stimulus. In terms of day-to-day interactions of the organism with its environment, such behavior is vegetative and plays primarily a protective role rather than acting on or altering the environment.

By contrast, a second type of unconditioned behavior embraces both extremely simple responses and extremely complex sequences. This type of behavior, too, is nearly always associated with highly specific aspects of the environment, has a fixed pattern, and is elicited rather than freely emitted. Such behavior differs from the simpler reflexes in its degree of complexity, in the unitary character of the entire behavioral sequence, and in the species-specificity of particular responses. Interrupting such a sequence of behavior usually results in an interruption of performance, and repetition of the sequence from the beginning. Such behavior is often called "instinctive," although the meaningfulness of this term has been seriously questioned (Verplanck, 1957). Such phenomena as orienting responses, tropisms, migration, following responses, and various courtship and aggressive behavior patterns fall within this category (Hinde, 1966; Lorenz, 1950; Thorpe, 1956; Tinbergen, 1951).

Instinctive behavior has been studied primarily by ethologists and comparative psychologists. While the literature is extensive, extremely interesting, and of potential value to the behavioral pharmacologist, so little has been done in this area with behaviorally active drugs that it seems inappropriate to speculate on analytical methods at this time. The paucity of research in this area probably reflects a lack of interest in conducting drug research in the fields of ethology and comparative psychology as well as the unfamiliarity of pharmacologists with ethological methods.

Much of the behavior studied in the behavioral or pharmacological laboratory is conditioned behavior—behavior that would not have occurred without training. Furthermore, most of the behavior essential for self-maintenance, and the day-to-day adaptation of the animal to its environment, is also conditioned behavior. There is justification then for devoting a large portion of our discussion to conditioned behavior.

In this book we deal with two classes of conditioned behavior, *reflex* and *operant*, and it is very important that we spell out their common and distinguishing characteristics, how they are measured, the variables controlling them, and the laws governing each class. Before elaborating on these classes of behavior, let us very briefly distinguish between behavior that is controlled by a specific eliciting stimulus and behavior that is controlled by its own consequences. Behavior of the former type is called *reflex* and behavior of the latter variety is called *operant*.

EXPERIMENTAL ANALYSIS OF REFLEX BEHAVIOR

In many psychology textbooks, the procedure for conditioning a reflex is referred to as Pavlovian conditioning in honor of the man who initiated the experimental investigation of this phenomenon.[*] The Russian physiologist Ivan Petrovich Pavlov was awarded the Nobel Prize for his studies of the regulatory mechanisms of the secretory and muscular activities of the gastrointestinal tract. He observed that the flow of saliva and gastric secretions in dogs increased markedly not only when the animals saw food, but when they saw the laboratory attendant who fed them. Clearly, the flow of digestive secretions elicited by the sight of the attendant was not an inborn reflex but a stimulus-response relation acquired through experience. To determine the precise manner in which such relations were acquired, Pavlov developed procedures for conditioning reflexes; his intensive investigations of environmental variables effecting the acquisition and maintenance of conditioned reflexes are of extreme importance to behavioral pharmacology. (For Pavlov, the conditioning procedure was a tool with which to study the physiology of the central nervous system; but we are not concerned here with his theories about the neural basis for the conditioning of reflexes.)

[*] A variety of other terms has been used to name this conditioning procedure. "Classical conditioning," "respondent conditioning," and "Type S conditioning" are the most widely used.

BASIC EXPERIMENTAL PROCEDURE
FOR STUDYING REFLEX CONDITIONING °

In order to study the variables affecting acquisition and maintenance of a new stimulus-response unit (i.e., a conditioned reflex), one must first elicit the response by another experimentally manipulatable stimulus. Pavlov and his numerous students and colleagues utilized two basic reflexes: (1) salivation elicited by food presentation and (2) salivation elicited by introducing a mild acid solution into the mouth. The food or acid presentation is called the *unconditioned stimulus* (US); the salivation induced, the *unconditioned response* (UR).

In the simplest conditioning procedure, a stimulus (for example, an auditory stimulus) that does not influence the rate of salivation is introduced immediately before presentation of a small quantity of food. If, after a number of trials, the auditory stimulus alone elicits salivation, the tone is said to have become a *conditioned stimulus* (CS) capable of eliciting salivation. The salivation elicited by the conditioned stimulus is called the *conditioned response* (CR).

Subjects employed in the establishment of a conditioned salivary reflex are adult dogs surgically prepared with parotid gland fistulas. The fistula is formed by redirecting the duct from the parotid gland, which normally carries saliva to the mucous membrane surface of the mouth to the outside of the cheek; by cementing a glass funnel and tubing to the cheek over the fistula it is possible to collect and measure the number of drops of saliva secreted per unit of time.

To avoid distracting subjects with irrelevant stimuli, each subject is placed in a soundproof room during the experimental session; there it is restrained in a standing position by a harness. The experimenter can view the subject from an adjoining room; he can present auditory stimuli and food by remote control, and can record the rate and volume of salivation. Critical to the success of this type of conditioning procedure is the adaptation of the animal to the restraining and recording apparatus. This can be accomplished by insuring the animal's comfort in the restraining harness, and by gradually increasing the length of daily sessions over the course of several weeks until they last for several hours.

The salivation rate should be recorded for several experimental sessions before initiating the conditioning trials. Aperiodically during these sessions a tone of a fixed frequency and intensity is sounded for 30 seconds. Initially, tone presentation elicits various responses, such as head and ear movements, but these disappear as the subjects adapt to hearing the tone. At this point

---

° This section embraces only the principles derived by Pavlov using reflexes. A discussion of the range of behaviors that can be brought under control using this procedure is given in Chapter 5.

it is most important to demonstrate that the tone does not increase the rate of salivary secretion. If not, subjects are now ready for initiating the conditioning procedure.

Acquisition

Over the course of several sessions, each subject should be presented with 50 trials in which the auditory stimulus begins several seconds prior to presentation of a small quantity of meat powder. The trials are variably spaced in time, with an intertrial interval sufficient to allow salivation elicited by the previous food presentation to cease. On certain test trials (1, 10, 20, 30, 40, and 50) the auditory stimulus is presented for 30 seconds prior to the delivery of food to the subject.

Table 4.1 shows the results of an experiment by Anrep (1920), who used the procedure outlined above. The measurements obtained were: (1) the quantity of saliva elicited by the tone on the test trials, and (2) the latency (in seconds) from the onset of the tone to the secretion of the first drop of saliva. As can be seen from Anrep's data, the magnitude of salivation elicited by the tone increased from zero drops on trial 1 to 60 drops after 30 trials. Concomitantly, the latencies show a progressive decrease during the test trials. There was no further increase in the strength of the conditioned reflex after the thirtieth trial, as indicated by the facts that the magnitude of CR showed no further increase and the latencies (CS-CR interval) showed no further decrease.

On the basis of these data, we may conclude that an initially ineffective stimulus (the tone) came to elicit salivation by being continually presented immediately prior to presentation of a stimulus (food) possessing the ability to elicit salivation. On the basis of many experiments of this type, Pavlov formulated the following general principle for the conditioning of new reflex stimulus-response relations: If any stimuli are repeatedly presented

ACQUISITION OF A CONDITIONED SALIVARY REFLEX		Table 4.1
Number of Paired Stimulations	*Response Magnitude (Drops of Saliva)*	*Response Latency (Seconds)*
1	0	—
10	6	18
20	20	9
30	60	2
40	62	1
50	59	2

Acquisition of a salivary reflex in the dog using an auditory CS (tuning fork), and dog biscuit powder as the UCS. The magnitude of the response was measured in number of drops of saliva and the latency in seconds. (Anrep, 1920, p. 380, Table IV)

contiguously with stimuli that elicit unconditioned reflexes, the former stimuli begin, of themselves, to produce the effect of these unconditioned reflexes. We designate the two sorts of reflexes, and the stimuli by which they are elicited, as *unconditioned* (inborn) and *conditioned* (acquired) respectively (Pavlov, 1927).

The *Law of Reflex Conditioning* (Type S) summarizes the foregoing generalization as follows: *The approximately simultaneous presentation of two stimuli, one of which is capable of eliciting an unconditioned response, may produce an increase in the strength of a new reflex composed of the unconditioned response and the stimulus paired with the previously eliciting stimulus* (Skinner, 1938).

Pavlov chose the term "conditioned" because acquiring a reflex is conditional upon the occurrence of certain operations in the past experience of the animal, the principal operation being the temporal association of the unconditioned stimulus and the (initially) neutral stimulus.

Extinction

Once a conditioned reflex has been established, what are the conditions necessary for maintaining its strength? Is it possible to reverse the effects of the conditioning procedure by continuing to present the conditioned stimulus in the absence of the unconditioned stimulus? To answer these questions, we should use a subject that has acquired a stable conditioned tone-salivary reflex as previously described.

The conditioned auditory stimulus should be presented for 30 seconds at an interval of two minutes. Let no food presentations follow the auditory conditioned stimulus. Trials in which the CS (tone) is presented alone (i.e., without the US, food) are called extinction trials. A total of seven such extinction trials should be given. After a 23-minute rest period, another extinction trial should be given.

Table 4.2 presents the results of such a procedure (Pavlov, 1927). As can be seen, the magnitude of salivation elicited by the conditioned auditory stimulus diminished progressively with repeated presentation in the absence of food; the gradual weakening of the conditioned reflex was also reflected by increased latencies during the course of the seven extinction trials.

Following the 23-minute rest period, the conditioned reflex showed a marked increment in strength as indicated by increased magnitude of salivation and decreased latency. Strengthening a conditioned reflex by introducing a "rest period" between extinction trials is called *spontaneous recovery*.° If repeated blocs of extinction trials are separated by "rest periods," the amount of spontaneous recovery will diminish and will ultimately reach zero.

These results demonstrate that the ability of the conditioned stimulus to elicit the salivary response is dependent on continued association with the

---

° An unfortunately chosen term, since it mistakenly implies a lack of experimental control.

EXTINCTION OF A CONDITIONED SALIVARY REFLEX

Table 4.2

Latent Period in Seconds	Secretion of Saliva in Drops During 30 Seconds
3	
7	10
5	7
4	8
5	5
9	7
13	4
	3
23 minute rest period	
5	6

Experimental extinction of a classically conditioned salivary reflex. The metronome (CS) was sounded for 30 seconds during which the secretion of saliva (CR) was measured in drops, and at the same time the interval between the beginning of the stimulus and the beginning of the salivary secretion (the latent period) was recorded. In no case was the metronome followed by food presentation (UCS) as previously. The latent period increases and number of drops of saliva decrease with successive CS presentations alone. (Pavlov, 1927, p. 49)

unconditioned stimulus (food). *If a conditioned reflex is elicited without presentation of the unconditioned stimulus, its strength diminishes.* This process of weakening a conditioned reflex is called *extinction,* and the preceding generalization is the *Law of Reflex Extinction.*

Stimulus Generalization

When an organism is conditioned to respond to a given stimulus, it will also respond to certain other stimuli in the same manner. This phenomenon is called *stimulus generalization.* For example, if a tone of 500 cps. is a conditioned stimulus for a salivary response, tones of various other frequencies will also elicit salivation. The strength of the conditioned reflexes to tones of various frequencies decreases as a function of the difference (in frequency) from the original conditioned stimulus.

This functional relation, called the *stimulus generalization gradient,* is illustrated by an experiment by Anrep (1923) in which the conditioned stimulus was tactile stimulation of the left thigh of a dog. Stimulation of this spot immediately preceded food presentation (the unconditioned stimulus eliciting salivation). When the conditioned reflex had become stabilized, stimulation of the dog's left thigh produced, on the average, 53 drops of saliva; and stimulation of five other areas of the skin progressively distant from the original area yielded average secretions of 45, 39, 23, 21, and 19 drops respectively.

The fact that salivation could be elicited by stimulation of skin areas other than the area originally conditioned is of great biological importance. In its natural environment, the organism rarely encounters a stimulus that does not vary in its physical characteristics even while its functional significance remains the same. For example, an olfactory stimulus associated with a predatory animal will never twice have exactly the same quality or intensity; but failure to react to this variable stimulus with appropriate autonomic responses (epinephrine release, sympathetic nervous system discharge) may lead to death.

It is of equal importance biologically that an organism be able to learn to discriminate among highly similar stimuli that do not have the same functional significance. Therefore a discussion of the conditions giving rise to stimulus discrimination is indicated.

Stimulus Discrimination

The study by Anrep (1920), used above to illustrate the acquisition of a tone-salivation conditioned reflex, was designed to test ability of dogs to discriminate between pure tones of differing frequencies. Following the establishment of a tone of 637.5 cps. as the conditioned stimulus eliciting salivation, subjects were given discriminative training. The procedure consisted of intermixing trials in which a tone of 637.5 cps. was presented in conjunction with food, and trials in which a tone of 1062.5 cps. was presented without food. Thus the strength of the original CS (tone of 637.5 cps.) was maintained by its presentation with food, while the salivation induced by the 1062.5 cps. tone was in the process of being extinguished. Table 4.3 shows the progressive weakening of the latter tone's ability to elicit salivation as a function of the number of times it was presented. Following establishment

Table 4.3 **DIFFERENTIATION OF TONE OF 1062.5 cps**

Working Days	Number of Tests	Strength of reflex in 30 seconds	Latency (Seconds)
1	1	51	3
3	3	30	6
5	5	18	7
6	6	0	10
7	8	3	10
11	13	0	38
12	14	0	—
20	25	0	—

Differentiation of tones with frequencies 637.5 and 1062.5 cps. The strength of the conditioned reflex diminished as successive tone presentations were made without the UCS. (Anrep, 1920, p. 380, Table VI)

DIFFERENTIATION OF TONE OF 850 cps   Table 4.4

Working Days	Number of Tests	Strength of Reflex in 30 Seconds	Latency (Seconds)
1	1	12	7
2	3	4	15
3	4	0	37
4	6	0	—
5	7	0	—
15	20	0	—

Differentiation of tones with frequencies of 850 cps. and 1062.5 cps. While the tone difference was smaller, it was possible to demonstrate differentiation. (Anrep, 1920, p. 381, Table VII)

of a clear-cut discrimination between two frequencies, subjects were presented with extinction trials using a tone of 850 cps. Table 4.4 charts the extinction of salivation initially produced by 850 cps. Subsequently, subjects were given discriminative training with a tone of 722.5 cps. Table 4.5 presents the extinction data for salivation initially induced by that tone.

These results indicate that the initial conditioning of the salivary response to a pure tone of 637.5 cps. resulted in a marked generalized conditioning of a tone of 1062.5 cps. However, discontinuation of food presentation served to extinguish subjects' salivary responses to various tones (1062.5, 850, and 722.5 cps.), while their conditioned salivary response to the original tone was maintained. Thus the discriminatory ability of the dog was clearly demonstrated.

A less obvious aspect of this procedure was the gradual method of forming the discriminations. It would have been difficult to obtain an auditory discrimination as fine as that between 637.5 and 722.5 cps. if the subjects had not had previous training in discriminating between 1062.5 and 850 cps. In other words, by making the initial discrimination relatively

DIFFERENTIATION OF TONE OF 722.5 cps   Table 4.5

Working Days	Number of Tests	Strength of Reflex in 30 Seconds	Latency (Seconds)
1	1	22	20
2	3	20	18
3	5	8	23
4	6	0	45
5	7	0	50
6	8	0	—
10	16	0	—

Differentiation of tone with frequencies of 722.5 and 850 cps. The difference of 122.5 cps. was differentiated as indicated by the rapid change in the strength of the reflex. (Anrep, 1920, p. 382, Table VIII)

gross, one can progressively increase the difficulty without the subject's developing a so-called experimental neurosis. This term was used by Pavlov to describe general hyperexcitability accompanied by a breakdown of previously established stimulus discriminations; it is a condition frequently encountered in subjects which have been given difficult discriminatory problems.

EXPERIMENTAL ANALYSIS OF OPERANT BEHAVIOR

Operant behavior differs from reflex behavior in several important respects. One can specify "usual" differences, including types of effectors, the mediating nervous system, the "voluntary versus involuntary" nature of the two, etc. (Keller and Schoenfeld, 1950). However, these differences have too many exceptions to be really valuable as anything but rough guides. In the last analysis, the distinction between operant and reflex behavior resides in the manner in which each is acquired, that is, in the conditioning procedure. It will be recalled that reflex behavior is elicited through repeated pairing of a stimulus normally incapable of eliciting a response with an unconditioned stimulus that normally elicits the response.

The Operant as a Class of Behavior

In operant behavior we are unable to specify an eliciting stimulus. The behavior occurs in an apparently continuous stream that has no clear-cut relation to a preceding stimulus. If we arbitrarily single out one component of the behavioral sequence, we may be able to bring it under the control of a stimulus; but that stimulus will be a consequent rather than an antecedent stimulus. We may discover that presentation of a particular stimulus (e.g., food) following the *emission* of a particular instance of behavior is closely followed by another instance of very similar behavior. As the stimulus is repeatedly presented after emission of closely related responses, the arbitrarily selected behavior begins to occur with increasing frequency. Clearly, the stimulus following the response is coming to exercise control over the foregoing behavior. The form of the response varies somewhat from instance to instance, sometimes involving almost entirely different muscle groups. Nevertheless, the behavior under consideration becomes less variable over successive response-consequence pairings.

Reinforcement and the Law of
Operant Conditioning

In the procedure just described, a correlation between a given stimulus and a given response was established in a seemingly amorphous sequence of behavior. This *operant* was demonstrated by increasing the frequency of its occurrence, which is one measure of its strength. In general, when presentation of a stimulus after a response increases the strength of that response, the stimulus is called a *reinforcing stimulus*. The law of which this generalization is a corollary is the *Law of Operant Conditioning* (Type R). That law states: *If the occurrence of an operant is followed by presentation of a reinforcing stimulus, the operant's strength is increased.* The defining property of the operant is the relation between a specific class of behavior and the reinforcing stimulus. This is to be contrasted with respondent or reflex behavior, in which the defining stimulus is an antecedent, eliciting stimulus. In operant behavior, an organism's actions on the environment lead to a reinforcing consequence; in respondent behavior, on the other hand, the environment elicits the action.

The problems of topographical specifications of reflexes alluded to in an earlier section bore particular reference to the highly specific unconditioned reflexes. Attempts to specify operants topographically end in the same quagmire as attempts to classify reflexes on the basis of all possible stimulus-response relations. The question is once again raised: If it is not possible to define a unit of behavior topographically, how can that unit be specified? An operant is defined in terms of the covariation of stimuli and responses, just as simpler reflex behavior is defined. A "door opening" operant, for example, would be defined as any behavior having the effect of getting the door open.

It should be clear that many forms of response can accomplish the same environmental consequence. Nevertheless, the only meaningful and consistent way of specifying a given operant is in terms of its consequences, that is, in "achievement language" (MacCorquodale and Meehl, 1954). For example, Mr. A says hello to Mr. B; Rat 38 bites Rat 47; a monkey presses a telegraph key 50 times—all these statements are instances of achievement-language descriptions of response classes. We might then endeavor to show that Mr. A's verbal behavior depends on the consequent changes in Mr. B's facial expression; that the more frequently Rat 38 bites Rat 47, the more food Rat 38 obtains; and that the monkey's completion of 50 responses is followed by presentation of 3 cc. orange juice. It is because of the relation of the behavior to these consequences that we say each belongs to the same "response class," by which we mean that each constitutes an operant.

Antecedent Operations

The occurrence of operants is affected by a variety of antecedent manipulations. One of the more common manipulations affecting the likelihood of an operant's occurrence is deprivation of food or water. Figure 4.1 illustrates the effects of various degrees of food deprivation on the frequency of occurrence of a food-reinforced response. It can clearly be seen that rate varies systematically with the degree of deprivation. Such operations or manipulations make reinforcement possible. Similarly, presenting an aversive stimulus and removing it following the emission of a response can also be considered an antecedent operation making reinforcement possible.

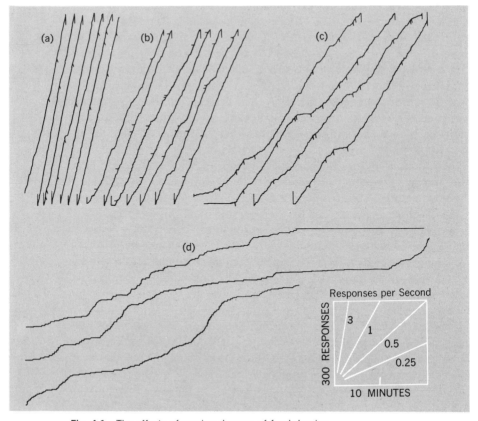

Fig. 4.1 The effects of varying degrees of food deprivation on variable interval food-reinforced performance by a pigeon. The weights are (a) 423 grams, (b) 463 grams, (c) 408 grams, (d) 499 grams. The very low response rate at 408 grams was during a period of generally declining rate, possibly due to inanition. (Ferster and Skinner, 1957, p. 371, Fig. 449)

At times, one might even class drug administration as an antecedent operation. For example, administering the morphine antagonist nalorphine to an animal which is physically dependent on morphine will induce a condition of morphine abstinence. Such chemically induced morphine deprivation increases the probability of morphine-reinforced behavior much as food deprivation increases the likelihood of food-reinforced responding (Thompson and Schuster, 1964).

It should be noted that all these antecedent operations affect a wide range of operants and not just the specific operant under examination. This is part of the defining characteristic of antecedent manipulations. The real importance of such deprivation operations is that they (1) strengthen the specific conditioned operant under investigation, (2) strengthen a vast number of other operants, and (3) make reinforcement possible. Whether or not we are able to state anything about the internal conditions resulting from deprivation (in the sense of physiological changes) is irrelevant. Drive or motivation does not enter into this description of behavior insofar as it is a *thing* or a *physiological condition;* rather, *the operation of deprivation* is of concern to us when it can be shown to covary with changes in the probability of occurrence of specific aspects of behavior.

Food or water deprivation, or presentation of a mild electric shock, will alter the probability of reinforcement; but sudden removal of food from a hungry animal, or the onset of an intense electric shock, will also produce certain predictable changes in behavior. Biting, jumping, scratching, vocalizing, urinating, defecating, piloerection, etc., result from such operations. Very frequently, the reflex aspects of behavior under such conditions are dramatic, particularly the responses of the smooth muscles and glands. Theoretical accounts of the roles of the autonomic nervous system, hormonal regulation, etc., in such states are often liberally intermixed with descriptions of behavior; but such accounts are beyond the scope of this text. Certain antecedent operations are conducted and an array of changes in behavior observed. The correlation of these two sets of variables is summarized by the term *emotion,* and nothing else is meant by that term as it is used here. Some of the manipulations inducing emotional behavior are discussed in more detail in Chapter 5.

Biological scientists are sometimes bothered by this "black box" approach to the concepts of drive and emotion. It should be clear that we are not advocating ignorance of the intervening physiological and biochemical processes associated with environmental manipulations. Indeed, *direct examination* of such intermediary events is the most profitable way of delineating these processes at a more microanalytic level. However, the basic biological scientist *should* be concerned about the use of misleading constructs purporting to explain behavioral events.

The aggressive behavior of a bull is not explained by reference to heightened libido, although specification of a relation between the degree of sexual deprivation and frequency of aggressive assaults may be explanatory. Or, to take another example, we have added little to our understanding of the rage reaction of a rat with a septal forebrain lesion when we say that the condition is the result of a "sympathetic discharge." The use of terms referring to processes that are measurable *in principle* does not necessarily yield a satisfactory explanation. However, when the brain lesion can be related to measures of neurohormonal changes (which are known from other research to be mediated by the sympathetic nervous system), then the term sympathetic discharge begins to contribute to the description of the process.

Thus, directly measurable events, whether physiological or environmental, can profitably enter into the explanation of a complex state, such as "emotion" or "drive." We must, however, be wary of explanations suggesting a great deal more than is inherent in the data. While they may give us some feeling of satisfaction, inasmuch as they provide an opportunity to talk about the data, the intellectual pleasure which one enjoys is really no reason to assume they possess verisimilitude.

Response Properties

We have seen that the usual measures of reflex strength in respondent behavior are the magnitude of the response and the latency of the reflex. In the analysis of operant behavior, we seldom concern ourselves with magnitude and latency, but rather with frequency and patterning of occurrence. Frequency of occurrence is said to measure the strength of an operant. (Or, operant strength may be stated in terms of the probability of occurrence.) It is now recognized, however, that frequency of occurrence alone does not tell us all we would like to know about an operant's strength. More recently, response force, duration of response, and interresponse interval have been used as measures of operant strength (Falk and Haas, 1965; Gollub, 1964; Margulies, 1961; Notterman, 1959; Notterman and Mintz, 1966; Schaefer, 1960; Sidman, 1955; Thompson, 1961, 1962). These differences become significant for the pharmacological investigation of behavior when one measure is affected by a given drug while the other measures remain unaffected. An example of this kind of result was obtained by Schaefer (1963), who demonstrated that neither the frequency nor the force of lever-pressing changed appreciably in rats receiving oral ethyl alcohol, while an examination of response durations clearly indicated an increase in the mean duration of the response and in variability of response duration (Fig. 4.2).

One of the distinguishing characteristics of operants is that they are *not* defined by response topographies. As a matter of fact, the form of an operant may differ considerably from instance to instance. Perhaps it is partially because of this response-form variability that there is a tendency for the emission of various related muscular topographies all leading to a given environmental consequence. This tendency is called *response generalization* or *response induction*. Thus, if for some reason a given response topography no longer leads to a certain consequence (for example, if the manipulandum is arranged so that a horizontal maneuver of the lever rather than vertical depression of the switch is required), the new operant will usually be quickly acquired.

The usual examples of response generalization in reflex conditioning involve the use of another limb in place of the one used in the original conditioning, as, for example, conditioning a dog to shift from the right paw to the left by immobilizing the right paw (Kellogg and Walker, 1938). A comparable operant situation might be generated if the hand that a monkey used to obtain food reinforcement were immobilized, requiring that the opposite hand be used. One would expect very rapid acquisition of the opposite-hand response, despite the fact that the opposite hand had never been used for that purpose.

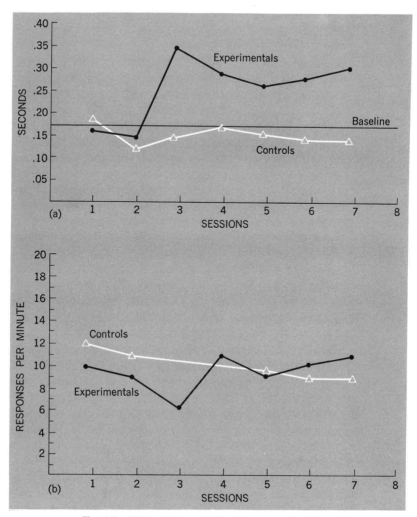

Fig. 4.2 Differential sensitivity of response duration and response rate to the effects of alcohol. The top graph shows the mean duration of lever-pressing by animals pretreated with ethyl alcohol or water. The lower graph shows the mean responses per minute by the same animals during the same time period. While the mean response duration increased for alcohol treated animals, response rates remained approximately equal. (Schaefer, 1960, p. 25, Figs. 12, 13)

Out of an organism's ongoing stream of behavior it is possible to select an arbitrary component and control it. For example, when a hungry dog runs to the place where its food is kept, jumps back and forth, stands on its hind legs, wags its tail, and barks, it is possible to strengthen one component of this sequence of behaviors. We might choose to reinforce standing on the hind legs. Initially, any response resembling standing on the hind legs would be followed by food presentation. As the number of reinforcements increased, the topography would come more and more to follow a specified pattern of standing on the hind legs, probably for relatively constant durations. Other aspects of the initial sequence would decrease in relative frequency. Such selection of one rather arbitrary component of a complex behavioral sequence is called *response differentiation.*

It is characteristic of operants that in their asymptotic form they take on a pattern that permits rapid procurement of reinforcement after completion of the response. The process of eliminating the unnecessary parts of the sequence while maintaining the desired response is extremely slow; this is particularly true when a wide range of topographies is reinforced, since inefficient ones are reinforced along with efficient ones. In an effort to speed up this process, a technique called *shaping* is used. By a series of *successive approximations,* response topographies resembling the ultimately desired response are reinforced. Unfortunately, an adequate technology and an objective language describing this process has not been developed. Shaping is usually a procedure learned in apprenticeship, with the behavior of both the experimental animal and the apprentice under the control of the experienced trainer. Training is rather subjective, since the entire procedure depends on the accuracy of the trainer to reinforce the student. In turn, the student's performance controls the animal's behavior. But despite the subjectiveness of the process, shaping is of considerable practical value in shortening initial conditioning.

When a student learns behavioral control techniques, he would be well advised to develop skill in shaping. This skill is acquired much as the clinician learns to manipulate his patient's health by recognizing, then treating the symptoms. The relation between the patient's health and what the student physician does may be vague, but the important part is that the student physician's behavior is effective. A good description of the process of shaping can be found in Holland and Skinner's introductory psychology textbook (1961). After the student has studied their treatment of the subject, he might profitably refer to the laboratory manual by Michael (1963) for a laboratory presentation of the shaping process. Michael's approach is very helpful in that the subject's performance is spelled out in such detail that it can become a reinforcer for the student shaper's behavior.

Recently, there have been attempts to eliminate the arbitrary subjectiveness of the shaping process. Lee (1963) developed a system involving a food magazine and a nose-press response key (for rats), which are separated by a series of photocell detectors (Fig. 4.3). This apparatus allows a rat to find food in the magazine; it then reinforces the subject for moving successively closer to the nose key and, finally, for moving into contact with the key. The sequence of successive approximations is programmed automatically by a preset progression of interruptions of the photocell detectors. Such a system, if fully developed, could automatically decide the question, Which response is more like the desired response? by revealing at once which sequence most effectively leads to the desired behavior.

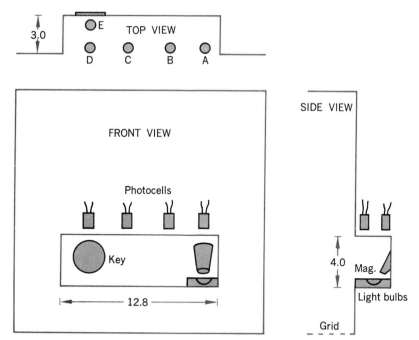

Fig. 4.3 Device for studying response topography during acquisition and maintenance of a dose-response by rats. An array of photocells in the immediate vicinity of the nose key and food magazine detects the position of the animal. The same system could be used to differentially reinforce responses that are successively closer to the operandum or magazine. (Lee, 1963)

Behavioral Consequences

As previously indicated, the real defining characteristics of any operant are the contingencies for reinforcement. Earlier in the chapter we stated the Law of Operant Reinforcement and defined a reinforcer. If the consequences of a given instance of behavior are such that that behavior will tend to occur more frequently, then we say that the consequences are reinforcing. If, however, the consequences are such that a response that had occurred with high frequency decreases in frequency, we say the response is undergoing *extinction*. Thus, removing or ceasing to present a reinforcing stimulus after a reinforced operant is emitted weakens that operant. The converse of the Law of Operant Reinforcement, then, is that *the emission of an operant not followed by presentation of a reinforcing stimulus will tend to decrease in frequency of occurrence*. This decrease in frequency is said to be a measure of the weakened strength of that operant.

A painful stimulus, removed following the emission of an operant, may act as a *negative reinforcer;* but it is a reinforcer only when it strengthens the preceding operant. If that same stimulus is *presented* following the emission of an operant, that operant will tend to decrease in frequency of occurrence. Presenting a negatively reinforcing stimulus *following* an operant

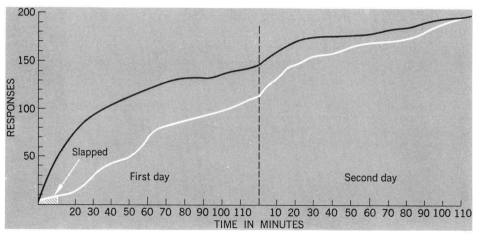

Fig. 4.4 Effect of punishment on the course of extinction of a positively reinforced response in rats. The two curves are from groups of four rats each. All responses made by one group during the first ten minutes of extinction were followed by a slap to the forepaws by the lever. The rate was depressed for some time but by the end of the second extinction session, complete recovery was made. (Skinner, 1938, p. 154, Fig. 47)

constitutes *punishment;* and usually produces a generalized decrease in the frequency of many operants. While punishment does suppress an ongoing sequence of behavior, it does not necessarily eradicate that behavior from the organism's repertoire. Once the punishing contingencies have been removed, the behavior will tend to recur at the same or, on occasion, at higher strengths.

Figure 4.4 shows a sample cumulative record of the responses of a rat punished for a previously conditioned bar-pressing response. It will be noted that the frequency of bar-pressing decreased during the punishment period, but that, on removal of punishment, bar-pressing not only assumed its previous rate but actually exceeded the prepunishment rate for a short time. In no sense, then, does punishment lead to "unlearning," but rather to suppression of learned responses. The only way to be sure that a given operant has disappeared from an organism's repertoire is to see that it undergoes extinction—that the operant is no longer reinforced when it occurs. Thus, when a positively reinforced operant is emitted, the positive reinforcer should no longer be presented; and, conversely, when a negatively reinforced operant is emitted, the aversive stimulus should *not* be removed. Such procedures eventually cause the operant to return to the frequency of occurrence observed prior to conditioning, i.e., to the *operant level.*

Stimulus Control

The discussion of the control of reflex behavior (by conditioned stimuli) versus the control of operant behavior may have conveyed the impression that operants cannot be controlled by specified antecedent stimuli. This is not the case. It is true, however, that the initial isolation of an operant is achieved by reinforcing consequences, not by presenting antecedent controlling stimuli. Once an operant has been isolated, it may be possible to bring the behavior in question under the control of antecedent stimulus conditions.

Before specifying the manner in which an antecedent part of the environment relates to behavior, we should provide a clear definition of the term "stimulus." Generally when we speak of a stimulus, we refer to *an aspect of an organism's environment that can be shown to covary with some aspect of the organism's behavior.*

The further classification of stimuli concerns the type of receptors involved rather than any aspect of the behavior as such. In the initial conditioning of a lever-pressing response, a pecking response, or any other operant, a procedure called *magazine training* is carried out. In magazine training, the animal must learn to approach that part of the experimental chamber where the reinforcer is to be obtained. This is particularly true of food or water reinforcement. In order to speed up magazine training, a buzzer or a light is usually presented during the presentation of the food or water reinforcement. For example, a buzzer might be sounded simultaneously with the presentation of a hopper full of grain to a pigeon in an experimental chamber. Soon we observe that, on presentation of the buzzer, the pigeon turns and approaches the food hopper and puts its head into the feeding chamber. By the procedure called successive approximation, discussed briefly above, the bird learns to peck a small disk on the wall of the chamber.

Taking the procedure one step further, we now change contingencies so that pecking the disk will activate the hopper only when a light is on. We set up our apparatus in such a fashion that the light is only presented for one minute every fourth minute. Initially the bird will tend to peck the key much of the time when the light is not on. However, pecking in the light-off periods will eventually diminish and stop completely, while as soon as the light is presented, pecking will occur at a high rate. *The stimulus in whose presence an operant is reinforced* (the light in this case) *is called a discriminative stimulus* (S^D). Conversely, the stimulus in whose presence a given operant is never reinforced is called an *S-delta* (S^Δ).

We find that if we vary the wavelength of the light, the bird in the foregoing example tends to continue pecking the key. However, if we measure accurately the tendency to peck the key, we find that as the wavelength of light is made increasingly different from that presented during conditioning, the percentage of responses occurring in the presence of the light decreases. Thus, if we were to plot percentage of total responses as a function of the wavelength of light, as in Fig. 4.5, we would see that an inverted-V curve describes the tendency to peck as a function of physical proximity to the stimulus presented during conditioning. This tendency for an operant to be emitted at strengths that decrease as the discriminative stimulus moves along

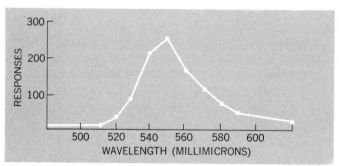

Fig. 4.5 A gradient of stimulus generalization for the pigeon using the Guttman-Kalish procedure. Each point represents the number of responses emitted during test periods when the key color is systematically varied from the color presented during baseline conditioning (550 millimicrons). The greatest number of responses is emitted when the wavelength of the test light is 550 millimicrons. As the wavelength differs more and more from 550 millimicrons, the number of responses diminishes. (After Guttman and Kalish, 1958; in: Sidman 1960, p. 207, Fig. 20)

a given physical continuum away from the intensity at which it was presented during conditioning is called *stimulus generalization*. The slope of the stimulus generalization gradient (Fig. 4.5) can be increased by discrimination training. In the foregoing case, discrimination training would be accomplished by intermittent presentation of S^Δ lights increasingly nearer the S^D. Thus, for example, if the S^D light was 5,500 Angstrom units, responses in the presence of key lights of 5,250 or 5,750A would go unreinforced. These wavelengths would be S^Δ's. If we were to test for the stimulus generalization gradient at this time, we would find that the slope of the curve had increased markedly, and we would say that we had sharpened the discrimination.

Reinforcers

A reinforcer is a stimulus whose presentation (positive) or removal (negative) following a response will tend to strengthen the foregoing operant. Some stimuli are effective in strengthening an operant on their first presentation. For example, submerged turtles will learn to emit a response leading to oxygen presentation (Van Sommers, 1962). Oxygen presentation is an effective reinforcing stimulus on its first presentation. Other stimuli may not be initially effective in strengthening an operant, although repeated pairing with the primary reinforcer (as in the foregoing example) causes them to gain reinforcing properties of their own. Morphine will act as a reinforcer for a lever-pressing response in a morphine-dependent monkey; and the animal will learn to emit responses leading to the intravenous infusion of morphine. A red light presented repeatedly with morphine infusion may come to have its own reinforcing properties when morphine infusion is discontinued (Schuster and Thompson, 1962). Reinforcers that are immediately effective when the subject has no prior experience with them are called *primary;* those whose effectiveness depends on their association with a primary reinforcer are called *conditioned reinforcers.*

Primary reinforcers do not generally change their ability to maintain behavior over repeated presentations short of satiation. By contrast, conditioned reinforcers presented repeatedly in the absence of the primary reinforcer eventually decrease their ability to maintain the operant. Thus, to maintain a conditioned reinforcer effectively, one must intermittently present it in conjunction with the primary reinforcer.

Conditioned reinforcers are extremely important in the conditioning of almost all operants, from the simplest regular reinforcement scheduling procedures to highly complex 24-hour procedures. The general function of conditioned reinforcers is to maintain a complex sequence of behaviors by interspersing conditioned reinforcers at various points along this sequence. A simple example is the presentation of a buzzer while food is being presented to a rat on a regular reinforcement schedule. The buzzer serves both as a discriminative stimulus and as a conditioned reinforcer. It is a discriminative stimulus because it sets the occasion for approaching the food cup; it becomes a conditioned reinforcer because the buzzing sound alone eventually suffices to strengthen other operants. Such conditioned reinforcers can be used to maintain long sequences of responses. For example a brief buzzing sound could be presented after every 100 responses, with food plus the buzzing sound after 500 responses. Such a procedure has been used to create and maintain highly stabilized extended behavioral sequences (Findley and Brady, 1965).

It should be stressed again that reinforcers are also distinguished on the basis of their ability to strengthen operants by their presentation (if they are positive reinforcers) or by their removal (if they are negative reinforcers). We frequently confuse the terms "negative reinforcer," "punishing stimulus," and "aversive stimulus." Although these terms may appear to overlap, they are conceptually independent. It must be remembered that negative reinforcers and punishing stimuli are defined by their effects on behavior. The term "aversive" is a subjective evaluation which may erroneously lead to an a priori assignment of a stimulus to one class or the other. One simply cannot decide on an a priori basis that a stimulus belongs to a certain class; only when one can show that the removal of a stimulus following the emission of a response strengthens that response can one legitimately call that stimulus a negative reinforcer.

The following is an example of a situation in which a stimulus certainly seems to be aversive from an anthropomorphic point of view: When a male Siamese fighting fish is presented with the image of another male Siamese fighting fish, the former will immediately attack the latter just as Siamese fighting fish attack each other when actually placed together. In nature, the result is severe damage and sometimes death to one of the adversaries. Certainly, from a human subjective standpoint, this would seem to be an aversive situation. Nevertheless, in the laboratory, a Siamese fighting fish will learn to emit an operant response leading to a visual presentation of the image of another fish in aggressive display. This would suggest that the opportunity to attack another fish may be a positive reinforcer (Thompson, 1966).

A similar phenomenon is seen in fighting cocks. When the birds are in a natural habitat, one rooster will often kill another within a relatively short time—an aversive outcome, it would generally be conceded. Nonetheless, one fighting cock will emit a key-pecking response in order to gain access to the visual image of another fighting cock (Thompson, 1964).

It is clear from these examples that it is impossible to use our subjective evaluation of aversiveness as a criterion for determining whether a stimulus will act as a negative or positive reinforcer.

Scheduling of Reinforcement

It should be obvious that among the most important determinants of operant behavior are the reinforcement contingencies. One of the systematic ways of expressing reinforcement contingencies is in terms of reinforcement scheduling. A reinforcement schedule is a formal arrangement of relations between the number of occurrences of a response of a specified class, and the temporal arrangements of responses and reinforcement. The most authoritative source available is Ferster and Skinner's *Schedules of Reinforcement* (1957). Any student seriously concerned with the analysis of drug effects on operant behavior will want to consult this work frequently. A more recent discussion of intermittent reinforcement has been presented by Morse (1966). The classification of operant behavior by means of the reinforcement schedule is discussed in more detail in Chapter 5.

Reliability and Generality of Behavioral Data

Like any other scientific investigator, the behavioral pharmacologist must face the question, Will the results of my experiment be the same if the experiment is repeated exactly as I conducted it? Pharmacologists have developed a number of procedures to assess the reliability of their experimental results. Such procedures are based on statistical analysis in which the results obtained are compared with "chance" results that might be obtained if no drug were administered at all. If the experiment were replicated and another set of quantitative observations made, one would then be able to compare the two sets of numbers from the two experiments. However, the question remains: Are the differences between the two sets of data reliable?

Another way of posing the same question is to ask: If a drug were administered to two groups of identically treated animals and one found a slight difference between the groups' performance, would that difference be reliable? The answer is found in terms of the chance probability of obtaining a difference as large as that observed. If the probability of obtaining a difference of the order of magnitude actually obtained is very low, then the differences are said to be due to factors other than chance. However, if the probability of obtaining a difference of that order of magnitude is high, then we say that the differences are not reliable, that they are probably the result of chance.

For many experimental purposes, such statistical methods are entirely satisfactory and necessary. Very frequently, though, these procedures are not only unnecessary but may be undesirable. The question of the reliability of experimental results is really a question of the ability to replicate a given result sequentially (that is, on several occasions). The procedure of running the experiment on a large number of subjects is the most widely used method of replicating an experiment. However, if we are concerned with sequential replication of a phenomenon then it would seem reasonable to do the same experiment on the same animal rather than replicating it across different subject samples.

An example may make the point clearer. If we wish to study the effects of meperidine on avoidance latencies in monkeys, we might conduct the experiment in two ways. The first would involve selecting a random sample of monkeys and administering meperidine to half and a placebo to the other half. We would then measure the change in avoidance latencies as a function of meperidine administration in one group compared with placebo administration in the other group. The resulting differences in latencies would be expressed in terms of mean differences and some measure of the variability of the latencies around the mean. We could subsequently make statistical tests to determine the probability of obtaining mean differences of that order of magnitude, taking the variability into consideration.

A second approach to the same problem might involve selecting two or three monkeys rather than the twenty or so required in the other procedure. Each monkey would be dosed in the following sequence: meperidine for one day, saline for ten days, meperidine again for one day, followed by saline for ten days. This procedure could be replicated ten times on each monkey, giving us a total of ten meperidine latencies and ninety saline measurements. We could then express the meperidine latencies and the saline latencies in terms of two means, and express the variability as before. This method demonstrates the possibility of carring out replications *within* the organism to determine the reliability of a given phenomenon.

Any biologist will immediately respond, "Yes, you have replicated an experimental result, but that is not the same as demonstrating that this phenomenon is characteristic of the species, or has generality across species." This point is well taken. We must first look at the terms "generality" and "representative." If a given experimental result is obtained with a single subject, for example, how representative is the finding for other organisms of the same species? Are we asking something about a particular aspect of our data, for example, the shape of the distribution of scores or the mean of our scores? Are we inquiring about the possibility of idiosyncrasies? In other words, are we concerned with the irregular and chaotic, or are we asking a question about the regular or the "normal"?

By asking about representativeness, we may in fact be asking about what happens on the average in a given population. But is this really what we are interested in? If the physician is going to give a patient a new behaviorally active drug, is he concerned with what happens to patients on the average, or is he concerned with how *this* patient will respond to the drug? Likewise, is the scientist concerned with how 90 rats will act under the effects of a drug, or does he want to learn how a given rat is likely to act under the effects of a drug? Carrying the example one step further, is the animal falling at the mean of a perfectly flat distribution "representative"?

Consider the meaningfulness of grouping data when there are large individual differences in several parameters of a "control" variable within a given group. What is the generality of these data? Let's postulate a situation in which a drug is administered to three groups of rats which have been orally pretreated with varying doses of olive oil. The experimental drug is administered orally as well. If we examine individual curves, we may find that they fall into three groups, with one group revealing the effects of the drug relatively early, the second intermediately, and the third only after a considerable period of time. In this case, the oil functions to decrease the experimental drug's rate of absorption from the stomach. Averaging curves from the three groups into a common curve would certainly not yield a representative curve that showed the effect of the test drug on a given measure of performance. As a matter of fact, such data would give a very misleading impression of the effects of the drug. They would lead us to make erroneous conclusions about the time of onset, the peak time of action, and the rate at which the drug disappears from the subject's body.

Frequently, comparable individual differences exist in experimental subjects, not by the design of the experimenter, but because of unknown and/or uncontrolled variables. The averaging of data under these circumstances leads to errors like those that arise in the hypothetical case above. Indeed, grouping data too often strips the raw data of this representativeness.

The question of interspecies generality is an entirely different problem. It is generally conceded that it is not particularly difficult to demonstrate differences between the behavior of men and rats. It may, on the other hand, be somewhat more difficult to specify the degrees of similarity and the degrees of differences. This is not to say that species is not a meaningful and important independent variable. However, it is to suggest that examining the behavior of individual organisms within a single species will very likely tell us much more about the quantitative and qualitative properties of the behavior of various groups of organisms than we will learn from group comparisons across species.

In this context, it is well to keep in mind that interspecies generality and interspecies comparisons can be extremely misleading. If we were to design an experiment to determine the effects of *d*-amphetamine on a visual discrimination in pigeons compared to the same discrimination in rats, using food reinforcement and a fixed-ratio schedule in both species, we might arrive at a very misleading conclusion.

If we first trained both groups of animals to a stable performance on a fixed ratio of 50 and subsequently administered a relatively low dose of *d*-amphetamine, we would be very apt to obtain a marked increase in rate of responding in the rats and relatively little change in rate of responding in the pigeons. We might well conclude that *d*-amphetamine enhances the ability of rats to make a visual discrimination while it has little effect on visual discrimination in pigeons. And if we ran a series of doses, we would probably obtain the same general result.

How do we account for the enhancement of performance in the rat and virtual lack of change in the pigeon? The answer resides in the fact that the pigeon tends to reach an asymptotic rate of pecking on a given ratio and seems to be unable to peck any faster. By contrast, the rat seldom approaches such a limit on a ratio schedule. Therefore, the administration of amphetamine or certain other behavioral stimulant drugs would be associated with an increase in rate at relatively low doses in the rat. It would clearly be erroneous to attribute the differences across species to differences in visual acuity. There are indeed differences, but they reside in the behavior and the reinforcement schedule, not the action of the drug on visual functioning.

One final comment on generality—in certain cases (lethal doses of drugs or partial irreversibility of behavioral effects) it is not possible to replicate an experiment on a given individual organism because the procedure itself precludes replication. Such experiments, of course, must be replicated across rather than within organisms.

Direct and Systematic Behavioral Replication

Replication can basically be accomplished by either direct or indirect means. Direct replication may be achieved either by performing the experiment again with new subjects or by making repeated observations on the same subjects under each of several experimental conditions. When the original subjects are retained, we use the term "intragroup" or "intrasubject" replication. If, on the other hand, the data are presented as group statistics or as descriptions of the behavior of a group of subjects, such replication is qualified as "intergroup" or "intersubject," respectively (Sidman, 1960).

In any experiment, the possibility exists that the result obtained with one subject could be an idiosyncratic reaction. Therefore, we invariably ask: Is one measurement enough? Are we then seriously doubting that the results obtained were real? That is, did the peculiar findings obtained reflect something unreal or mystical? Or, do we believe that our results are "real" if our procedures were scientifically acceptable, and the phenomena observable by a number of experimenters? Surely it must be agreed that, however idiosyncratic the reaction of a given animal to a given drug in a given behavioral situation, the results are nonetheless "real." Indeed, markedly uncommon responses frequently reveal the effects of previously unknown variables. It is the purpose of intersubject replication to determine whether such uncontrolled and/or unknown variables might be operating and, therefore, whether they might be sufficiently potent to preclude replication.

When an organism's behavior can be repeatedly manipulated in a quantitatively consistent fashion, we would generally agree that the phenomenon produced is a real one, and that the experimenter has the relevant variables under control. For example, if we find that administering 1.5 mg/kg I.P. of chlorpromazine to rats causes a 25 per cent reduction in the rate of lever-pressing, which leads to intracranial stimulation, and that this depression occurs plus or minus 5 per cent on 10 successive replications, we can be quite confident that the phenomenon is a real one.

Such an experimental manipulation is a revealing demonstration of the variable in question. The fact that a phenomenon can be essentially turned on and off at will certainly testifies to the degree of control the experimenter has been able to establish, and indicates far greater experimental power than the expression of a statistical difference resulting from a single presentation or manipulation of an independent variable across a large number of subjects.

A complication may arise when one is unable to replicate a result in one of two or three subjects. One should be cautious about relegating the irregular result to chance. Such results are no less real for the one subject than are the expected results for the others. Once we are able to demonstrate that a phenomenon can be replicated in a given organism, failure to get agreement across organisms may be more interesting than discouraging. Very frequently, such differences mark the beginning of the delineation of a new variable or a previously ignored or unknown parameter of a variable. Such results should lead to *more,* rather than less, searching investigation.

After completing a series of direct replication experiments in which the basic variables controlling a given behavioral phenomenon have been out-

Fig. 4.6 The effect of two phenothiazine derivatives on lever-pressing reinforced by posterior hypothalamic brain stimulation in rats. Five dosages of perphenazine and thioridazine were administered intraperitoneally to rats, and onset and duration of action of the two drugs were compared, using the same subjects to test both drugs. (Thompson, Pliskoff, and Hawkins, 1962)

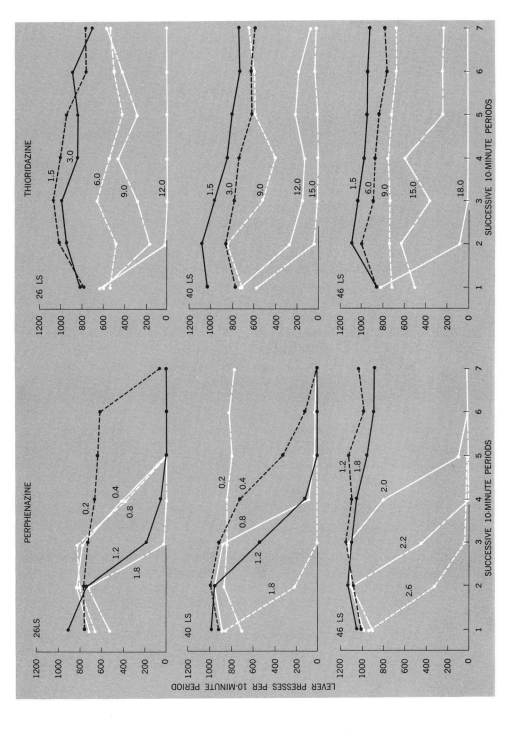

lined, the investigator may be prepared to proceed in a less conservative fashion. Instead of simply repeating subsequent experiments in exactly the same way, he may opt to use the data collected in the experiment's first stage or procedure as a basis for further systematic manipulations in subsequent experimental steps. Investigation of the latter type, i.e., repeated partial replication combined with systematic variation within a given subject in a given series of experiments, is called *systematic replication.*

An example of how systematic replications might be conducted in drug-behavior research would be an investigation of the effects of several phenothiazine derivatives on intracranially reinforced lever-pressing in rats. We might like to examine the effects of these drugs at three or four representative dosage levels in each subject. How should we design our experiment so that it provides a systematic way of obtaining all this information? One way to accomplish this would be to administer the drugs in a randomized sequence interspersed with trials in which the subjects received isotonic saline. A sufficient number of trials on saline could be interspersed to assure the occurrence of drug metabolism and excretion, and to provide an ongoing baseline from session to session.

Figure 4.6 presents data from an experiment that examined the effects of thioridazine and perphenazine on posterior hypothalamic self-stimulation. It can be seen that systematic replication made it possible to get dose-effect curves for the two drugs, without contamination of the data. This is one relatively simple example of the way in which systematic replication can be used.

Another type of systematic replication, one that is inherently more difficult to perform, requires session-to-session or even within-session manipulations by the experimenter on the basis of his past knowledge of the controlling variables of the phenomenon under investigation. For example, monkeys conditioned to self-administer morphine were pretreated with varying doses of morphine prior to providing them with the opportunity for self-administration. Self-administration periods were indicated by the onset of a light S^D. The effect of pretreatment with morphine was to reduce the rate of responding in the presence of the appropriate discriminative stimulus leading to the morphine reinforcer. Without knowledge of the appropriate doses for use in pretreatment, and without knowledge of the duration of effects, the investigators were forced to make educated guesses and then to replicate on the basis of each succeeding bit of information. Each replication involved variation and, therefore, new experimental findings.

Systematic replication requires considerable knowledge of the phenomena at hand. It therefore behooves the investigator who intends to make use of systematic replication to first be secure in his own knowledge of the basic variables controlling the behavior under consideration. Systematic replication assumes a great deal of integrity on the investigator's part, for it requires a good deal of discipline and experience. The success with which an investigator uses systematic replication is a measure of his skill and knowledge.

Operant-Conditioned Reflex Interaction

We have dealt with operants and conditioned reflexes separately, as a matter of didactic convenience, not out of any belief in real biological isolation. A moment's reflection will lead to the realization that in most, if not all, operant-conditioning situations, certain stimuli uniquely occur in close temporal contiguity with the reinforcement. Whatever responses are reflexively produced by the presentation of the reinforcer could come to be elicited by stimuli regularly preceding the reinforcing event. In an early paper by Konorski and Miller (1930), a food-reinforced operant and salivation were concomitantly recorded. These authors postulated that the operant response would produce proprioceptive feedback, which would become a

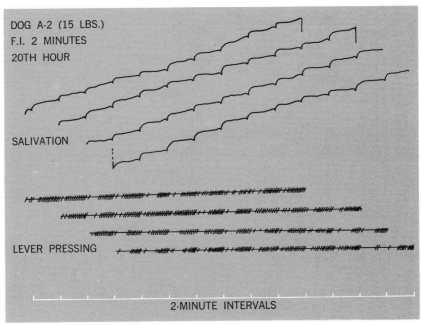

Fig. 4.7 Cumulative salivary responding and lever-pressing by a dog, reinforced with food for lever-presses on an F12 schedule. Cumulative salivary responses are shown in the upper portion, and discrete lever-presses in the lower portion. Reinforcements are designated by the diagonal downstrokes of the cumulative pen. The salivary response clearly covaries with the schedule of food reinforcement. (Shapiro, 1961, p. 363, Fig. 2)

conditioned stimulus eliciting anticipatory salivation. Their experimental data confirmed this hypothesis. However, subsequent experiments by these authors and others (Kintsch and Witte, 1962; Ellison and Konorski, 1964) have failed to confirm these findings consistently.

The interrelations of operants and conditioned reflexes have seldom been simultaneously observed. A particularly noteworthy exception was reported by Shapiro (1960, 1961). Shapiro employed dogs which had been surgically prepared with chronic indwelling catheters in the duct of the parotid gland. In this manner, a continuous record of salivary secretion was obtained while the subjects were emitting a lever-pressing operant reinforced with food on a fixed-interval schedule. Figure 4.7 shows a record of salivary secretion and lever pressing following stabilization on the fixed-interval schedule. This record demonstrates the occurrence of salivation not only after the food reinforcement, but toward the end of the fixed-interval period. Clearly, this anticipatory salivation is a conditioned response, and further, this record shows a high correlation between the magnitude of conditioned salivation and the number of lever-pressing responses in a fixed interval.

An additional correlation between these two responses was found by Shapiro in a period of extinction. Figure 4.8 shows a record of fixed-interval performance followed by a 30-minute extinction period. The decrement in responding caused by the extinction procedure proceeds at essentially the same rate for both the conditioned salivation and the lever-pressing responses.

It remains for future research to determine the precise conditions in

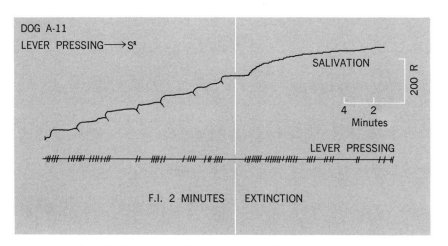

Fig. 4.8 Cumulative salivary responses and lever-presses of a dog on an F12 minute schedule of food-reinforced lever-pressing. At the vertical line, food reinforcement was discontinued. Note that the diminution in lever-pressing indicated on the event pen varies systematically with the decrease in salivation. (Shapiro, 1961, p. 363, Fig. 6)

which operants and reflexes are conditioned concomitantly and the possible causal relations between them.

Less obvious perhaps is the fact that operant responses may also be conditioned in experiments dealing with conditioned reflexes. The presentation of food acts as a reinforcing event for whatever operants are occurring at that time. The operant (or operants) thus strengthened will occur with greater frequency and may therefore be occurring again at the time of the next food presentation. In this manner an operant might be maintained in strength by such adventitious intermittent reinforcement. Operants strengthened by adventitious reinforcement have been referred to as "superstitious behavior" (Skinner, 1948). Unfortunately, experimenters dealing with conditioned reflexes have not systematically reported on the occurrence of ancillary behaviors that may have been superstitiously strengthened.

5

The Classification of Behavior

When the behavioral pharmacologist communicates experimental findings, the most essential information he must provide, aside from the name of the drug administered, is the kind of behavior investigated. In certain instances, the investigator may choose to describe the behavior anatomically, speaking, for example, of "frontalis muscle contraction," which would be comparable to categorizing drugs by their chemical structures. Unfortunately, the topographical classification of behavior suffers from a variety of conceptual weaknesses, the most damaging of which is the difficulty of deciding when two instances of behavior belong to the same response class.

A more common classification scheme involves the selection of some obvious and dramatic aspects of behavior that are believed to reveal a particularly interesting and, presumably, important internal state of the organism, i.e., "fear motivated," "sex directed," or "conflict induced" behaviors.

Such terms refer not only to behavioral events but to unobserved mediating processes between environmental manipulations and the behavioral events. The investigator may feel justified in using such terms to distinguish behavioral classes, since clearly measurable behavioral changes are under his experimental control (e.g., he may shock the subject, impose sexual deprivation, or simultaneously present negative and positive reinforcers). Obviously, however, such classes refer to states of the organism that are singularly unavailable for direct objective measurement. Furthermore, the defining properties of such a classification do not reside in the unmeasured inner states, but in the relation between the antecedent manipulations of the experimenter and the subject's behavior and the controlling consequences of that behavior.

Thus, the value of classifying behavior according to hypothetical mediating states is not at all apparent, although ambiguity can be considerably diminished if behavioral classes are specified in terms of functional relations. These relations exist between certain environmental events (e.g., stimulus presentation) and discrete behavioral events (e.g., closing a switch). Such a functional descriptive system can provide the foundation for a meaningful classification system.

A functional classification of behavior might be initiated by relating changes in environmental factors to changes in behavior. An animal may manifest an intact sequence of certain behavioral changes without prior experience; or the same animal may require a series of opportunities or trials to establish the final form of a different kind of response. The first type of response is called *unconditioned;* the second, which requires training, is called *conditioned.* The simplest form of unconditioned behavior is the *reflex.* More complex forms of species-specific unconditioned behavior are usually called *instinctive behavior patterns.*

Conditioned behavior falls into two general classes. *Conditioned reflex* or *respondent* behavior is elicited by a known stimulus. Conversely, *operant* behavior cannot initially be shown to covary with a specific environmental event. These major behavioral categories are defined in terms of the covariation of occurrence of their members with specific changes in the environment. A more detailed description of any experimentally produced behavior requires specifying an array of other variables uniquely characteristic of each subcategory.

FUNCTIONAL CLASSIFICATION OF CONDITIONED REFLEXES

Before we can make a functional classification of conditioned reflexes, we must come to grips with the taxonomy of unconditioned reflex behaviors. Essentially, the question we wish to ask is: What are the controlling contingencies of reflex responses? Since reflex has been defined as a stimulus-response covariation, we might surmise that the principle controlling condition of a reflex response is the stimulus that elicits it. It should be no surprise, therefore, that reflexes are classified on the basis of a physical description of the stimulus, and the dimensions of the response that it elicits.

It is beyond the function of this book to tabulate the wide variety of experimentally isolated reflexes. Furthermore, as technological progress makes it possible to stimulate internal receptors more precisely and to measure the elicited physiological changes more finely, new reflexes are continually being isolated. It suffices to say that complex chains of reflexes are the principal means by which the various aspects of our physiological processes are integrated.

There is another important avenue of research besides the experimental isolation of new reflexes. It is clear that reflex responses vary in magnitude. What are the principal variables controlling reflex-response magnitude? If we isolate a reflex whose stimulus may be varied intensively and whose response magnitude we can measure precisely, we can demonstrate certain basic laws. These laws have been termed the *Static Laws of the Reflex* (Skinner, 1938).

The Law of the Threshold: The intensity of a stimulus must reach or exceed a certain critical value, called the *threshold*, in order to elicit a response.

The Law of the Latency: An interval of time, called the latency, elapses between the beginning of the stimulus and the beginning of the response.

The Law of the Magnitude of the Response: The magnitude of the response is a function of the intensity of the stimulus.

The Law of After-Discharge: The response may persist for some time after the cessation of the stimulus. The amount of after-discharge increases, in general, with increments in stimulus intensity.

The relations described above demonstrate that latency, magnitude, and after-discharge are functions of stimulus intensity. Stimulus duration is also important, and it can be shown that under certain conditions the prolongation of a stimulus or its repeated presentation may affect latency, magnitude, and after-discharge in the same manner as an increment in the stimulus intensity.

The static laws of the reflex must be distinguished from other empirically derived laws relating *changes* in the static properties of the reflex to the manipulation of certain variables. For example, what will occur to latency, magnitude, and after-discharge if a reflex response is repeatedly elicited at a high frequency? Clearly, the reflex response will, through fatigue, diminish in magnitude and after-discharge, and show an increment in latency. We could then derive a functional relation between various time intervals between successive stimulus presentations and the decrement in reflex strength. This is simply an example of the basic quest of behavioral science, which is to derive functional relations between experimental manipulations and changes in the properties of behavior. We shall deal in subsequent chapters with the manner in which drugs may affect the static properties of reflexes.

Conditioned Reflexes

Our first basic problem concerns the types of behavior that can be conditioned with the Pavlovian paradigm. From our discussion of this procedure in the previous chapter, we can deduce that only responses that may be elicited by experimentally manipulatable stimuli can be controlled by a new stimulus through Pavlovian conditioning. This assumes that any reflex response can, through Pavlovian conditioning, be elicited by an initially ineffective stimulus (i.e., the CS). It remains for future research to show whether there are exceptions to this rule. As it now stands, the generalization implies the possibility of environmental modification of physiological processes. This is of extreme importance in the field of psychosomatic medicine.

For example, Bykov (1957) has shown that it is possible to condition the secretion of bile from the liver. He preceded the administration of a drug (the US) that stimulated bile secretion with a stimulus (CS) initially having no effect on biliary secretion. Following a number of such US-CS pairings, the CS alone acquired the ability to elicit bile secretion. This is but one of hundreds of examples in the Russian literature showing how the environment can be used to control physiological processes. The interested reader is referred to the works of Bykov and to a recent review of the Russian literature by Razran (1961).

Selecting a Stimulus to Be Used as the Conditioned Stimulus

What types or classes of stimuli can be used as the CS in the Pavlovian conditioning paradigm? Since stimuli vary both qualitatively and quantitatively, the answer to this question is somewhat complex. Its two aspects must be explored separately before a general principle can be formulated.

Stimuli may be classified in one of three ways on the basis of the location of the receptor modality they affect. Sherrington (1906) has classified the receptors of the organism as exteroceptors, interoceptors, and proprioceptors. We can therefore speak of exteroceptive stimuli, interoceptive stimuli, and proprioceptive stimuli, depending on the class of receptors excited.

Of all these classes, the exteroceptive stimuli have received the most study. Wide varieties of visual, auditory, and cutaneous stimuli have been used as the CS. The relative rarity of American investigators who have used interoceptive and proprioceptive stimuli as the CS is attributable to the greater technical difficulties involved in presenting and controlling these stimuli. The Russian psychophysiologists have, however, carried out extensive investigations with proprioceptive and interoceptive stimuli as the CS. From these investigations we can conclude that, with the necessary techniques, proprioceptive and interoceptive stimulation can function adequately as the CS. Thus, there appear to be no qualitative limitations on the type of stimulus able to so function.

We must take stimulus intensity into account when we select a CS for, as stated previously, stimuli vary quantitatively as well as qualitatively. Recalling the static laws of the reflex, we can clearly see that a stimulus must exceed a certain intensity before it reaches the threshold. Furthermore, when we increase the intensity of a stimulus, the response magnitude increases. If we continue to increase its intensity, the organism's receptors may be damaged with concomitant elicitation of pain reflexes. Therefore, we must determine not only the type of stimulus we can use as a CS, but over what range of intensities it can be presented. The stimulus, of course, must be both above the threshold and below the intensity that causes physical damage.

A more subtle problem must be considered. *The stimulus used as a CS cannot elicit a response of greater strength than that elicited by the US if the two responses are incompatible.* For example, if our US is food (which elicits salivation as the UR), we cannot use an intense electric shock as the CS. The electric shock (at a high enough intensity) elicits responses stronger than and incompatible with the food-salivation reflex. We could, however, use electric shock as the CS if we lowered its intensity to the point where the responses elicited were weaker than the food-salivation reflex. Conversely, we could increase the strength of the food-salivation reflex by depriving the animal of food for a longer period of time, which would allow us to use a more intense shock.

The essential point is that a stimulus can function as a CS only if it does not elicit incompatible responses of greater strength than the US. Thus, there exists a range of stimulus intensities over which a stimulus can act as a CS; and this range is modified by any variable capable of affecting the strength of the US.

We may conclude from this discussion that any stimulus, within an appropriately intense range, can acquire the ability to function as a CS in the Pavlovian conditioning paradigm.

The CS-US Interval

The procedure dealt with thus far in our discussion of Pavlovian conditioning is called *simultaneous conditioning.* Simultaneous conditioning exists when the CS immediately precedes the US. What would be the effect of lengthening the time interval between the onset of the CS and the presentation of the US? Such a study was carried out by Pavlov's student Zadovsky. He lengthened the CS-US interval to 180 seconds. The US was a dilute acid solution introduced into the mouth of a dog, and the UR was salivation. The CS was a continuous whistle sound. Salivation rate was recorded at intervals of 30 seconds during the training in this procedure. As can be seen in Table 5.1, the salivation rate showed a progressive increment over the 180-second CS-US interval. Thus, the CS can best be conceived of as the whistle sound plus the passage of time. Pavlov called such a procedure with a CS-US interval greater than five seconds a *delayed conditioned reflex.*

CONDITIONING OF A DELAYED SALIVARY REFLEX **Table 5.1**

Time	Conditioned Stimulus Whistle	Salivary Secretion in Drops During Successive Periods of 30 Seconds of the Isolated Action of the Conditioned Stimulus
3:12	whistle	0, 0, 2, 2, 4, 4
3:25	whistle	0, 0, 4, 3, 6, 6
3:40	whistle	0, 0, 2, 2, 3, 6

Conditioning of a delayed salivary reflex in the dog, using the sound of a whistle as a CS and acid as a UCS. The whistle was sounded for 3 minutes, whereupon acid was presented concurrently with the whistle for a short time. The measure of conditioning was the number of drops of saliva during isolated CS presentation periods. (Pavlov, 1927, p. 90)

Many kinds of variables have been investigated in relation to the rate at which delayed conditioned reflexes are acquired. The nature of the CS was found to be an important variable. It has been shown that tactile, thermal, and visual stimuli lead to faster acquisition of delayed conditioned reflexes than do auditory stimuli. Furthermore, continuous stimuli were found by Pavlov (1927) to be more efficacious than intermittent stimuli (continuous light vs. flashing light).

A third procedure investigated by Pavlov was one in which, after a brief presentation of the CS followed by a time lapse, the US was presented. This procedure Pavlov termed *trace conditioning*, since he believed that a neural trace of the CS must remain in the nervous system to bridge the temporal delay in the CS-US interval. Establishing a trace conditioned reflex is usually more difficult than establishing a delayed conditioned reflex.

Both delayed and trace conditioned reflexes have been found extremely sensitive to stimuli presented during the CS-US interval. For example, if a novel stimulus is presented during the CS-US interval, we may observe the immediate occurrence of the CR. Pavlov believed this to be evidence that the CR was inhibited during the earlier temporal portion of the CS-US interval and that the novel stimulus broke this neural inhibition, precipitating the premature occurrence of the CR. We shall not attempt to evaluate the Pavlovian concept of inhibition and disinhibition; the interested reader is referred to Skinner (1938) for other explanations. It is interesting to note, however, that delayed and trace conditioned reflexes are extremely sensitive to disruption by pharmacological agents active in the central nervous system.

Higher-Order Conditioning

We have stressed that the Pavlovian conditioning procedure typically involves an unconditioned reflex (e.g., food ⟶ salivation; acid in the mouth ⟶ salivation, etc.) and that the response component is brought under the control of an initially ineffective stimulus. On the other hand, we stated that any response elicited by a manipulatable stimulus can be conditioned: the underlying reflex need not be an unconditioned reflex. For example, a tone may be used as a CS to elicit salivation, food being used as the US. After the tone has acquired the ability to elicit salivation, the tone-salivation reflex can be used as the underlying reflex to establish another stimulus, e.g., a light as the second-order CS. The light, by being associated with the tone-salivation reflex, may acquire the ability to elicit salivation independently.

At the present time, the feasibility of establishing higher-order conditioned reflexes is questionable. In the most frequently cited examples of higher-order conditioning (Frolov, as quoted in Pavlov, 1927), there is a disturbing lack of information about the experimental procedure. Razran (1955), in a review of higher-order conditioning, found very few successful experiments. In fact, in many instances attempts to establish a second-order conditioned reflex have resulted in disruption of the first-order conditioned reflex. More recently, several experimenters who used interoceptive stimulation as the CS and electric shock as the US reported successful higher-order conditioning. It is readily apparent that further research is needed to give a clearer picture of the procedures by which higher-order conditioning can be obtained. It is quite evident, however, that higher-order conditioning is an extremely limited phenomenon whose practical significance is open to doubt.

FUNCTIONAL CLASSIFICATION OF OPERANT BEHAVIOR

Antecedent Variables (Behavior Maintained by Positive vs. Negative Reinforcers)

Operant behavior is classified on the basis of four kinds of factors: (1) the antecedent manipulations, (2) the current stimulus circumstances, (3) the properties of the behavior, and (4) the response consequences. By specifying these classes of variables, the investigator can characterize his experimental procedure, predict the behavior to be obtained, and meaningfully communicate his findings (Fig. 5.1).

Some Characteristics of Behavior Under the Control of Positive Reinforcement: Before operant behavior can be reinforced and brought under experimental control, the behavior must occur. One way in which the investigator can increase the probability of an operant's occurrence is to deprive the subject of a positive reinforcer, such as food. The animal is usually deprived of food for a fixed period (e.g. 24 hours), or until his free-feeding body weight is reduced by a fixed percentage (e.g. 15 per cent). Under conditions of food deprivation, the frequency of many responses increases, making the occurrence of any given response more likely. In general, positively reinforced behavior requires deprivation for the reinforcer to be effective.

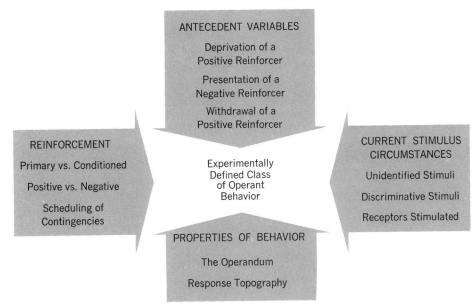

Fig. 5.1 An experimentally defined response class takes into consideration antecedent variables, current stimulus circumstances, properties of the behavior and reinforcement. By specifying each of these variables an operant can be empirically defined.

Experimental psychologists tend to use easily manipulated, readily presented reinforcers that are known to be "primary," or effective without a subject's prior experience. Consequently, much of what we know about the principles of learning is based on experiments using food and water reinforcement. Behavior maintained by food or water reinforcement can be very predictable and orderly. One of the predictable attributes of food- and water-reinforced behavior is the tendency for local satiation effects to appear. A food-deprived animal may become satiated after 15 minutes on a regular reinforcement schedule, but several hours later may again work for food. If CRF (continuous reinforcement) is the required reinforcement schedule for a particular experimental procedure, then food may not be an appropriate reinforcer. Figure 5.2, which presents a cumulative record of lever-pressing by a rat maintained on a CRF schedule for food, shows that the response rate during the first 10 to 15 minutes is at a stable rate but that negative acceleration occurs during the last 15 minutes. If, on the other hand, social stimulation (visual presentation of another animal) or electrical stimulation of certain subcortical brain structures had been the reinforcer, a highly stable rate of responding over long periods would have been obtained.

There are difficulties inherent with conditioning procedures based on the conception of "drive" or "need" reduction as a necessary condition for learn-

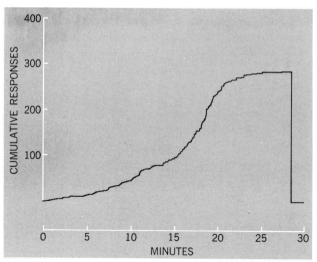

Fig. 5.2 A cumulative record of acquisition of lever-pressing by a rat for food reinforcement, illustrating a gradually increasing response rate followed by satiation. Note that between 15 and 20 minutes the record becomes negatively accelerated as satiation progressively suppresses rate.

ing. While this position was long accepted, it is now clear that many reinforcers are effective without drive or physiological need reduction. Saccharine solution (Sheffield and Roby, 1950; Smith and Capretta, 1956), the opportunity to exercise (Kagan and Burkun, 1954), manipulation (Harlow and Meyer, 1950), the presentation of visual stimuli (Thompson, 1963, 1964), and electrical stimulation of subcortical brain structures (Olds and Milner, 1954; Brady, 1955) have all been shown to act as positive reinforcers without drive or need reduction. The characteristics of behavior maintained by these reinforcers, the specific variables examined, and the nature of the reinforcer itself determine which reinforcer is most appropriate for an investigator. Frequently such "nonessential" reinforcers have properties undesirable as baselines for studying drug effects. For example, electrical brain stimulation produces a rate of responding that, while very high, is often subject to rapid extinction. Consequently, if the number of responses to extinction is an important dependent variable to be studied for a considerable time in relation to drug effects, brain stimulation may not be the optimum reinforcer.

The visual image of another fighting cock can act as a positive reinforcer for the key-pecking response in a rooster (Thompson, 1964). However, while the daily response output for this reinforcer is very stable and highly predictable, the absolute number of responses is relatively low. Therefore, if a continually high response rate is a necessary condition for an experimental procedure, this type of reinforcer may not be satisfactory. The specific behavioral characteristics desired must be carefully specified before the most appropriate reinforcer is selected. The less experienced investigator is cautioned not to expect ostensibly similar reinforcers to produce similar behavioral effects. What may seem similar to the investigator may very well produce dissimilar behavioral effects in the experimental animal.

"Emotional Behavior" and Positive Reinforcement: The experimenter may be interested in examining the effects of drugs on "emotional behavior." As indicated in the preceding chapter, *emotion* is construed in terms of manipulations performed and explicit descriptions of resulting behavior rather than in terms of nonobservable internal processes. It is well established that, following a history of positive reinforcement, the onset of extinction produces an abrupt increase in the vigor of responding (Miller and Stevenson, 1936; Amsel and Roussel, 1952; Screven, 1954). This increased vigor has been thought to reflect a state of "aggression," since it is concurrent with an increased tendency to attack other animals (which can include a variety of behaviors like gnawing and biting inanimate objects).

For example, Azrin has shown that pigeons vigorously attack one another during extinction (Fig. 5.3), and Thompson and Bloom (1966) have shown that the tendency for attack during extinction covaries with the tendency for response-rate increase. The marked increase in vigor typical of many kinds of responses covaries with the tendency for attack during extinction; and this increase in vigor has been experimentally exploited as a drug evaluation procedure. By designing an experimental procedure to compare response rates during periods immediately before and after extinction onset, it is possible to express numerically the behavioral effects of the extinction operation (Fig. 5.4). This index can be subsequently used as a measure of the effects of drugs on this correlative of aggressive behavior (Fig. 5.5).

Various stimuli that precede time-out from positive reinforcement are associated with marked behavioral changes. In such procedures, a chimpanzee might be conditioned to operate a switch-manipulandum on a variable-interval reinforcement schedule for food reinforcement. A stimulus is presented immediately before a period of nonreinforcement of responses. This is called a *pretime-out stimulus*. The response rate increases markedly during the pretime-out stimulus, and, if the reinforcement contingencies are arranged so that high response rates terminate the pretime-out stimulus and put the animal into a time-out (S^Δ period), then responding will decrease markedly. The animal learns to avoid such interruptions of positively reinforced stimulus periods (S^D periods) in much the same way that it learns to avoid painful stimuli like electric shock and loud noises (Ferster, 1958).

Some Characteristics of Behavior Under the Control of Negative Reinforcers: Behavioral researchers normally use painful stimuli to induce the dramatic

Fig. 5.3 The aggression-inducing effects of withdrawal of food reinforcement can be seen in the upper photograph, in which the subject is vigorously attacking the stuffed model of another pigeon following the onset of extinction. (Azrin, Hutchinson, and Hake, 1965, p. 583) The photograph at left shows similar attack behavior induced by shocking two albino rats placed in immediate proximity in a confined space. (Ulrich and Azrin, 1962, p. 512, Fig. 1)

Fig. 5.4 The relation between extinction of a food-reinforced lever-pressing response and fighting by hooded rats. One rat had previously been conditioned to press a lever for food reinforcement, while a paired animal was satiated and relatively inactive in the test chamber. During extinction, the previously reinforced animal attacks the satiated animal. The curves on next page are for ten five-minute extinction periods, and show concurrent lever-pressing and fighting duration. (Thompson and Bloom, 1966, p. 336, Fig. 1)

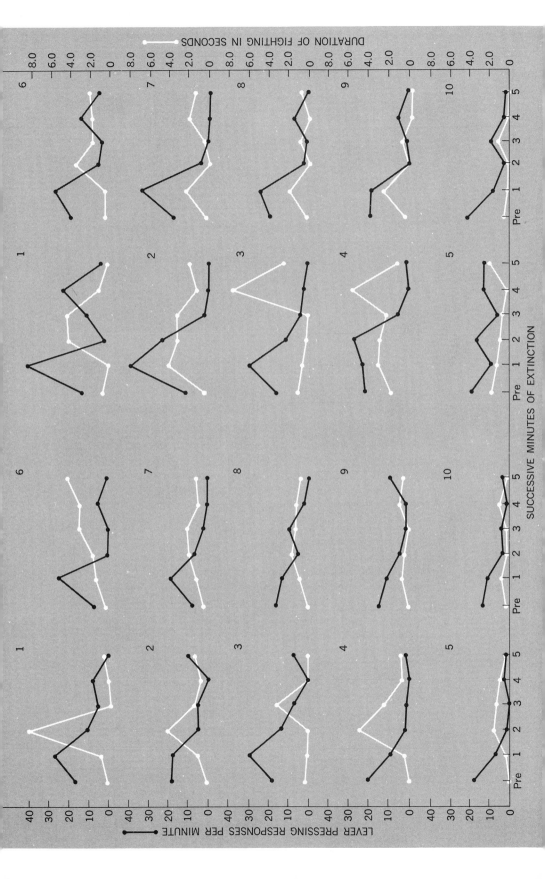

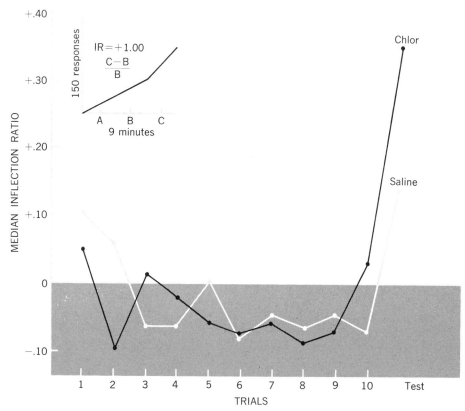

Fig. 5.5 The effects of chlorpromazine (1.5 mg/kg/I.P.) on extinction-induced rate increase of a previously food-reinforced operant. The response rate increase is expressed as a ratio of the difference between the number of responses during an extinction period (C) and responses during a comparable period prior to extinction (B), divided by the pre-extinction responses (B). The extinction inflection ratio is zero if there is no rate change, and positive with a rate increase during extinction. While all subjects increase rate in extinction, those treated with chlorpromazine exhibit a relatively greater rate increase. (Thompson, 1961, p. 399, Fig. 1)

behavioral changes usually called emotional responses. Many such stimuli, including electric shocks, puffs of air, loud noises, and heat or cold, have been used as negative reinforcers. Animals subjected to such procedures exhibit characteristic changes in behavior, which include vocalization, trembling, piloerection, urination, and defecation. These signs are cited as validation of the "emotion-producing" nature of the antecedent operation. Operant behavior maintained by such stimuli involves a response leading to removal of the painful stimulus, or to removal of the stimulus that precedes and warns that the painful stimulus is forthcoming. Such procedures are called *conditioned escape* or *conditioned avoidance*.

Commonly Used Negative Reinforcement Procedures: In *escape conditioning*, a primary negative reinforcer, such as a painful electric shock to the feet, is presented without a warning stimulus. The emission of a specified operant following the painful stimulus (such as running to a "safe" compartment or pressing a lever) will terminate the shock. Therefore, it is said that removing the shock reinforces the running or lever-pressing operant. Concomitant with the operant measured is an array of responses, many of which are mediated by the autonomic nervous system. For example, an animal is likely to tremble, hyperventilate, and generally exhibit behaviors ascribed to states of extreme fear or anxiety in humans. Whenever the subject is placed in an experimental situation in which a shock has once been delivered, these responses occur even before the shock is presented. The total environment, including many stimuli not experimentally manipulated, comes to act as a complex of conditioned stimuli for the array of reflex responses that initially occurred only following electric shock. Animals conditioned in this way may run to the lever in the experimental situation and begin pressing before a single shock has been delivered. The lever-pressing operant may thus come to be partly controlled by the stimulus effects of the respondents as well as by exteroceptive stimuli.

On presentation of some previously neutral stimulus (like a tone sounded five seconds before shock), an animal will crouch, urinate, defecate, and vocalize during the tone. In addition, it will approach the lever during tone presentation and begin to press or stand in a position to press the lever when the shock begins. If pressing the lever during the tone terminates the tone and postpones the shock, lever-pressing will henceforth occur with a short latency after the tone's onset. This type of conditioned response is called an *avoidance response*.

In avoidance conditioning, removing the warning stimulus constitutes reinforcement; whereas in escape conditioning, the response is controlled by shock removal. If the shock ceases to be presented after the tone, the latency of the lever-pressing response from the onset of the tone will increase until the response finally stops occurring altogether. If the shock is reinstated, the latency will decrease sharply and the shock will be successfully avoided. Thus, shock avoidance also depends on continued presentation of the shock following the tone. The tone acts as an exteroceptive discriminative stimulus for the lever-pressing operant; termination of the tone is in itself reinforcing.

Complex Procedures for the Analysis of Control by Negative Reinforcers: One variation of the avoidance procedure requires the subject to emit a response at least once during a fixed period in order to postpone shock for a short time. The shock is not preceded by an exteroceptive warning stimulus, as in the above procedure, so the animal tends to respond at a relatively high and constant rate (Fig. 5.6). This rate can be adjusted up or down by introducing or withdrawing unavoidable shocks (Sidman, Herrnstein, and Conrad, 1957). Both types of conditioned avoidance can be used to establish baselines for analyzing drug-behavior interaction, and both have been extensively explored (Sidman, 1960). This avoidance conditioning situation is extremely stressful. In fact, under prolonged exposure to avoidance contingencies, monkeys tend to develop peptic ulcers (Brady, 1958). This technique is potentially useful for research in psychosomatics, and on the role of drugs in ameliorating psychosomatic syndromes, both behaviorally and by direct effector action (such as with anticholinergic agents).

A third experimental situation that has been studied in detail is the phenomenon of conditioned suppression, or conditioned emotional response (CER) (Estes and Skinner, 1941; Brady and Hunt, 1955). Some ongoing behavioral

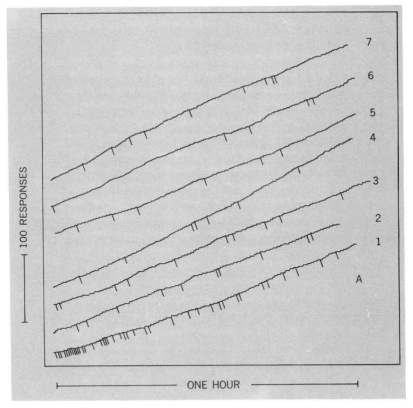

Fig. 5.6 Cumulative record of a rat's avoidance behavior during a seven-hour experimental session. The oblique "pips" indicate shocks, and are most closely spaced at the start of the session. (Sidman, 1960, p. 291, Fig. 35)

sequence leading to a positive reinforcer is conditioned as a baseline, e.g., VI-1 food. While the animal is working on VI-1 schedule for food, a clicking sound is presented for three minutes. At the termination of the sound, the subject receives a painful shock that is not contingent on his behavior. In other words, the stable VI performance continues during the clicker and is briefly disrupted by the shock. Repeated pairing of the clicker and the shock is associated with a suppression of the food-reinforced responding during clicker presentation. The suppression progressively increases until the animal ceases to respond during the clicker.

A well-trained CER subject will respond until the onset of the clicker, will temporarily cease responding during clicker presentation, and will resume responding after the shock (Fig. 5.7). An example of the effects of drugs on conditioned suppression is presented in Fig. 5.8. Saline administration before the experimental session has no effect on suppression during the clicker presentation; but reserpine administration before the experimental session simultaneously reduces the overall rate of responding and tends to ameliorate the suppression effect so that the animal continues to press at the preclicker rate.

In the three foregoing cases, a negative reinforcer was used. In the first two examples, the animal could make a response that would lead to removal of a negative reinforcer. In the third, the aversive stimulus was not contingent on the animal's behavior. The kinds of behavior generated in these experimental situations differ greatly and provide measures of quite different behavioral phenomena.

Conditioned avoidance usually requires far longer to extinguish than conditioned escape. This difference in persistence is believed to be due to the immediacy of reinforcement in escape conditioning as compared to the delayed reinforcement of the response in avoidance conditioning and to the fact that avoidance responses are intermittently reinforced (i.e., the shock is avoided most of the time). The persistence of a suppression phenomenon has been illustrated by a study in which pigeons continued to exhibit suppression for two and one half years after conditioning without intervening exposure to these contingencies (Hoffman, Fleshler and Jensen, 1963).

A very widely used procedure for the analysis of negatively reinforced behavior is the "titration" or "escalator" method. In this procedure, a painful stimulus is presented to the subject in a series of increasingly intense steps. For example, foot shock is presented at fixed time intervals increasing in voltage by equal increments at each shock. The subject's lever-pressing responses decrease shock voltage by equal values. Initially, the shock voltage is below the subject's threshold; but voltage is increased at fixed time intervals, and soon exceeds the threshold. The subject quickly learns to respond regularly in order to drive shock voltage below his threshold. The resulting record of shock voltage is presented in Fig. 5.9 (Weiss and Laties, 1964).

(a) TYPICAL OUTPUT DURING
15 MINUTE PERIOD

(b) FIRST CONDITIONING TRIAL

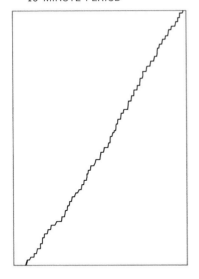

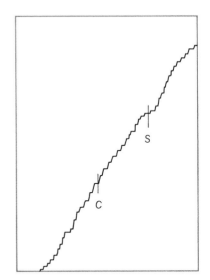

(c) CONDITIONED EMOTIONAL RESPONSE

1. Early Stages

2. Fully Established

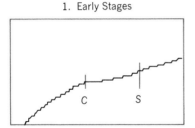

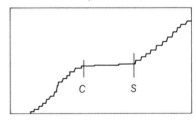

RESPONSE

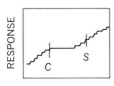

TIME

LEGEND

Clicker Introduced at C, Terminated by Shock at S after 5 Minutes

Fig. 5.7 The conditioning of suppression during presentation of a preaversive stimulus. Typical VI performance reinforced by food is presented in A. B shows the effect of a brief shock (S) on this VI performance. C_1 and C_2 illustrate early and late conditioned suppression with progressively fewer responses emitted during the clicks. (Hunt and Brady, 1951, p. 90, Fig. 1)

Fig. 5.8 The effect of saline, amphetamine, and reserpine on conditioned suppression in monkeys. Amphetamine administration is associated with an over-all rate increase, and increased tendency to suppress responding during the clicker. Reserpine, on the other hand, produces a generalized decrease in over-all response rate, but a relative increase in responding during the clicker. (Brady, 1956)

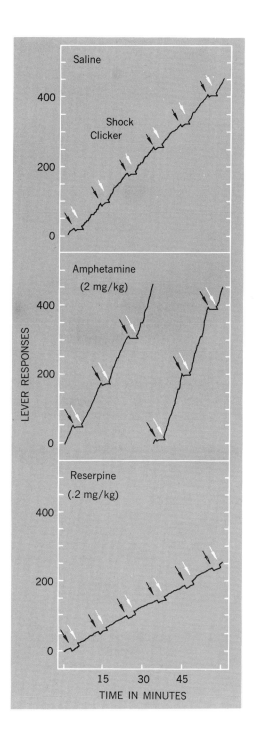

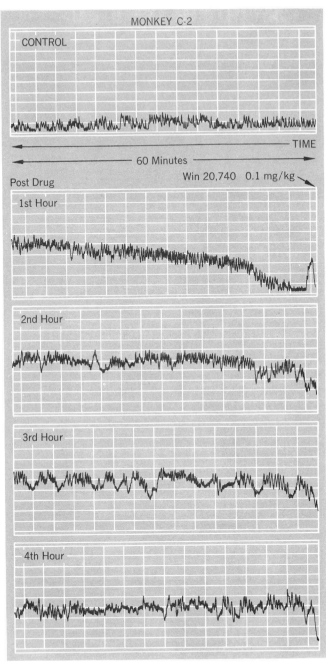

Fig. 5.9 Recording attenuator record of the response of
one monkey to 0.1 mg/kg of Win 20,740. Each segment
represents one hour; the control segment is the last hour
of the two-hour predrug sample. Time reads from right
to left; maximum shock is represented by the top of the
record. Each hour segment begins with the shock level
reset to zero. (Weiss and Laties, 1964, p. 172, Fig. 4)

Current Stimulus Circumstances

In defining the operant, we said that the experimenter is initially unable to specify stimuli controlling behavior. However, stimulus events that are consequences of the behavior soon come to control the operant. These consequences are called *reinforcers*. At first, the subject's environment may be one in which the reinforced response can be freely emitted at all times. If the response is almost immediately followed by reinforcement, leaving the subject in a position to emit that response again, the behavior is described as a *free operant* (Ferster, 1953). As we observe the animal, we find that his behavior is not without *antecedent* stimulus control. In fact, we find a stereotyped sequence of behaviors, in which the last behavior is the stimulus for the next response in the sequence, the sequence terminating in reinforcement. This behavioral chain is summarized below.

sS^D: visual lever. R: lifting sS^D: tactual lever. R: pressing
sS^D: tray S^D: sound of magazine. R: approach to tray
S: food. R: seizing   –(Skinner, 1938)

We see that, although we have not intentionally introduced stimuli as such in the experiment, external environmental events and the animal's own behavior gain control over the operant. To the extent that these stimuli set the occasion for reinforced responding, they may be classified as discriminative stimuli.

Behavior Controlled by Unidentified Stimuli: Occasionally there is a question about the value of studying "nondiscriminated" operants. The implication is that some operant behavior may not be under the control of discriminative stimuli. As illustrated in the foregoing example, even the simplest of free-operant situations involves discriminative stimuli. The assumption that discriminative stimuli exist only if the experimenter programs them is hardly warranted. However, the important consideration is the extent to which such stimuli can be *shown* to control behavior discriminatively. It is sometimes difficult to define clearly the environmental events controlling certain instances of behavior. For example, a very stable response rate is maintained by a fixed-interval avoidance schedule with no exteroceptive warning stimulus and with no shocks for long periods of time. That is, no specific auditory, visual, or other exteroceptive environmental events seem to set the occasion for the high rate of responding.

Other examples offering difficulties in clear identification of the *discriminative stimulus* are tandem and mixed reinforcement schedules. In neither instance is there a distinct change in the exteroceptive stimulus from one component of the schedule to another; yet the behavior reflects schedule control. Perhaps the greatest difficulty in identifying controlling stimuli arises when the behavior is under the control of interoceptive stimuli. While the experimenter can sometimes manipulate interoceptive stimulation, it is certainly true that most interoceptive stimulus events are not under experimental control. To the extent that the experimenter has no access to these events (and this is usually the case), he is unable to specify accurately the stimuli controlling certain behaviors. This difficulty makes human introspective reports very difficult to evaluate and utilize experimentally (Skinner, 1954).

The Use of Discriminative Stimuli to Control Behavior: Specifiable discriminative stimuli are used in most procedures and behaviors studied by the behavioral pharmacologist. The simplest case is a CRF schedule that, intermittently indicated by a tone, leads to food reinforcement. In other words: S^D tone $\longrightarrow$ R one-lever press $\longrightarrow$ S^R food pellet.

Well-discriminated behavior maintained by this type of procedure is illustrated in Fig. 5.10. Responding begins promptly with the onset of the tone and terminates almost immediately when the tone stops. In this example, the most probable dependent variable is rate of responding during the tone presentation as compared with the response rate during nontone periods. The obvious advantage of using this procedure rather than a "free" one (in which the animal can be reinforced all the time) is elimination of the satiation effect discussed earlier. By varying the time between tone presentations, and the duration of each tone presentation, CRF behavior can be maintained over a relatively long period of time. In this way, time-course drug effects on CRF behavior may be studied with the contaminating factor of satiation at a minimum.

The Class of Receptors Stimulated: The preceding example illustrates the general principle of discriminative control. However, such control can be exercised by many kinds of stimuli that act on receptors located on the external surfaces of the body, the retina of the eye, and the basilar membrane of the ear, and on various receptors located in the smooth muscles, the con-

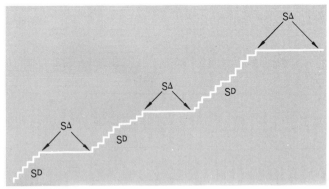

Fig. 5.10 A stylized detail of a cumulative record of discriminated lever-pressing on a CRF schedule. During alternating periods response rate is moderate (S^D) or zero (S^Δ) according to the prevailing stimulus conditions.

nective tissues, and the glands. Because of technical difficulties encountered in using interoceptive stimulation, most American scientists have employed exteroceptive stimuli instead. Practical obstacles notwithstanding, Russian psychophysiologists have studied interoceptive stimulation extensively, using conditioning techniques developed by Pavlov (Bykov, 1957; Razran, 1961).

In the United States, several investigators have begun to use operant methods to study the control exerted by interoceptive stimulation. Conger (1951) has shown that the presence or absence of alcohol in the body can provide the discriminative basis for learning differential responses. Heistad (1957, 1958) has demonstrated that the degree to which conditioned suppression is retained depends on the degree to which the internal environment resembles the state it was in when the behavior was conditioned. Heistad and Torres (1959) and Torres (1961) have obtained the same results with this line of investigation extended to other drugs and different procedures for measuring behavior. Barry, Miller, and Tidd (1962), Belleville (1964), and Otis (1964), have demonstrated similar phenomena in situations involving positive reinforcers. Cook and coworkers (1960) found that an avoidance response can be brought under the stimulus control of physiological changes associated with intravenous administration of epinephrine, norepinephrine, and acetylcholine. Pickens (1965) conditioned locomotor activity changes to amphetamine administrations. Schuster (1962) demonstrated a similar phenomenon in which the intravenous infusion of epinephrine into monkeys acted as a discriminative stimulus for a food-reinforced operant. He further found that the simple infusion of body temperature isotonic saline into the internal jugular vein (at rates as low as 0.5 cc/min.) was discriminable (Schuster and Brady, 1964).

Behavior During Pretime-Out Stimuli and Stimuli Preceding Positive-Rein-forcer or Negative-Reinforcer Presentation: In addition to classification of stimuli on the basis of the location of stimulated receptors, stimuli can be classified in terms of the events following the stimulus and its response. Using this scheme, stimuli are sometimes called either preaversive or preappetitive. Preaversive stimuli are those that precede withdrawal or time-out from positive reinforcement; or they may precede the presentation of a negative reinforcer. In both instances, behavior during the stimulus presentation has been characterized as "emotional" and affords a behavioral baseline for studying drug effects. Conversely, behavior during preappetitive stimuli (e.g., FI of FI-FR chain) is less frequently described as emotional, although there are exceptions. When the reinforcer is a female rat in estrus presented on the emission of an operant by a male rat, or when the reinforcer is the visual image of one Siamese fighting fish presented on emission of an operant by another fighting fish, the behavior during the preappetitive stimulus is usually described as emotional.

Stimulus Thresholds, Discrimination, and Generalization: When we speak of two stimuli as similar, we actually refer to our tendency to generalize our response in the presence of those two stimuli. On the other hand, when we say that two stimuli are quite different, we refer to our ability to discriminate the difference and report on it verbally. If we continue moving a discriminative stimulus progressively closer to an S^Δ and require the subject to respond only in the presence of the S^D and never in the presence of the S^Δ, we arrive at a physical difference along the continuum at which the organism can no longer successfully discriminate. This smallest value of a stimulus change to which a response can be made discriminatively is called a *difference threshold* or *difference limen*.

The titration technique described earlier is applicable to the analysis of drug effects on stimulus thresholds, and the tendency for stimulus generalization. Blough (1958) described a technique for obtaining psychophysical thresholds in pigeons. In Blough's experimental situation, the pigeon had two response keys available. By using appropriate reinforcement-scheduling techniques, Blough trained the pigeon to peck one key when a stimulus light was on and the other key when the stimulus light was dark. Pecks on the first key lessened stimulus intensity, while pecks on the second key increased it. A record of the oscillations in stimulus intensity describes the visual threshold continuously in time. Thus, the subject's responses govern the stimulus intensity, and the stimulus intensity controls the subject's responses. Blough (1956) used this procedure to analyze drug effects on the visual threshold in the pigeon.

In another procedure for measuring the gradient of stimulus generalization, a pigeon was conditioned to peck an illuminated key on a variable-interval reinforcement schedule. During response-reinforcement periods, key illumination was maintained at a constant wavelength. The reason for using a VI reinforcement schedule was the tendency of such a schedule to generate a great deal of resistance to extinction. That is, a VI schedule maintains responding for a long period without reinforcement. In the next stage of the experiment, the food magazine mechanism was disconnected, so that responses on the key could continue, although they were unreinforced. During this period, the key was illuminated intermittently and systematically with different colors of light that varied across the visual spectrum. The period of each stimulus presentation was equal, so that the number of pecking responses in the presence of each color could be directly compared. The greatest number of extinction responses was emitted when the wavelength of light was the same as the S^D. As the wavelength moved away from the S^D value, either to higher or lower wavelengths, fewer responses were made during stimulus presentation. This curve was presented in Fig. 4.5; it is a typical gradient of stimulus generalization (Guttman and Kalish, 1958).

Properties of the Behavior

The Operandum: One sometimes hears "operant-conditioning situation" defined as an experimental apparatus involving an animal and a lever. However, if there is no lever, then apparently some other kind of behavior is being measured. This reflects a lack of understanding of the term "operant." It will be recalled that an operant is any member of the class of responses—whether it is lever-pressing, switch-closing, running, talking, touching, licking, or striking—having common antecedents and being under the control of common reinforcing consequences. It is true, however, that many operant situations involve levers, switches, etc. or, as such devices have come to be called, *manipulanda* or *operanda* (Skinner, 1962). The importance of the characteristics of the manipulandum in an experimental situation is not to be underestimated. The physical dimensions of a manipulandum in terms of length, thickness, the extent of excursion required, the amount of force, and the duration for which it must be held closed should be very carefully considered in designing the behavioral procedure.

In certain experimental procedures, the operant may be closing a telegraph key. Telegraph keys have certain characteristics of potential behavioral importance. For example, when the key is depressed and released, the contacts tend to "chatter," (to close and open and close again several times without making a single clean contact). If one is concerned with measuring the duration of each press as a dependent variable, then this "noise" in the system must be taken into account. Furthermore, one must make sure that the amount of pressure required to close the contact is the same on each press, and that the pressure needed is not so great as to produce fatigue.

Certain types of manipulanda are not very practical. Bakelite and Lucite devices are not recommended for work with rats, since the animals tend to chew or gnaw at them in the test chamber, particularly during the extinction periods. The position of the manipulandum in the experimental situation is of considerable importance. If the response key is close to the floor in an experiment using pigeons, the frequency of key-pecking will be very low. Similarly, rats should not be subjected to a switch-type manipulandum located so high on the side wall of a chamber that the animals can depress the switch only by jumping off the floor. In dealing with primates, one has to consider the great strength of the subjects and their tendency to destroy any manipulandum in the experimental chamber. Very heavy-duty steel switches and handles are usually required, particularly for chimpanzees and the larger monkeys.

Response Topography: The way in which an organism emits a response, the musculature used, the posture, and the patterning of the response all go into making what is called the *topography* of the response. Response topography is an interesting aspect of the subject's behavior, and it has not been studied very extensively. As indicated earlier, certain procedures, including drug administration, may not significantly alter response frequency, but they may indeed alter other, often ignored, aspects of response topography.

Operant Level: Operants tend to occur with some basic frequency prior to conditioning. The frequency with which an operant occurs under these conditions is called its *operant level*. The operant level of a given response is of considerable practical importance in designing an experiment. If one were to place an albino rat inside a 10 ft. sq. room with a 1 in. sq. lever protruding midway along one of the side walls, the likelihood that the rat would approach the lever and depress it would not be very great. If, however, the same rat and the same lever were placed inside a 12 in. sq. box, the likelihood that the rat would press the lever "by accident" (closing the switch and recording a response) would be much greater. In the second instance, one would say that the operant level (that is, the frequency with which the response occurs) would be greater as a function of the smaller size of the experimental chamber.

In the same 12 in. sq. test cubicle with the lever described previously, a rat deprived of food for 15 minutes will be less likely to move about and press the lever than one deprived of food for 24 hours. Increased activity is a function of deprivation conditions, which also affect operant level. Further, if the pressure required to depress the lever is 20 gm., it is unlikely that many responses will be recorded. However, if the same lever is adjusted so that 5-gm. pressure is required to depress it, the operant level will increase markedly. Thus it can be seen that a variety of factors affects the operant level of any behavior to be measured. The experimenter is well advised to take these factors into consideration when he plans the initial stages of his experiment. On the one hand, a response which has an operant level of once per six-hour period in a satiated animal in a room 10 ft. sq. with a 20-gm. lever may have an operant level of 10 times per hour in the same subject when it has been deprived of food for 24 hours and put in a 12 in. sq. box with a lever requiring 5 gm. of pressure. Differences in order of magnitude such as those just suggested can make a difference of hours or days in acquisition.

Multiple Operant-Multiple Operanda Interactions: The investigation of drug effects on behavior is, at times, a shot in the dark. We are not very sure which behaviors may be affected by a given drug, but we would like to be able to provide an approximate answer without months of random searching. One way to examine a drug's effect on an array of behaviors is to condition subjects on multiple-operant schedules with multiple operanda. An example of such a schedule is presented in Fig. 5.11 (Thompson, 1964). In this example, the subject could respond either on the same operandum or on different operanda. The organism had the opportunity to receive food, water, or visual reinforcement on a fixed-ratio schedule. In this instance, the organism was in a position to select its own reinforcer, and the size of the ratio was progressively increased.

Discriminability of the Response: One technique for conditioning animals involves the presentation of a "feedback stimulus" following a response. This refers to the presentation of an auditory or visual stimulus immediately fol-

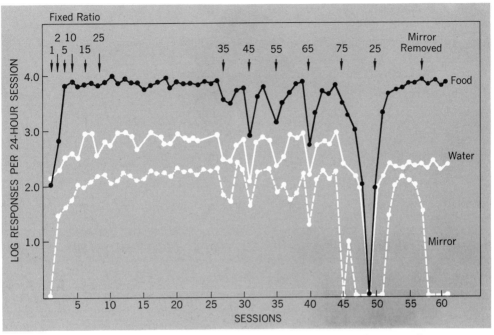

Fig. 5.11 The logarithms of the numbers of responses for food and water on mirror reinforcement by an adult fighting cock. Progressively larger fixed ratios were programmed over successive sessions using a three-member nonreversible option. (Thompson, 1964, p. 47, Fig. 1)

lowing the completion of the response. For example, when a monkey closes the switch of a telegraph key, a buzz or click may occur. When a laboratory technician who has conditioned a great many animals is asked why he uses this procedure, he may well answer, "Because the animals condition a lot faster that way." But why should a feedback stimulus facilitate conditioning? In essence, the organism is emitting a response of such an order of magnitude that it is initially unable to discriminate the proprioceptive feedback from the emission of the response. The click is an additional exteroceptive stimulus to provide it with this information. The empirical demonstration of the value of such additional stimuli has been most eloquently presented by Hefferline. By adding a visual stimulus that varied as a function of the subject's response magnitude, a previously indiscriminable response was readily conditioned (Fig. 5.12).

There are ways of making responses more discriminable in and of themselves. The force required to complete the response may be increased, or the excursion of the manipulandum may be increased, or the subject may be trained to discriminate his own behavior by prior conditioning of proprioceptive feedback as a discriminative stimulus for another operant.

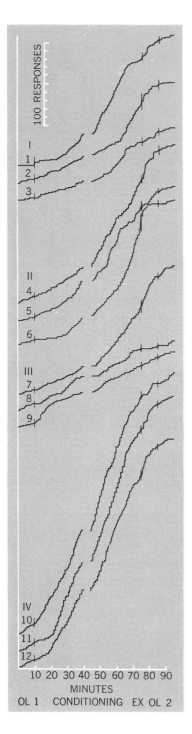

Fig. 5.12 Cumulative response records for adult human subjects in a situation where a small unnoticed thumb twitch either terminated or postponed noise stimulation. O.L.'s 1 and 2 indicate initial and terminal operant levels, while EX. indicates extinction. Subjects in Group I received no instructions, while those in Group II were told that a response would terminate or avoid the noise. Group III subjects were told that a movement of the thumb would terminate or avoid the noise, while S's in Group IV were given the same instructions as those in Group III, but were given an exteroceptive feedback stimulus in addition. (Hefferline, Keenan, and Harford, 1959, p. 1339, Fig. 1)

The ability of an organism to make fine-grained response discriminations on the basis of his own proprioception can be disrupted by drug effects. Therefore, operants requiring the animal to make such discriminations may be of great value in assessing pharmacological agents. In human behavior, we encounter inability to make fine response discriminations under the effects of drugs like alcohol, the barbiturates, and some of the newer behaviorally active drugs.

Reinforcement Contingencies

Conditioned and Primary Reinforcers: Historically, reinforcers have been viewed as stimuli that fulfill the subject's primary physiological needs, e.g., for food, water, air. As we have used the term, a *reinforcer* is a stimulus that has the capacity to increase or maintain response strength above operant level. At least in principle, there might be stimuli that increase response probability but are not "primary" or "essential." A discriminative stimulus that has repeatedly preceded and set the occasion for reinforced responding may come to increase response frequency above operant level without further association with a primary reinforcer. By definition, such a stimulus would *be* a reinforcer. It has gained its reinforcing properties through conditioning; hence the term *conditioned reinforcer* is applied.

Some writers use the terms "secondary reinforcer" and "conditioned reinforcer" interchangeably. There is nothing inherently wrong with making synonyms of these words, but certain connotations of the term "secondary" render the practice less than desirable. "Secondary" implies something less important or vital. This is misleading and, if taken literally, incorrect. Furthermore, use of the term secondary does not encourage the analysis of the functional relations involved in developing a stimulus as a reinforcer. Emphasis on the manner in which the stimulus comes to act as a reinforcer requires the experimenter to remain close to the observational level and encourages rigor. As a practical consideration, the term secondary introduces the problem of using awkward terminology like "tertiary" and "quaternary" reinforcers (based on successive members of a chain). Thus, despite the widespread acceptance of the phrase "secondary reinforcer," for reasons of clarity and ease of communication, the term "conditioned reinforcer" is preferable (Kelleher and Gollub, 1962).

To understand conditioned reinforcement, one must grasp the concept of behavioral chaining. It will be recalled that in an operant chain, responses act as discriminative stimuli for other responses. In such a chain, the sequence of individual responses is emphasized, rather than the external stimuli controlling the behavior. The occurrence of the sequence is generally presumed to be controlled by proprioceptive stimuli. The components of such a chain are the individual responses that make up the sequence.

The conditioning of an operant usually establishes a chain. For example, in using food reinforcers to train a food-deprived rat, a complex sequence of behaviors is established in which the last response in the sequence is the discriminative stimulus for the first response of a new sequence. In some experimental procedures, an exteroceptive stimulus is presented after the completion of each response or each unit of the chain. In others, responding in the presence of one exteroceptive stimulus produces a second stimulus, which produces a third stimulus, and so forth (Kelleher and Gollub, 1962; Ferster and Skinner, 1957). At the end of the chain, a primary reinforcer is presented. Each component stimulus of such a chained schedule may be a conditioned reinforcer for responding to the component that precedes it. Thus, subcomponents of a chain are maintained or reinforced by the several conditioned reinforcers intervening between the beginning of the chain and the terminal primary reinforcer.

The application of the conditioned-reinforcing aspects of chains permits construction of very long sequences of behavior, with only one primary reinforcer at the end. For example, it is possible to maintain a chimpanzee on an FR120,000 reinforcement schedule by interspersing conditioned light reinforcement (Findley and Brady, 1965). Such long periods of relatively stable behavior have obvious advantages in behavioral pharmacological research. They allow the examination of time-course drug effects without the contaminating factor of satiation. This type of procedure also allows repeated measurements over many sessions at approximately the same level of performance. Finally, the degree of alteration of control by stimuli associated with the successive components of chains is of importance. For example, there is suggestion that differential effects on fixed-interval clock performance depend on alteration of control by the exteroceptive stimulus that varies systematically with time during the interval (Weiss and Laties, 1964).

Simple Reinforcement Schedules: Historically, the most widely studied schedules have been the simple reinforcement schedules. The basic schedules in this class are presented below; they are known as nonintermittent *reinforcement schedules.* The first of these has been called an *operant-level schedule* (Op. 1.), in which occurrences of an operant with no previous reinforcement history go unreinforced. The operant-level schedule is used to determine the frequency with which an operant occurs prior to conditioning (its operant level). The basic schedule from which all other schedules stem is the one usually called a *regular reinforcement schedule* (CRF). On a regular reinforcement schedule, every response is followed by the presentation of a reinforcing stimulus.° The acquisition of an operant on CRF is characteristically positively accelerated and is somewhat irregular. After several sessions on this

---

° In order to understand the discussion of reinforcement scheduling, the reader must be familiar with cumulative response records. Appendix II-A discusses cumulative recording for those who may have had little exposure to this method of presenting data. It is recommended that this material be studied in detail at this time, since it is basic to an understanding of the remainder of the book.

schedule, responding stabilizes at a very regular rate (Fig. 5.13). If an operant that has been conditioned on a CRF schedule is no longer followed by reinforcement, the frequency of occurrence diminishes to the operant level. In this case, one would say that the operant is on an *extinction* (Ext) schedule.

The other main class of simple schedules comprises the *intermittent* schedules. In recent years, the intermittent schedules have enjoyed increasing experimental attention. The term "aperiodic reinforcement" was once used by some writers as synonymous with "intermittent reinforcement." As we shall see, however, the first term has connotations that are not entirely appropriate.

Basically, there are two types of intermittent schedules: interval schedules and ratio schedules. The first type of interval schedule is one in which a fixed interval of time elapses between the last reinforced response and the occasion on which the occurrence of that response will again lead to reinforcement. Responses made during the interval have no consequence in terms of procuring the reinforcer; it is only after a fixed period following the last reinforcement that reinforcement will again be forthcoming. This type of schedule is called a *fixed-interval (FI) reinforcement schedule.*

The other interval schedule is one in which variable periods elapse be-

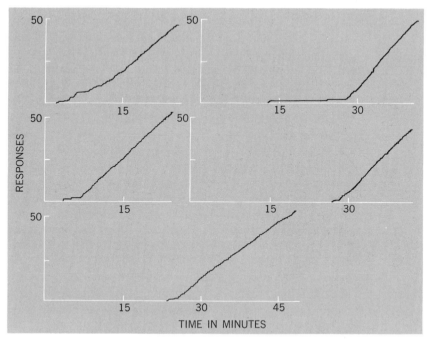

Fig. 5.13 Cumulative records of lever-pressing acquisition on a regular food reinforcement schedule for five rats. (Skinner, 1938, p. 68, Fig. 4)

tween the last reinforced response and the recurrence of reinforcement following emission of the operant. In the latter case, the interval will have a specified mean and range. Such a schedule is called a *variable-interval* (VI) *reinforcement schedule.* A number following the abbreviations FI and VI indicates the length of the interval in minutes or seconds. In a VI-1 schedule, for example, reinforcement occurs at intervals that average one minute following the last reinforced response (with a range of perhaps five seconds to three minutes). On an FI-1 schedule, however, a constant interval (one minute since the last reinforced response) would elapse before a reinforcement would be forthcoming. Figure 5.14 illustrates the development of FI and VI performance of the same interval lengths. It will be noted that in the case of the FI record, there is a characteristic positively accelerated scallop that reaches the highest rate of responding immediately prior to reinforcement; this segment is followed by a pause and then by a gradual second buildup, etc. By contrast, the rate on the VI schedule is very stable.

The other general class of intermittent schedules comprises the ratio reinforcement schedules. One type of ratio reinforcement schedule is one in which a reinforcement is forthcoming after a fixed number of responses. Therefore, the higher the rate of responding, the more frequently the organism will be reinforced. There are no time contingencies. This type of schedule is called a *fixed-ratio-reinforcement* (FR) *schedule.* A variation of this is a schedule in which a variable number of responses is required to procure reinforcers within a mean and specified range of ratios. Such a schedule is called a *variable-ratio-reinforcement* (VR) *schedule.* Examples of fixed- and variable-ratio cumulative records are presented in Fig. 5.15.

FR records reveal a characteristically constant high rate with a short postreinforcement pause that is followed by the same high rate. A comparison of the interval and ratio records demonstrates that there tends to be greater stability on both the VI and the VR schedules; however, responding is at a higher rate on a VR schedule. Broadly speaking, ratio schedules are "piecework" schedules, whereas interval schedules are essentially "time clock" schedules.

In general, intermittently reinforcing a response produces far greater resistance to extinction than regular reinforcement. That is, the operant will be maintained for a far greater period, or for many more responses, if conditioning is followed with an intermittent reinforcement schedule rather than with a regular reinforcement schedule. This may be extremely important when the number of responses to extinction is an important measure of the effects of a drug, and a fairly large sample of behavior is required.

Compound Reinforcement Schedules: Compound schedules of reinforcement are made up of variations and combinations of the simple schedules just discussed. A characteristic of the compound schedules is *the alternation of two or more simple schedules or the interspersion or superimposition of two simple schedules.* The first type of compound schedule involves the orderly

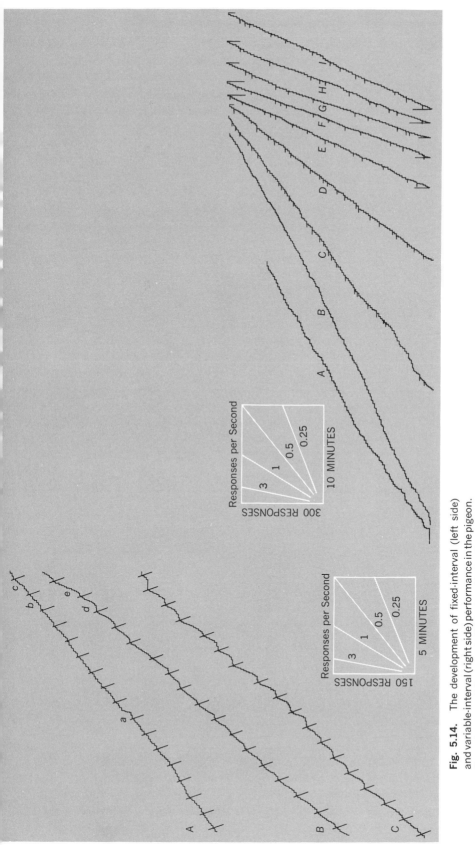

Fig. 5.14. The development of fixed-interval (left side) and variable-interval (right side) performance in the pigeon. Records proceed from early (A) to late (C, I). (Ferster and Skinner, 1957, p. 143, Fig. 126, [left] and p. 327, Fig. 386, [right])

Responses per Second

3
1
0.5
0.25

150 RESPONSES

5 MINUTES

alternation or sequencing of subcomponents of the schedule. Such schedules are called *sequential*. The primary example of a sequential schedule is a *chain*. In a *chained schedule* at least two components occur in the same order, with a discrete stimulus change from one component to the next. The only consequence of completing the first component of the chain is a change to the stimulus condition characteristic of the next component of the chain. For example, the records of performance by monkeys trained to press a lever on a fixed interval of two minutes (FI2) in the presence of a tone reveals the characteristic positively accelerated scallop referred to earlier in discussing the fixed-interval schedule. At the end of the two-minute FI, the stimulus changes to a green light. The green light is an S^D for a fixed ratio of 25 (FR25) leading to morphine S^R. Following the twenty-fifth response, a morphine solution is infused intravenously. This is an example of an FI2-FR25 chain in which morphine is the terminal reinforcer.

If morphine infusion is discontinued following the FR component of this chain, the stimulus change from the FI to the FR component gradually loses its ability to maintain the FI component. This is characteristic of a chained schedule. It is said that the stimulus change acts as a conditioned reinforcer for the first member of the chain (Kelleher and Gollub, 1962).

Another type of compound schedule involves the interaction of two or more simple components without distinctive stimuli. An example of such an interaction may be found in a *tandem reinforcement schedule*. In a tandem schedule, two or more components are programmed sequentially with no discrete stimulus condition indicating the currently active component. For example, we might superimpose an FI reinforcement schedule and an FR reinforcement schedule as follows: Let rats first be trained to press a lever on FI5 for food reinforcement. Subsequently, add an FR50 contingency in tandem to the FI5, so that 50 responses emitted five minutes following the last reinforced response would lead to food S^R. We see that two contingencies are necessary to obtain reinforcement, the contingencies being those of both of the members of the tandem schedule.

The second most widely used type of compound reinforcement schedule is the *multiple reinforcement schedule,* in which two or more component schedules occur in a sequential or randomized fashion indicated by discrete stimulus changes with primary reinforcement at the end of each component. For example, an organism may be conditioned on a fixed-interval schedule in the presence of a tone and on a fixed-ratio schedule in the presence of a clicking sound. The tone and the clicking sound may be presented alternately, they may be interspersed with "blackout" periods, or they may be presented

Fig. 5.15 Comparison of well-established fixed-ratio (left side) and variable-ratio (right side) performance in the pigeon. (Ferster and Skinner, 1957, p. 50, Fig. 22 [left] and p. 393, Fig. 472 [right])

in a random order, without blackout periods. By contrast, a *mixed reinforcement schedule* is one in which the different components occur in a randomized sequence *without* discrete stimulus control. Components of various schedules—DRL (differential reinforcement of low rate), FR, and FI—may alternate in a randomized order with no exteroceptive stimuli indicating which component is currently in effect. Conditioning by such mixed schedules ordinarily requires far longer than conditioning by comparable multiple schedules. Although the behavior generated by the mixed schedule is quite complex, it is nevertheless extremely orderly. This orderliness results from a precisely specified set of conditions, maintained unchanged for a very long time (Ferster and Skinner, 1957).

Interpolated reinforcement schedules are those in which a single bloc of reinforcements on one component of a schedule is inserted into a background schedule. For example, an FR20-interpol-FI15 schedule employs a background schedule of FI15. After a certain period, a bloc of FR20's is interspersed in the background schedule; and after the completion of the bloc of FR20's, the FI15 schedule is used until that experimental session is completed. The interpolated schedule is most commonly used as a control procedure following conditioning on a multiple reinforcement schedule.

Complex Reinforcement Schedules: Complex reinforcement schedules necessarily involve ratio and interval contingencies that vary as a function of the organism's performance. *Differential and adjusting reinforcement schedules* are among the most widely studied complex schedules. A differential reinforcement schedule is one in which some component or parameter of the ongoing operant is manipulated within a defined range as a function of the subject's performance. Usual examples are frequencies of occurrence, forces, or durations. In a DRL schedule, for example, an animal must learn to space its responses at some minimal interval in order to obtain reinforcement. In a DRL one-minute schedule, responses occurring less than one minute after the last reinforced response will reset a timer which must then time for one minute. The first response after one minute will produce a reinforcement. Responses before the end of that minute will reset the timer again.

A DRH schedule differs from a DRL schedule in that a *high* rate of responding is specified. We can also place the subject on a differential schedule according to the duration of lever-pressing. For example, a rat may have to hold the contacts of a telegraph key closed for a minimum of 10 seconds and a maximum of 20 seconds. In this case, we are differentially reinforcing response duration. Likewise, we may specify certain ranges of force, for example, a minimum of 10 gm. and a maximum of 20 gm. In all these cases, one of the most important indices of the schedule's effect is the distribution of interresponse times, response durations, or response forces. Through the examination of the distribution of these variables we gain greater sensitivity.

Adjusting reinforcement schedules (Adj.) are slightly different from differential schedules inasmuch as the schedule changes over the course of a given experimental session according to the performance of the subject. In Sidman's adjusting avoidance schedule (1962), an animal is permitted to press a lever to produce a five-second period of safety from painful electric shock. The animal may accumulate "safe time" by successive responses, in which case an additional five seconds of safe time is added for every response. This type of schedule tends to produce a characteristic temporal pattern of responding to avoid the shock. There tends to be a rather wide spacing of responding occurring in long bursts, which has the effect of reducing the density of shock per unit of time. This differential reinforcement of long interresponse times is probably responsible for the development of an efficient spacing of responding (Fig. 5.16).

Another sort of adjusting reinforcement schedule is the progressive-ratio procedure. The progressive-ratio schedule requires the subject to emit an

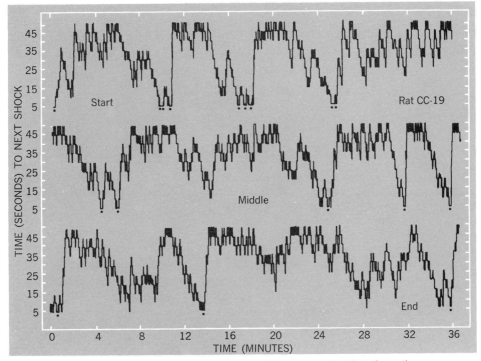

Fig. 5.16 Adjusting avoidance records taken from the beginning, middle, and end of a session, giving a continuous picture of the temporal distance the animal kept between itself and shock. The pen moved up one five-second step each time the animal pressed the lever, and moved down an equal distance whenever the animal allowed five seconds to elapse without pressing the lever. Shocks are indicated by the dots below each segment of the record. (Sidman, 1962, p. 274, Fig. 3)

increasing number of responses for each successive reinforcement. Eventually, the response requirement becomes so large that the subject fails to respond before the reaching of a "breaking point" arbitrarily set for that subject. This has been said to be a measure of motivational variables, since the longer an animal is deprived of food, for example, the more responses he will make for food reinforcement (Hodos, 1961).

One of the more interesting applications of adjusting schedules to behavioral pharmacological research grew out of a "fractional escape and avoidance titration" procedure (Fig. 5.9) developed by Weiss and Laties (1958). Weitzman and associates (1961) applied the general method to the study of escape from a painful electric shock delivered through chronically implanted electrodes in the Gasserian ganglion of monkeys. The shock intensity increases by fixed increments at fixed intervals (e.g., 0.2 volts every five seconds). Concurrently, responses on a telegraph key lever reduce the voltage by the same amount. The resulting record of shock-voltage steps is a saw-toothed function (Fig. 5.17) varying around a point thought to be an aversive stimulus threshold (Weitzman, Ross, Hodos, and Galambos, 1961). The procedure has been examined as a baseline for exploring the effects of morphine and other analgesics on aversion threshold (Weitzman and Ross, 1962). In addition, Weiss and Laties have extended the technique to the analysis of drug effect and behavioral thermoregulation (1961).

This brief introduction to complex schedules of reinforcement can best serve as a guide to *some* of the ways in which complex repertoires can be built up. For a more detailed discussion of complex schedules of reinforcement, and methods of controlling behavior on such schedules, the interested student is referred to Ferster and Skinner, 1957; Findley, 1962; and Kelleher and Gollub, 1962.

Multioperant Repertoires: Thus far we have dealt with relatively simple cases of reinforcement scheduling. The most complex schedules have involved combinations of two or three simple schedules presented over a relatively short period. Recently, techniques have been developed for experimentally manipulating highly complex sequences and parallel arrangements of behavior that utilize 24 hours of reinforcement scheduling daily. It is possible to examine literally dozens of different operants involving an array of types of repertoires and multiple stimulus modalities (Findley, 1962).

An important development in the evolution of methods for studying multioperant repertoires was the conception of a 24-hour experimental session and an experimental living space (Findley, 1958). The 24-hour session makes the "home" environment the experimental space and permits the exploration of extensive segments of the organism's behavior within this space. To this end, Findley developed an outline for the construction and exploration of multiple operants within the individual organism. The behavior investigated within this framework can vary from simple chains to several-level multiple option situations that may repeat themselves once a day, or

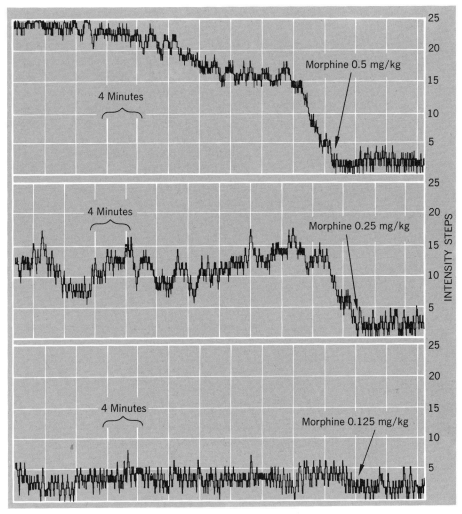

Fig. 5.17 Effect of intravenously administered morphine sulfate (0.125, 0.25 and 0.50 mg/kg) on titrated shock intensity to the Gasserian ganglion in the monkey. (Weitzman, Ross, Hodos, and Galambos, 1961, p. 37, Fig. 1)

even less often. The degree of control can vary from sampling of behavior for five minutes at a time four times a day, to virtually continual experimental control. Using such methods, it may be possible to bring larger and larger segments of behavior under the control of the experimenter, with much smaller segments of behavior remaining beyond experimental manipulation.

For the behavioral pharmacologist, such an experimental regimen suggests exciting research possibilities. One has only to give cursory attention to some of the data Findley obtained to begin to comprehend the tremendous potential that remains untapped. Perhaps the most effective illustration of the power of the multioperant approach is contained in an experiment conducted by Findley (1966). This study involved the exploration of complex repertoires in a normal human adult subject who was maintained in an experimentally controlled environment for five months. A program of activities controlled by automatic equipment permitted the subject to engage in a particular sequence of activities. The terminal parts of the sequence allowed the subject to engage in more reinforcing activities, and to choose among a greater selection of activities. Behavioral requirements in several of the activities were manipulated during the experiment. Performance changes were recorded in terms of frequency of selection and duration of activities, and in other more qualitative terms. Using these methods it was possible to bring up to 90% of the subject's time under the control of programmed contingencies. Other complex experiments of this sort have been reported by Findley (1962) and Kelleher (1967).

Section IV

6

Behavioral Mechanisms of Drug Action

INTRODUCTION TO SECTION IV

Behavioral pharmacology represents the wedding of two scientific disciplines, a wedding occasioned by the need for preclinical procedures to select new compounds that would produce clinically desirable behavioral changes. In the earliest days of behavioral pharmacology, investigators seemed to be content to show that drugs *could* cause certain behavioral changes; but it rapidly became apparent that something more than a simple demonstration of a drug effect was needed. One of the principal aims of pharmacology is to determine the mechanisms of action by which a drug produces a given effect; and this is swiftly emerging as the principal goal of behavioral pharmacology.

In Chapter 6 we will present representative experiments suggesting investigatory approaches indicated if researchers in behavioral pharmacology are to be successful in delineating the mechanisms by which a drug affects behavioral changes. Chapter 7 discusses special problems such as screening methods for predicting the potential clinical usefulness of a new drug. Implicit in the order of these chapters is our conviction that a thorough grasp of the mechanism of action of well-known behaviorally active drugs is a prerequisite to improving the validity and reliability of preclinical screening procedures for new drugs.

The apparatus and terminology of behavioral pharmacology sometimes obscure its fundamental methodological similarity to the more traditional "hard core" pharmacological approaches. To show this similarity, let us consider a hypothetical experiment that deals with the effects of a drug on the blood pressure of an anesthetized dog.

We anesthetized our subject by administering 30 mg/kg intravenous sodium pentobarbital. We then placed a catheter filled with heparinized saline into the carotid artery, attaching the catheter's free end to a pressure transducer that yielded an electrical output varying linearly with the blood pressure in the artery. The electrical output could thus be used to drive a kymograph pen, providing a continuous graphic record of the subject's arterial blood pressure.

Before beginning the experiment proper, we conducted a series of control observations to determine that the subject's blood pressure was stable. Then we administered intravenously a volume of the solvent we had selected as the vehicle for our test drug. Figure 6.1 shows that the administration of 1.0 cc. of 0.9 per cent NaCl solution caused no change in the subject's blood pressure. A dosage of $1 \times$ mg/kg was then administered in 1.0 cc. of saline. Figure 6.1 shows that the administration of $1 \times$ mg/kg of our test drug caused a decrement in blood pressure of approximately 8 mm. mercury. The blood pressure returned to its predrug level after approximately 10 minutes.

A dosage of $2 \times$ mg/kg of the test drug was next administered; and this dosage caused a blood pressure decrement of approximately 17 mm. mercury, which returned to the baseline reading in approximately 15 minutes. We could repeat this procedure for testing a variety of dosages as long as the blood pressure returned to its control level between each dosage tested. Figure 6.1 shows the effects of three dosages of our test drug.

The most obvious conclusions to be drawn from this simple experiment are that the decrement in blood pressure and the duration of this effect were dose-dependent. That is, with increasing dosages, the blood pressure showed a progressive decrement and took longer to return to the predrug control level. Our findings might raise the question, How did the test drug cause a decrement in blood pressure? What, in other words, was the test drug's mechanism of action? Was the blood pressure drop caused by drug-induced peripheral vasodilatation, or by a drug-induced slowing of the heart rate?

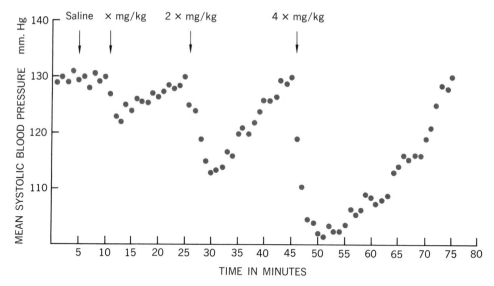

Fig. 6.1 Hypothetical results from an experiment involving the effects of three dosages of drug X on blood pressure in the dog. In each case, blood pressure was allowed to return to the baseline between administrations of the test drug.

Clearly, we will be able to determine this drug's mechanism of action only by further experimentation. By measuring its effect upon heart rate, stroke volume, peripheral vascular resistance, etc., we might be able to delineate more precisely the cardiovascular mechanisms involved in the drug's action.

The following illustrative experiment shows that research tactics in behavioral pharmacology closely parallel the fundamental steps followed in the model experiment described above. Our subject was an adult male Rhesus monkey maintained at 85 per cent of its free-feeding body weight. The monkey was trained to emit a lever-pressing operant that was reinforced with a 0.7 gm. food pellet on a variable-interval schedule of reinforcement. The monkey spent two hours daily in the experimental situation and, after a number of such sessions, its lever-pressing response rate stabilized both within and between sessions. Figure 6.2 shows the number of lever-pressing responses per five-minute interval in several daily sessions.

Following behavioral stabilization, the monkey was given 1.0 cc. intravenous saline after the first 30 minutes of each daily session. The animal rapidly adapted to the injection procedure so that its response rate was minimally affected, as illustrated in Fig. 6.2, Day 1. We were then ready to study the effects of our test drug in a variety of dosages. On Day 2, the subject was given 1 × mg/kg of the test drug after the first 30 minutes of the ex-

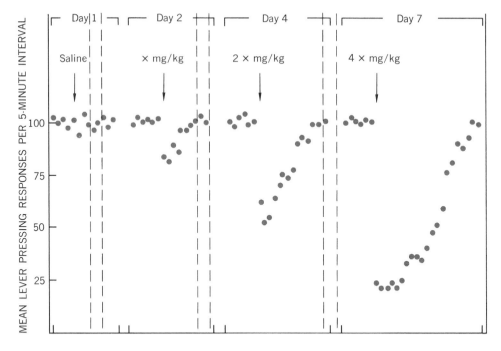

Fig. 6.2 Hypothetical results from an experiment in which the effects of three dosages of drug X were administered to a monkey working for food on a VI-1 minute reinforcement schedule. In each case, the performance was allowed to return to the baseline before another dose of the drug was given.

perimental session. Figure 6.2 shows that the subject's lever-pressing rate declined from 100 responses per five minutes to 80 responses per five minutes. After approximately 40 minutes, the subject's response rate returned to its predrug level.

The next step was to give the subject saline for several sessions as a control measure and then to increase the dosage of the test drug to $2 \times$ mg/kg. Figure 6.2, Day 4, shows that this dosage of the drug caused the response rate to decline to about 55 responses per five minutes. After 60 minutes, the subject's response rate returned to its predrug level. Figure 6.2 summarizes the effects of three dosage levels of the test drug on the VI lever-pressing response rate.

What can we conclude from this experiment? The response decrement and the duration of the drug's action were clearly dose-dependent; that is, the response decrement and the drug's duration of action showed a progressive increment as a function of dosage. Clearly, further experiments would be required before we could delineate the mechanism by which this drug produces its behavioral effects. The remainder of this chapter describes an approach that would allow more precise specification of the behavioral mechanisms of action of this drug. Before we proceed to a more detailed analysis, however, let us review the procedural steps that are common to both of our illustrative experiments. These procedural steps are summarized in Table 6.1, which stresses the fundamental similarity of the two approaches.

HOW DO WE DETERMINE THE BEHAVIORALLY ACTIVE DRUG'S MECHANISMS OF ACTION?

The cardiovascular pharmacologist has an extensive fund of knowledge about the variables that control blood pressure. This knowledge enables him to proceed systematically when he studies these variables in relation to a given cardiovascular effect. It cannot be too strongly stressed that the investigator's success is based on a thorough understanding of such variables,

ANALYSIS OF EFFECTS OF HYPOTHETICAL DRUG ON BLOOD PRESSURE AND LEVER PRESSING

Table 6.1

	Experiment I	Experiment II
	The effect of test drug on systolic blood pressure in the dog	The effect of test drug on food-reinforced VI-1 lever-pressing in the monkey
A. Preparation of the subject	Anesthetization Surgical introduction of carotid catheter	Food deprivation Conditioning of lever pressing
B. Establishment of control base line	Assessment of blood pressure's stability under experimental conditions	Assessment of stability of lever-pressing rate under VI-1 schedule of reinforcement
C. Solvent control testing	Assessment of the effects of the drug solvent on blood pressure	Assessment of the effects of the drug solvent on lever-pressing response rate
D. Effects of X mg per kilogram of test drug	Measurement of extent and duration of blood pressure change (mm Hg)	Measurement of extent and duration of lever-pressing rate change
E. Re-establishment of control base line	Observation of blood pressure for its return to control levels	Observation of lever-pressing for its return to control levels

Repeat steps D and E with various dosages of test drugs.

Procedural comparison of the investigation of the effects of an hypothetical drug X on blood pressure in the dog and on variable interval food-reinforced lever pressing in the monkey. The basic steps are very similar although details differ.

and of the interrelationships that combine to control the biological system under consideration. If behavioral pharmacology is to succeed in determining a drug's behavioral mechanisms of action, a comparable background of knowledge about the variables that control *behavior* must be obtained.

The older discipline of physiology provides a background of information on which the pharmacologist draws; similarly, the behavioral sciences *should* make the same kind of information available to the investigator in behavioral pharmacology. However, these sciences are only beginning to determine the essential variables controlling given behaviors, and the investigator who wishes to analyze behavioral actions of drugs must therefore engage in preliminary parametric studies of the variables that control the behavior he wants to use. With this knowledge, the interpretation of a drug's behavioral mechanisms of action can proceed, in an orderly fashion. It is our intention in this section to give guidelines to an approach for determining a drug's behavioral mechanisms of action. This approach should be viewed as suggestive rather than exhaustive; as procedural rather than as substantive.

We discussed in Chapter 4 some of the basic variables that control behavior. The procedural outline we used there can also be applied to a systematic investigation of a drug's behavioral mechanism of action. Let us begin with the relatively simple experiment described above that dealt with the effects of several dosages of a test drug on the lever-pressing rate in a monkey reinforced by food pellets on a VI schedule.

Antecedent Conditions

Clearly, one of the most potent variables affecting lever-pressing response rate on a VI food-reinforcement schedule is the level of food deprivation. Figure 4.1 shows representative cumulative response records of VI performance under different levels of food deprivation. As the level of food deprivation is decreased, the VI response rate shows a progressive decrement. Figure 6.2 showed that increasing dosages of the test drug also produced a progressive decrement in response rate. Perhaps the action of this drug was to produce a change in the effective level of food deprivation.

This question frequently arises when pharmacologists look at data about a drug's effect on food-reinforced behavior. All these data show, it is commonly asserted, is that the drug has produced anorexia—"a lack or loss of the appetite for food" (*Dorland's Medical Dictionary* (1964)). This definition, by its inclusion of the unmeasurable inferred state of "appetite," places the question of what anorexia is outside the realm of scientific inquiry. However, if we define an anorexigenic drug as an agent that specifically decreases eating behavior, we may approach the problem in a meaningful experimental way.

How can we go about determining whether our test drug is an anorexigenic agent and, further, whether the anorexia produced is responsible for the decrement in food-reinforced VI response rate? Several experimental possibilities suggest themselves. The simplest and most direct approach would be to determine whether an animal under comparable food-deprivation conditions would eat when given free access to food under the various dosages of the test drug. A more profitable approach would involve determination of the effects of the test drug on VI lever-pressing behavior maintained by reinforcers other than food (e.g., water, visual access to other animals, brain stimulation, etc.). If the test drug produced a comparable change in VI performance, regardless of the kind of reinforcer used to maintain the behavior, it could not be argued that the drug was a specific anorexigenic.

Another alternative would be to investigate the effects of the drug on other types of schedules with the same reinforcer. We might wish to choose a fixed-interval schedule of food reinforcement, since this schedule is particularly sensitive to changes in deprivation conditions. Frequently, drugs that decrease the response rate on one food-reinforcement schedule are found to produce no effect, or an increase in response rate, on a different type of food-reinforcement schedule (see, for example, Fig. 6.2). Such differences in the effect of a drug between schedules of food reinforcement clearly obviate an explanation of the drug's action as specifically anorexigenic.

Let us turn this problem around. How would we go about demonstrating that a drug *is* in fact an ideal anorexigenic? Such a compound would weaken all behaviors maintained by food reinforcement and have little or no effect on behaviors maintained by other reinforcers. The ideal anorexigenic agent is currently unknown; the amphetamines, widely used clinically for anorexigenic effects, appear to act in part by strengthening alternative behaviors rather than by specifically depressing food-reinforced behaviors.

The approach outlined above is equally applicable to determining the way a drug acts on behavior maintained by other reinforcers. It might, for example, prove intellectually stimulating for the student to devise an experimental approach to determine whether a drug has the properties of an aphrodisiac.

Another common assertion about the mechanism of action of drugs on food-reinforced behaviors is that a given drug is said to produce changes in the normal gastrointestinal patterns associated with alimentation. For example, chlorpromazine produces a decrement in food-reinforced VI response rates. Possibly chlorpromazine decreases food ingestion by virtue of anticholinergic effects on the salivary glands. It is well established that food ingestion is decreased in water-deprived animals. This fact lends plausibility to the suggestion that chlorpromazine's action on food-reinforced behavior might be attributable to its production of dryness of the mouth.

One control experiment, in addition to those previously described, might consist of the administration of a dosage of methylatropine to subjects performing on a VI food-reinforced schedule. Methylatropine produces its peripheral anticholinergic effects with no discernible effects on the central nervous system. This compound is therefore a valuable control for use with drugs having both central and peripheral anticholinergic actions. When the VI performance is differentially affected by the chlorpromazine and methylatropine at dosages that produce comparable peripheral anticholinergic effects, the behavioral change associated with chlorpromazine cannot then be attributed to its peripheral anticholinergic action.

Response Properties

Let us assume that only lever-pressing responses at forces of 50 gm. or greater are registered by our equipment. The decrement we observe in the monkey's VI response rate induced by the test drug may be a change in the frequency of responses less than 50 gm. in force. Many drugs that have neuromuscular effects could conceivably render a monkey less able to press the lever with the necessary force.

Recently, systems have been developed that enable the experimenter to measure continuously the exact force expended on each lever-press (Falk and Haas, 1965). Such systems allow the analysis of changes in the relative frequency of responses of different forces under drug conditions. If a drug is found to produce neuromuscular effects, one can use this force measuring system to study highly skilled lever-pressing responses. For example, one might differentially reinforce responses which did not exceed a given pressure (e.g., 20 gm.). Or, one might differentially reinforce responses of a specific force *and* duration (the subject might be required to exert a pressure of between 15 and 20 gm. and to maintain the response within this range for a minimum of five seconds).

These new force systems have not yet been used in procedures for generating a behavioral baseline for drug evaluation; but they may very well prove useful tools in this respect. For example, one might evaluate the effects of drugs on fatigue generated by requiring responses of great force to be emitted at a high rate. Another possibility is that of investigating the Parkinson-like tremors associated with chronic phenothiazine therapy.

Gross Motor Incapacitation and Nonspecific Schedules

Another drug action possibly capable of producing response-rate decrements is motor incapacitation. For example, if a drug renders an animal ataxic, the placement of the lever becomes of extreme importance. If the lever is placed so high that the subject must stand on its hind legs in order to depress it, ataxia may render the animal incapable of emitting the response. Parenthetically, a similar incapacitation might result from a drug-induced orthostatic hypotension. Thus, the physical properties of the response in question may be an important variable in determining a drug's mechanism of action. It is beyond the scope of this section to deal with the problem of selecting the response to be studied. However, it is important to realize that seemingly similar behavioral procedures may differ only in the choice of the response, yet yield markedly different drug effects. This is dealt with more explicitly in Chapter 7.

In many instances, one can rule out motor incapacitation or nonspecific sedation as a drug's mechanism of action by using a multiple schedule. For example, Dews has shown that pigeons trained on a multiple FI-FR schedule show differential sensitivity to the actions of pentobarbital. Dosages that markedly depress FI responding increase subjects' FR response rates. Clearly, the depression of FI response rates cannot be attributed to generalized sedation, motor incapacitation, or changes in the ability of food to act as a reinforcer.

The behavioral pharmacologist is ordinarily interested in the behavioral effects of drugs at dosages below those necessary to produce gross motor incoordination and marked general sedation. The latter effects are, however, important as measures of a drug's behavioral toxicity. This is an important area of behavioral pharmacology, particularly in the preclinical evaluation of new drugs.

Stimulus Control

In many behavioral baseline procedures for drug investigation, the behavior of an animal is brought under explicit discriminative stimulus control. For example, in our hypothetical experiment, the monkey might be reinforced for lever-pressing in the presence of a white light. In the presence of a green light, lever-pressing responses would not be reinforced (S^Δ condition). Periods of S^D and S^Δ conditions would be systematically programmed. After training under the baseline conditions, the subject would show a high lever-pressing response rate in the S^D condition, and a very low frequency of responding in the S^Δ condition. Immediately one might ask, What possibilities exist for the action of a drug on this behavior baseline? Table 6.2 summarizes the nine logical outcomes of drug administration. This section deals with these possibilities, the interpretation each outcome allows and, more important still, what further experiments are suggested by various outcomes to delineate responsible mechanisms.

1. S^D Response Rate Unchanged, S^Δ Response Rate Unchanged

This outcome indicates that at this dosage of the drug there is no change in the subject's performance. It is therefore appropriate to test higher dosages of the drug.

2. S^D Response Rate Unchanged, S^Δ Response Rate Increased

This outcome suggests that the drug has disrupted the animal's discriminative abilities. How might we determine more precisely that the animal's dis-

Table 6.2   **EFFECTS OF A DRUG ON FOOD-REINFORCED PERFORMANCE**

S^D Response Rate		S^Δ Response Rate
(1) $\longrightarrow$ (no effect)		$\longrightarrow$
(2) $\longrightarrow$		$\uparrow$
$\longrightarrow$		$\downarrow$ °
(3) $\uparrow$ (increase)		$\longrightarrow$
(4) $\uparrow$		$\uparrow$
$\uparrow$		$\downarrow$ °
(5) $\downarrow$ (decrease)		$\longrightarrow$
(6) $\downarrow$		$\uparrow$
$\downarrow$		$\downarrow$ °

° These possibilities are excluded since we have stated that the animal's S^Δ response rate under base line conditions is extremely low. We, therefore, cannot determine any further drug-induced decrements.

The possible effects of a drug on discriminated variable interval food reinforced performance. The possible effects are no change ($\longrightarrow$), increased response rate ($\uparrow$) and decreased response rate ($\downarrow$).

criminative abilities were affected by this dosage? One possibility would be to determine whether comparable discriminative disruption was induced by the drug when we used discriminative stimuli affecting another sensory modality (e.g., auditory stimuli). If this dosage caused similar discriminative disruption, regardless of the sensory modality stimulated by the S^D and S^Δ, we could conclude that the drug had not caused a specific sensory disruption. It should be stressed, though, that we must be certain that the baseline performance is the same with the different types of stimuli used.

If the disruption in stimulus control were found to be specific to visual stimuli, we might wish to investigate the effects of the drug on the subject's absolute and difference visual thresholds. A first approximation to this could be obtained by increasing the differences between the S^D and S^Δ stimuli. For example, we could increase the intensity of the S^D and decrease the intensity of the S^Δ stimuli. If, after this change, the drug produced less of an increment in the monkey's S^Δ response rate, we might wish to employ a finer measure of the effect of the drug on the monkey's discriminative abilities. The Blough technique (see Chapter 4) could be used to determine more precisely the effect of the drug on discriminative abilities.

3. S^D Response Rate Increased, S^Δ Response Rate Unchanged

In this case, the drug has exerted a specific stimulating effect upon response rate in the S^D period. Therefore, it did not cause any discriminative disruption. The first question to be asked is, Was the stimulation observed specific to behavior reinforced by food? By employing the same schedule and response but by changing the reinforcer, we should be able to find the answer.

A second question might be, Was the increased S^D response rate peculiar to the variable-interval schedule? By varying the reinforcement schedule while using the same reinforcer and response, we could answer this question. If the drug was found to increase the response rate only when food was used as the reinforcer, it would suggest that the drug might be enhancing the strength of the reinforcer in the same manner that increased deprivation conditions would do so. One could next determine whether animals under free-feeding conditions showed an increment in total food intake. If they did, we could conclude that the drug's mechanism of action in increasing the animal's response rate for food was its ability to increase the reinforcing strength of food.

If, on the other hand, the drug increased the animal's response rate regardless of the type of reinforcer employed, our conclusions would have to be more general. It would be worthwhile to determine whether the drug increased the frequency of unconditioned behaviors like locomotor activity. If this was found to be the case, we could only conclude that we had a general behavioral stimulant that did not affect visual discriminations.

4. S^D Response Rate Increased, S^Δ Response Rate Increased

This outcome is the one most frequently seen with sympathomimetic amine compounds; no breakdown in stimulus control is necessarily implied if the ratio of S^D to S^Δ responding is not changed by the drug. The fact that the ratio *is* changed, however, can also be misleading. If the subject's response rate in the S^D is high, it cannot be increased by the same magnitude as the S^Δ response rate, which is low. In other words, there is a ceiling effect for response rate beyond which it is impossible to cause further rate increments. Drug-induced increments in response rate therefore depend partly on the baseline rate in comparision to the maximum rate possible.

As was the case in example (3), we would wait to determine whether the increments in S^D and S^Δ responding were peculiar to the VI schedule and/or to food as the reinforcer. The question would be solved as it was in (3).

5. S^D Response Rate Decreased, S^Δ Response Rate Unchanged

In this effect, the failure of S^Δ responding to show a decrement may be misleading. Since the S^Δ response rate under baseline conditions is extremely low, it is impossible for a drug to produce significant decrements. The only valid conclusion to draw from these data is that the S^D response rate is diminished. As in (3) and (4), we would want to determine whether this drug-induced response-rate decrement was specific to the VI schedule and/or to the use of food as a reinforcer.

Let us assume that we found that the response-rate decrement was specific to food-reinforced behaviors, independent of the type of schedule used. This would suggest that the drug altered the reinforcing strength of food in a manner similar to decrements in food deprivation. We might test this hypothesis by finding out what effect the drug had on total food intake under free-feeding conditions. Further, we could determine the interaction between level of food deprivation and drug dosage. We would expect that as food deprivation increased (and drug dosage remained constant), there would be less decrement in lever-pressing rate. This interaction would constitute evidence for our interpretation of the action of the drug, namely, that its action was based on its ability to diminish the reinforcing strength of food deprivation.

Alternately, let us assume that our drug produced a decrement in lever-pressing rate, regardless of the type of schedule or reinforcer employed. This result would indicate that the drug exerted a general depressant action on behavior. We would then want to find out whether the drug had the same depressant action on responses with different topographies, e.g., what degree of motor incapacitation was caused by this range of dosages? Previously discussed techniques for measuring skilled motor activities could be applied here.

Finally, let us assume that our test produced a response-rate decrement only when the animals were reinforced on a VI schedule. This might indicate that the behavior generated by the VI schedule had some peculiar properties that interacted with the drug. The most likely candidate would be the response rate generated by this particular VI schedule. One could use another type of reinforcement schedule, adjusting the parameters so that a response rate comparable to that obtained on the VI schedule was generated. Then it could be ascertained whether the drug exerted comparable depressant effects on the behavior generated by the second schedule. If the effects *were* comparable, we could conclude that the baseline response rate, independent of the types of schedule or reinforcer, was the important determinant of the drug's action.

6. S^D Response Rate Decreased, $S^{\triangle}$ Response Rate Increased

In this case, our drug appears to disrupt the animal's discriminative abilities. A situation that might lead to such a decrement in the S^D response rate would exist if the animal was undergoing extinction in the $S^{\triangle}$ periods. If we assume that the stimulus control had broken down and the animal continued responding in the $S^{\triangle}$ period when no reinforcement was given, a decrement in lever-pressing response strength in the S^D period could result. One should analyze the cumulative records carefully to see whether or not there is any suggestion that this is the case. For example, a gradual decrease in responding typical of the $S^{\triangle}$ period might continue into the succeeding S^D period. An abrupt increase in response rate after the first reinforcement in the S^D period would suggest the correctness of this interpretation. The easiest way to verify this interpretation would be to determine the effects of the drug on the subject's performance on a simple VI schedule without the interpolated $S^\triangle$ periods. Absence of response-rate decrements under such a schedule would indicate that our interpretation was correct.

It is obvious that when there is an increase in $S^\triangle$ responding and a simultaneous decrease in S^D responding, we can rule out the possibility that the observed S^D response-rate decrement is based on general depression of all behavior, or on motor incoordination.

It should be pointed out here that the preceding discussion involves gross oversimplification of the experimental procedures that a behavioral pharmacologist actually follows. In the first place, we have been assuming that our test drug had only one effect on the behavior we were studying. The action of a drug is very rarely so simple. For example, at low dosages, the amphetamines may increase an animal's S^D response rate and have no effect on its $S^\triangle$ response rate (see [3] above). At higher dosages, amphetamines may cause an increase in both S^D and $S^\triangle$ response rates (see [4] above); and at even higher dosages, they may cause a decrease in the S^D response rate and an increase in the $S^\triangle$ response rate (see [6] above). The multiplicity of action that may characterize a single drug necessitates the explication of a variety of behavioral mechanisms of action that are dose-dependent. In other words, there may not be a single behavioral mechanism of action, but rather, a dose-dependent family of mechanisms of action. This should not astound pharmacologists, since this is true for most drugs acting on physiological systems. Indeed, Terrace (1963) has shown that the effects of chlorpromazine and imipramine on performance of pigeons trained in S^D-$S^\triangle$ discrimination vary as a function of the discrimination training procedure. In pigeons trained in the usual discrimination procedures, these drugs produced an increase in $S^\triangle$ responding; in pigeons trained in an "errorless" discrimination procedure, these drugs caused no increment in $S^\triangle$ response rate. At the time of drug administration, S^D-$S^\triangle$ performance was comparable in both groups; yet each drug produced a different effect, depending on the training method used in establishing the discrimination.

These considerations point to the extreme complexity of determining a drug's behavioral mechanisms of action. This complexity should, however, stimulate the researcher rather than discourage him, since the reinforcement gained by solving complex problems is often greater than that obtained from the solution of simpler ones.

Response Consequences—Types of Reinforcement

In a previously described experiment, food was used to reinforce monkeys for pressing a lever. The observed decrease in response rate produced by our test drug, we said, might have been specific to food-reinforced behaviors. The simplest procedure for determining whether this was true would have been to reinforce the same animals on a multiple schedule that involved the same response but different reinforcers. One could then have determined whether drug-induced changes were specific to a particular reinforcer. In a recent experiment Schuster and Estrada (1966) conditioned monkeys to depress levers on a concurrent FR10 schedule, using food and visual reinforcers. Parametric studies revealed that if the visual access time was set at five seconds per reinforcement, the monkeys would work for an equal number of food and visual reinforcements in each daily session. Following stabilization of this baseline, the effects of administering various dosages of morphine sulfate were studied. Figure 6.3 shows that morphine administration had a differential effect on the two behaviors. At lower dosages the monkey showed a marked increase in responding for the visual reinforcer and a decrease in responding for food. At higher dosages of morphine, both behaviors were reduced to low levels.

On the basis of these findings, how can we interpret the effects of morphine sulfate on food and visually reinforced performance? In the first place, the decrement in food-reinforced behavior observed at lower dosages cannot be attributed to motor incapacitation or general sedation, since the subject's response rate increased in the presence of the visual reinforcer. Neither can we attribute the increased responding for the visual reinforcer to non-

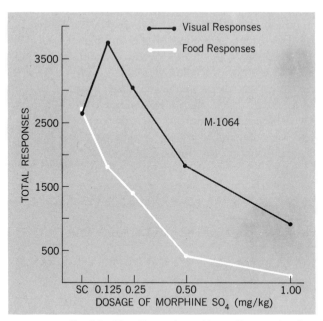

Fig. 6.3 The effects of morphine sulfate on visually reinforced and food-reinforced lever-pressing in the monkey. At 0.125 mg/kg, there is an increase in the number of responses leading to visual reinforcement, but a very significant decrease in food-reinforced responding. (Schuster and Estrada, 1966, unpublished)

specific behavioral stimulation, since the animal's food-reinforced behavior was depressed. Since both food and visual reinforcement were contingent on the same value of fixed-ratio schedule, the schedule itself cannot have caused the drug's differential effect. Finally, because the subject worked for the same number of food and visual reinforcements, we cannot attribute the drug's differential effect to differences in the strength of the behavior generated by each type of reinforcer.

It therefore appears that, at certain dosages, morphine has a specific differential effect that is dependent on the type of reinforcer used to maintain lever-pressing behavior. Obviously, other reinforcers would have to be investigated before we could conclude that the compound had specific stimulating or depressing effects on visually reinforced and food-reinforced behaviors. Further, we cannot be assured that this differential effect would be observed under a different kind of reinforcement schedule.

Another approach has been to compare the effects of drugs on food-producing and discriminative stimulus-producing responses. Kelleher, Riddle, and Cook (1960) trained pigeons to peck one key for food, and a second key to intermittently present the discriminative stimulus for food-reinforced responding. Using this basic technique the investigators were able to differentiate two groups within the phenothiazine derivatives on the basis of their selective effects on the two operant classes.

Ray (1963) reported another illustration of the differential effect of drugs on a behavior maintained by different reinforcers. He trained rats to depress a lever for a food reinforcement whenever a tone of 500 cps. was presented. Responding produced the food reinforcement and terminated the tone. The tone terminated automatically after 20 seconds if the subject failed to respond. A tone of 1000 cps. was also presented intermittently, and failure to depress a second lever in the presence of the higher tone resulted in a brief electric shock. After stabilization, the shock was used only during the first 20 to 30 minutes of the five-hour session. Latencies for food reinforcement and shock-avoidance lever-pressing were comparable and stable over each session. Administration of meprobamate, reserpine, and chlorpromazine caused a marked increase in the latencies for shock-avoidance responses but food-reinforced lever responses changed very little. The fact that the animals were being run on extinction for the shock avoidance (no shock given after the first 20 to 30 minutes of the session) was an important variable, although the subject's shock-avoidance performance did improve by the end of the session, presumably as a result of falling drug levels in the organism. On the other hand, administration of pentobarbital increased latencies for both shock-avoidance and food-reinforced behaviors. Thus, a comparison of the experiment described above and Ray's experiment demonstrate that only certain drugs show a differential effect on food-reinforced and shock-avoidance behaviors.

In contrast to Ray's procedure, Waller and Waller (1962) used a multiple schedule that consisted of a Sidman shock-avoidance component and a variable-interval food component. Their subjects were beagle dogs, to which they administered chlorpromazine. This drug produced comparable decrements in both the food-reinforced and shock-avoidance components.

As we have pointed out, an ostensible conflict in experimental findings (as is the case with Ray's findings vs. Waller and Waller's findings) is often based on an assumption that drugs effect some process common to all shock-avoidance behaviors and all food-reinforced behaviors. However, the two experiments were dissimilar in many respects: in the species of subjects, in the dosage and route of administration, in the food-reinforcement and shock-avoidance schedules, and, finally, in the dependent variables. It should be remarked, too, that Waller and Waller used a nondiscriminated avoidance and a VI schedule, with response rate as their dependent variable. Noting all of these differences, it is hardly surprising that the effects of chlorpromazine in these two experiments were not the same.

Schedule of Reinforcement

An assumption implicit in the foregoing discussion is that the schedule of reinforcement used to maintain a behavior is an extremely important variable in determining a drug's action. Innumerable reports have dealt with the differential effects of drugs upon behavior maintained by different schedules of reinforcement—We cited above the study by Dews, in which it was demonstrated that phenobarbital had a differential effect on behavior generated by fixed-interval and fixed-ratio schedules. Of course, we now want to know how we can go about determining the critical variables responsible for drug-schedule interactions. Since it is obvious that different schedules of reinforcement generate markedly different response rates, let us compare lever-pressing responses generated by a differential reinforcement of low rate vs. a fixed-ratio-differential reinforcement of high rate schedules, using an amphetamine as our test drug. A DRL schedule of 60 seconds will generate a response rate of approximately one response per 60 seconds. On the other hand, an FR200 with a DRH contingency of 60 seconds will generate response rates of approximately 200 responses per 60 seconds. Obviously, if the FR-DRH schedule generates response rates approximating the maximum rate of which organism is physically capable, we cannot expect amphetamine to induce an increase. On the other hand, no such ceiling effect exists in the behavior generated by the DRL schedule. As a matter of fact, amphetamines have frequently been observed to produce response-rate increment in low rate baselines. (Sidman, 1955).

Another variable that may be of importance in drug-schedule interactions is the density of reinforcement. It is difficult to disentangle the contingencies of reinforcement. One approach to this problem is that used by Ferster and Skinner (1957). These investigators used the reinforcements generated by one animal to set the occasion for reinforcement for a second animal. One could, for example, reinforce Animal A on a variable-ratio schedule. Whenever Animal A received a reinforcement, this set the occasion for the reinforcement of response by Animal B. The schedule generated for Animal B was thus a variable-interval schedule. The density of reinforcement for the two subjects would be approximately equal, but the contingencies would be different. Differences in drug effects observed in these two animals could not be attributed to differences in the density of reinforcement. Unfortunately, differences in contingency in this procedure would probably be confounded with differences in baseline response rate.

The response rate generated by a VR schedule is usually markedly higher than that generated by VI schedule. One way of getting rid of these differences in baseline response rates is to place a limited-hold contingency on the VI schedule. This simply means that the opportunity for reinforcement on the VI schedule exists only briefly. It has been shown that as the limited-hold period decreases, the VI response rate increases (Schoenfeld, *et. al.*, 1956). By exploring these parameters, it might be possible to develop a VI schedule that would generate response rates equal to those observed under a VR schedule. Differential drug effects on the VI and VR baselines would then be attributable to differences in the contingencies of reinforcement for the two schedules.

One of the most effective illustrations of the significance of schedule variables in the control of behavioral actions of drugs is Kelleher and Morse's comparison (1964) of drug effects on FI and FR behavior under positive and negative reinforcement control. Squirrel monkeys were trained on multiple FI-FR schedules of food reinforcement and shock escape under visual stimulus control. After extensive conditioning, indistinguishable patterns of responding were established for both food reinforcement and shock-escape reinforcement. Administration of 0.01 to 1.0 mg/kg of *d*-amphetamine and 0.03 to 0.3 mg/kg i.m. of chlorpromazine produced virtually identical effects on food-reinforced and shock-escape response rates (Fig. 6.4). It would seem that the contingencies for reinforcement, rather than the type of reinforcer, determined the effects of these drugs.

Multiple Schedule Interaction

Throughout this chapter we have suggested that multiple scheduling of reinforcement is a powerful tool in the analysis of behaviorally active drugs. Its advantages lie in the fact that it allows us to compare the effect of a drug on two behaviors without the problem of individual differences in drug sensitivity. This chapter contains verification that such comparisons are frequently essential to an appropriate interpretation of a drug's action. It should be pointed out, however, that the effects of a drug on behavior generated by a particular schedule may differ if this schedule is one component of a multiple

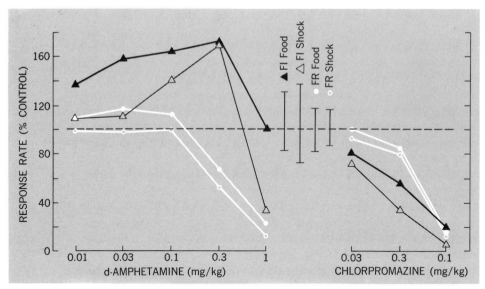

Fig. 6.4 Effects of *d*-amphetamine and chlorpromazine on rates of responding under multiple fixed-interval and fixed-ratio schedules of positive and negative reinforcement in squirrel monkeys. Curves represent means of the percentage changes in average response rates from control to drug sessions. The dashed line at 100 per cent indicates the mean control level. The vertical lines in the middle of the figure indicate ranges of control observations. Note the similarity of the pairs of dose-effect curves for fixed-interval and fixed-ratio components. (Kelleher and Morse, 1964)

schedule. There is ample evidence that the behavior generated by one component of a multiple may be influenced by the schedules used in other components.

It is entirely feasible that such interactions between components could be amplified or diminished by drugs. Recent work by Schuster and Woods (1966) is relevant. In their study, rats were initially maintained on an FI60-second DRL60-second multiple schedule. Components were alternated every 15 minutes with a 60-second blackout period between. A dose-response function using *d*-amphetamine was obtained. Subsequently, the FI component was replaced with the DRL component. Thus, the rats were run on a DRL60-second blackout period every 15 minutes. The dose-response function for *d*-amphetamine was again obtained. Finally, the subjects were again conditioned on the multiple FI60-second DRL60-second schedule, and the dose-response function with *d*-amphetamine repeated. Figure 6.5 shows a dose-response function for *d*-amphetamine for the DRL-DRL and FI-DRL performances. The response-rate increment induced by amphetamines is markedly larger when the subjects were run on the FI-DRL than on the DRL alone.

This evidence suggests that the actions of a drug on behavior generated by a schedule of reinforcement may be modified if the schedule is one component of a multiple schedule. Inspection of the cumulative records for the rats on the FI-DRL schedule revealed that amphetamine administration produced what appeared to be a breakdown in schedule control in the DRL. Figure 6.6 shows cumulative records of the DRL performance following amphetamine administration for the FI-DRL schedule, and for the DRL schedule alone. We can see that DRL rate shows an abrupt increment following a reinforcement. The increased response rate continues at this level for several minutes, then gradually falls in a manner suggesting extinction. Thus, the data suggest that the rat is responding in the DRL component in a manner appropriate to FI contingencies. When the rats are on the DRL alone, there is less tendency for the increased response rate, since they have not been reinforced for such behavior in the recent past. Thus, it is possible in a multiple schedule to observe drug-induced interactions that indicate schedule-control breakdown.

Weiss and Laties (1965) have shown that drug effects can be altered by adding an exteroceptive stimulus that covaries with schedule contingencies. In their experiment, the color of the S^D light was changed as time elapsed on an FI schedule. The organism therefore had an exteroceptive stimulus, in addition to its own behavior, to indicate the time elapsed since the last reinforcement. The investigators demonstrated that drugs had less disrupting

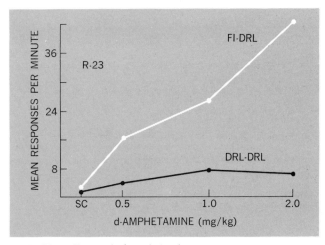

Fig. 6.5 The effects of *d*-amphetamine on response rate as a function of the schedule of reinforcement. Response rate increases systematically with dosage under fixed-interval contingencies, but remains low under DRL contingencies. (Schuster and Woods, 1966, unpublished)

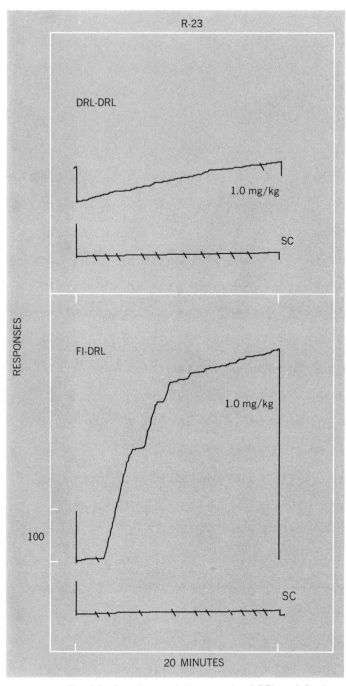

Fig. 6.6 Sample cumulative records of DRL and fixed-interval performance under 1.0 mg/kg of d-amphetamine. (Schuster and Woods, 1966, unpublished)

effect on FI performance when the subject was provided with this extero-ceptive "clock." Thus, by making explicit the passage of time in the FI, the amount of disruption induced by drugs was reduced.

In a science as young and as complex as behavioral pharmacology, we can only suggest tactics for solving problems. If the reader is impressed simply with the complexity of drug-behavior interactions and the necessity for pursuing experimental answers systematically, but with a great deal of imagination, we shall be happy. At the very least, this chapter—designed to be suggestive rather than exhaustive—will prevent him from making over-simplified and premature judgments about the behavioral actions of drugs; hopefully, it will lead to more fruitful explorations of behavioral mechanisms of action.

7
Drug-Environment Interaction

Analyzing the mechanisms by which drugs affect behavior would be immeasurably easier if organisms could be isolated from their environments. However, in the world of intact, behaving animals, the organism and its environment are inseparably interdependent; and it is inevitable that the effects of drugs administered to intact animals will be modified by environmental conditions. Although the importance of environmental influences should be obvious, inadequate consideration of such factors is one of the commonest weaknesses of drug-behavior research. Indeed, the failure of experimental designs to control for environmental factors is so prevalent, and the principle involved so basic that we feel compelled to devote an entire chapter to a detailed discussion of drug-environment interactions.

In the broadest sense, the term "drug-behavior interaction" is approximately equivalent to "drug-environment interaction." That is, the environment can determine the kind and degree of control a drug imposes on behavior. In its narrower and earlier sense, the term refers to the fact that, as Sidman pointed out (1956, page 282), drug effects depend not only on the organism's physiological state but also on the envrionmental contingencies that maintain its behavior at any one time. As we shall see, these two definitions occupy positions on a continuum of environmental influence that range from direct and relatively simple modifications of the absorption and distribution of drugs, to highly complex interlocking changes between the enviornment and behavior.

The diameter of the blood vessels that distribute a drug to its site of action can be determined, in part, by the ambient temperature of the environment. An animal in an extremely warm room will tend to distribute a drug more quickly than one in a very cold room. Furthermore, if a change in ambient temperature is great enough to alter body temperature, the rate of chemical reactions and the metabolism of drugs within the body will be changed correspondingly. Room temperature, which can alter both the time of onset and duration of action of a behaviorally active drug, thus provides an example of one simple and very direct kind of environmental influence on drug action.

Related to effects on distribution are direct effects due to the mode of introduction of the drug. Rats receiving their first intraperitoneal injection often behave differently from those accustomed to this route of administration. It is, therefore, necessary to use saline control injections to separate effects of the injection procedure from the pharmacological influences of the route of administration.

The toxic effects of drugs can also be altered by environmental conditions. For example, the degree of stress to which an animal is subjected can alter the lethal effects of a drug. Rats which have undergone repeated traumatic electric shock while under the influence of amphetamine have significantly lower LD-50's than nonshocked controls (Weiss, Laties, and Blanton, 1961). Another type of toxicity may arise from the interaction of certain social behaviors and drug effects. The LD-50 of amphetamine is markedly decreased when several animals are placed together in one cage. Increased toxicity is associated with the tendency of rodents to aggregate. This *aggregate toxicity* is also influenced by room temperature, degree of fluid deprivation, and cage size (Chance, 1946, 1947; Gunn and Gurd, 1940; Höhn and Lasagna, 1960).

The magnitude of a dog's salivary reflex varies with the length of food deprivation. A dog that has just finished a meal salivates very little when a weak acid solution is placed on his tongue; but, if acid is placed on the same dog's tongue immediately before a meal, a relatively large volume of saliva is elicited. Thus, the effects of a drug on the magnitude of an unconditioned salivary reflex depend on food-deprivation conditions as well as on the direct pharmacological actions of the drug. The effect of a drug on the latency of termination when a painful electric shock is given may be quite different on the first occasion the shock is presented than on the hundredth occasion. The amount of experience with shock escape will undoubtedly alter the action of the drug. Similarly, the shock-escape latency will vary with the intensity of shock on the first and hundredth trial, and this contingency would surely interact with the physiological action of a drug. The foregoing types of drug-environment interactions can be distinguished from interactions of drug variables with any of the classes of factors known to control operant behavior (i.e. antecedent variables, current stimulus circumstances, response variables, and response-consequence variables).

Antecedant Variables

Because deprivation conditions can vastly affect operant behavior, one might expect drug variables to interact with deprivation conditions to alter performance. Investigations of this question have been relatively limited, but indicate that such interactions can significantly alter the behavioral actions of a given dosage of some drugs. Bindra and Mendelson (1963) and Mendelson and Bindra (1962) have studied interactions between water-deprivation conditions and methylphenidate administration. Methylphenidate produced a significant response-rate decrement at relatively low deprivation levels, with very little effect on response rate under longer deprivation conditions. Similar interactions between water-deprivation conditions and drug effects have been reported for 5-hydroxytryptophan (a metabolic precursor to norepinephrine) (Joyce and Summerfield, 1965) and chlorpromazine (Singh, Manocha, and Satinder, 1966).

Prior drug treatment is another major class of antecedent operations that may affect the behavioral actions of a drug. For example, establishing physical dependence on morphine will markedly affect an animal's disposition to self-administer morphine. Similarly, long term pretreatment with drugs frequently leads to the development of tolerance so that a given dosage may have far less effect than might be expected. Such prior drug treatment procedures are not commonly considered "behavioral" variables, and will not be discussed further at this point, though they are dealt with in Chapter 9.

Stimulus Control

Interactions of current stimulus conditions and drugs have been studied more extensively. Alteration of stimulus control by drugs is often a function of the complexity, physical intensity, or similarity of the discriminative stimulus used, as well as the drug dosage. Dews (1955) conditioned pigeons in a "conditional" visual discrimination, involving several discriminative stimuli and a compound S-delta. Pentobarbital and methamphetamine more profoundly altered the "conditional" discrimination than a simple visual discrimination. Weiss and Laties (1964) found that chlorpromazine had less effect on fixed-interval performance with an added "clock" than without an exteroceptive stimulus varying with passage of time. Hearst has made a particularly eloquent demonstration of the weakening of stimulus control and drug effects (1964).

The tendency for animals to respond in the presence of visual stimuli varying in intensity from the discriminative stimulus in an avoidance situation was differentially affected by *d*-amphetamine, scopolamine, and caffeine. Generalization to other stimuli was increased under the influence of these drugs, and was found to vary inversely with the distance of the test stimulus from the discriminative stimulus used during training (Fig. 7.1). Using an "errorless" discrimination learning procedure Terrace (1963) found that imipramine has markedly different effects as a result of the way in which a simple visual discrimination has been established. Imipramine has very little effect on visual discrimination established without errors, but has a graded dose-dependent effect on a discrimination established by extinguishing responses in the presence of an S-delta.

Stimulus control can be altered by the interoceptive stimulus change following drug administration. In certain repects, one can think of drug administration as causing a stimulus change having a "novel" stimulus effect (e.g. disruption of an ongoing operant), or possibly altering interoceptive stimulation along a generalization gradient. The latter interpretation has been explored by Heistad (1957) and Overton (1966).

The specification of the exact nature of drug-induced stimulus control has been more difficult. Stewart (1962) has shown that rats can come to behave discriminatively with respect to an intraperitoneal dosage of chlorpromazine (3 to 20 mg/kg) or saline. Efforts to more precisely specify discriminative stimulus control via drug-produced interoceptive stimulation have been made by Cook, *et. al.* (1960) and Schuster and Brady (1964). Cook and co-workers trained dogs in an avoidance response using acetylcholine, epinephrine, and norepinephrine as discriminative stimuli. Schuster and Brady (1964) conditioned monkeys to emit a food-reinforced operant during a period following intravenous administration of epinephrine. The latency from the beginning of epinephrine infusion until the animal emitted its first response varied inversely with the infusion speed. Drug-produced stimulus changes can clearly function as discriminative stimuli, and can be disruptive as a function of dosage. The interaction of drug-produced stimuli with parameters of exteroceptive stimulation remains to be explored, but might well prove to be a significant factor controlling some types of behavior.

Response Variables

The relation between the type of response that is reinforced and the actions of a drug is all too frequently overlooked. Most people familiar with the treatment of psychiatric patients would agree that amphetamine

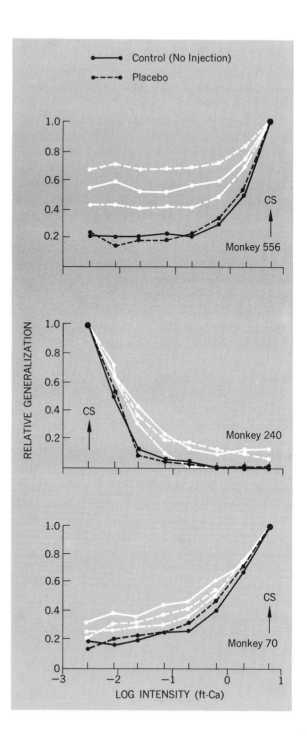

Fig. 7.1 Effects of scopolamine on absolute and relative gradients of stimulus generalization in monkeys. Eight intensities of a test stimulus varying up to 3.5 log units away from the training stimulus were used. The shaded areas in the absolute curves indicate the range of scores in control sessions. Note that while low doses of scopolamine facilitate responding to the discriminative stimulus, all gradients become flatter following drug administration. (Hearst, 1964)

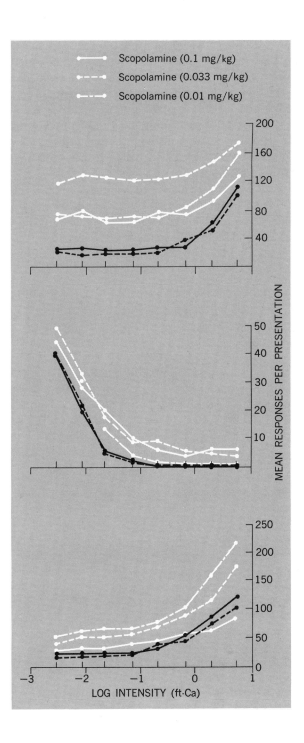

would be contraindicated in a hypomanic, agitated, and physically assaultive patient, pointing out that the drug would tend to increase the "incorrect" response rather than decrease it. A psychiatrist would give such a patient a drug that produced less, not more, agitated behavior. Nevertheless, experimenters working with infrahuman subjects often disregard the fact that the response they choose to define as correct (the response to be reinforced) may be incompatible with the known action of the drug administered. One drug may "improve" performance on one response, while another drug may "impair" performance on the same response.

Bindra and Anchel (1963) demonstrated this phenomenon by administering several behaviorally active drugs to rats which had been trained to avoid a painful electric shock by remaining motionless. Representative dosage ranges of chlorpromazine, imipramine, and methylphenidate were administered; and measures of the degree of immobility were recorded. While each drug re-

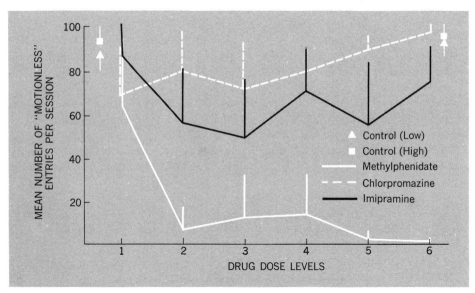

Fig. 7.2 The mean and S.D. (vertical lines) of frequency of occurrence of the immobility response during the control sessions and under the influence of the six doses of each of three drugs. The doses were as follows:

Chlorpromazine 2, 4, 6, 8, 10, or 12 mg/kg;
Imipramine 15, 20, 25, 30, 35, or 40 mg/kg; and
Methylphenidate 4, 6, 8, 10, 12, or 14 mg/kg

Group L was tested at the three lower doses of each drug, and Group H at the three higher doses of each drug. A control session was given at the beginning, and again at the end, of the test sessions. (Bindra and Anchel, 1963, p. 217, Fig. 2)

duced the amount of immobile shock-avoidance behavior, methylphenidate-treated animals exhibited the poorest shock-avoidance performance (Fig. 7.2). This should be contrasted with the more common observation that drugs with the property of increasing spontaneous motor activity enhance avoidance performance. It appears that the choice of an immobile response rather than an active avoidance response accounts for the decrement in avoidance in one situation, and facilitating effect in the other.

Responses requiring holding a lever within a narrow force band for a fixed duration are very susceptible to graded disruption as a function of drug dosage (Falk, 1967). However, interactions between parameters of such responses and drug administration have not been reported.

Response Consequences

A less obvious kind of drug-environment interaction, but one of the most important types of environmental influences on drug action, has been called "schedule effects." Some writers have failed to grasp the significance of the temporal and sequential relation between stimuli and behavior across various reinforcement contingencies and classes of reinforcers.° This is most unfortunate, since it is now clear not only that interschedule considerations are of extreme importance, but that parameters within a given schedule can be equally important. For example, a range of effects from behavioral "stimulation" to "depression" can be obtained with the same dose of the same drug simply by varying the length of delay in a DRL schedule (Sidman, 1956). As Dews and Morse (1962) pointed out, "These are not trivial matters; on the contrary, the importance attributed to schedules in determining behavior has been growing steadily since the days of Pavlov . . . it has been shown repeatedly . . . that the behavioral effects of a drug are frequently critically dependent on schedule influences on behavior" (p. 152).

In his analysis of drug-behavior interaction (1956) Sidman focused his attention on the scheduling of environmental contingencies that maintain behavior. The dependence of a drug's behavioral actions on reinforcement-schedule differences was first specifically demonstrated in pigeons, using pentobarbital (Dews, 1955). Pigeons trained on FI15-minute, and FR50 schedules of food reinforcement were administered various doses of pentobarbital, and changes in response rate were observed. Figure 7.3 shows changes in response rate before and after drug administration under the two schedules. Clearly, responding on FI15 was markedly reduced by doses of

° For example, in a drug-behavior methodology paper Miller and Barry (1960) followed a citation of Ferster and Skinner's (1957) extensive parametric study of reinforcement schedules and factors influencing behavior maintained by those schedules with this comment: "In the absence of adequate systematic studies showing exactly which schedule is the most sensitive to motivation, a variable-interval schedule is a good one to use." This approach to the selection of behavioral contingencies is analogous to selecting a drug by flipping pages in the *Pharmacopeia*.

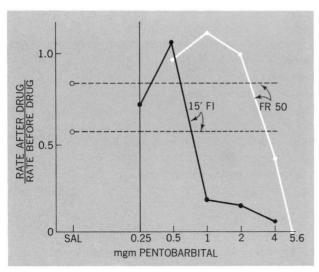

Fig. 7.3 Effect of pentobarbital on pecking behavior of pigeons. Log dose-effect curves. Each point represents the arithmetic mean of the ratios for the same four birds at each dosage level on each schedule. Open circles: mean baseline ratios. Solid circles: effects of five dosages on FI15 and FR50 performance. (Dews, 1955, p. 399, Fig. 4)

pentobarbital equal to those that had caused an increase in response rate on FR50. In other words, the behavioral effects of a given dose of pentobarbital were shown to depend on the environmental contingencies maintaining that behavior—even when the same reinforcer was used.

Subtle schedule parameter differences can obscure what otherwise seem to be more fundamental differences among experimental procedures. Many investigators have attempted to compare the influence of drugs on positively and negatively reinforced behaviors, assuming the type of reinforcer to be a major determinant of drug effects. Most of these investigations have proceeded on the additional premise that differences in schedule and quality of the performance maintained by negative and positive reinforcers would be overshadowed by the presumed enormous influence of the type of reinforcer. This has been a serious error.

An essential first step in comparing the influence of drugs across reinforcers is establishment of equivalent behavioral baselines and equivalent controlling contingencies. Cook and Catania (1964) conditioned squirrel monkeys in FI-food reinforcement and FI-shock escape, generating virtually indistinguishable baselines. The procedures necessary for establishing comparable baselines were elaborate and cannot be recounted here, however the point must be made that the creation of equivalent baselines *prior* to any drug manipulations was essential.

Figure 7.4 shows sample cumulative records of shock escape and food-reinforced performance following treatment with a control injection and treatment with four commonly studied behaviorally active drugs. These data indicate very few, if any, significant differences between effects of *any* drugs on escape and food-reinforced performance. Equally importantly, Cook and Catania went on to show that subtle changes in parameters of shock inten-

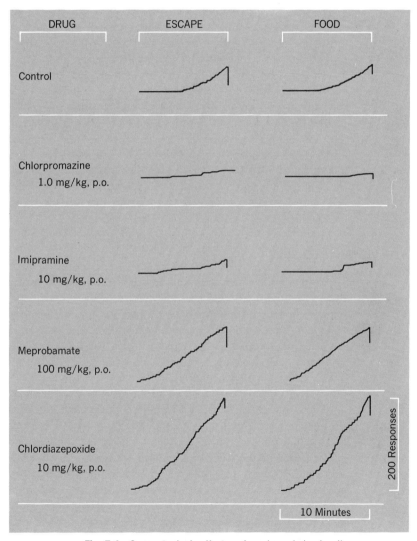

Fig. 7.4 Some typical effects of various behaviorally active drugs on fixed-interval performance maintained by negative reinforcement (escape) and positive reinforcement (food) in squirrel monkeys. (Cook and Catania, 1964)

sity, interval length, or baseline response rate can profoundly influence the differential effects of some drugs on negatively and positively reinforced behavior.

More complex types of drug-behavior interactions arise when the organism, under the effect of the drug, is no longer able to satisfy the environmental contingencies, or when its behavior under the effect of the drug changes the degree and kind of consequences of that behavior. Perhaps the most complex interactions occur when an organism can regulate its own drug intake while emitting other behaviors necessary for survival. Such interactions are the most difficult to study experimentally, although they probably occur commonly outside the laboratory.

To begin to understand these interactions and some of the methods for assessing their effects, it would be helpful to examine several research programs in greater detail. The two programs we have selected will serve as examples of the way in which two of the more complex kinds of drug-behavior interactions can be attacked. These methods are highly specific and approximate; obviously they are not exhaustive. The reader is asked to place himself in the role of the experimenter throughout the series of investigations. If the steps are taken carefully, the reader should begin to appreciate the process of decision making that goes into the evaluation of drug-behavior interactions.

BEHAVIORAL TOLERANCE

Amphetamines are commonly employed in clinical medicine because of their "stimulant" effects. The true nature of the relation between what the clinician means by the "stimulant effect" of amphetamine and the various effects of the drug on infrahuman behavior remains unclear. For example, it has been observed that the frequency of a variety of behaviors increases at low and moderate doses of amphetamine (Dews, 1956; Brady, 1956; Sidman, 1955). At higher doses, similar performance measures reveal a reduction in behavioral output (Dews, 1956; Miller, 1956). Furthermore, the effects of amphetamine seem to depend in part on the consequences of various types of performance (Dews and Morse, 1962) and, as discussed in the preceding section, the precise values of the controlling reinforcement schedules.

The acute effects of amphetamine on behavior requiring spacing of responses (DRL) are quite marked. It will be recalled that responses must be spaced at specified minimal intervals in order to obtain reinforcement on a DRL schedule. Using the distribution of interresponse times as a dependent variable, it has been reported that a shift toward shorter interresponse times occurs under the effects of moderate and low doses of amphetamine (Sidman, 1955). This means that the total number of reinforcements decrease, since the animal is no longer effectively spacing his responses. Whether or not this change in performance after amphetamine administration would occur under a chronic drug regimen is another matter.

We may ask: Would the effects of acute versus chronic administration be the same? Or: Does the animal develop a behavioral tolerance to the drug that permits him to behave more effectively? And, finally: Is such tolerance specific to certain kinds of performance and not to others? To answer these questions we will discuss a research program that dealt with the effects of chronically administered amphetamine on some arbitrarily conditioned performance. The experiments were conducted in a well-controlled environment; and the subject was carefully selected.

It is less than realistic to begin any experiment without giving careful consideration to the facilities available, for the type and amount of behavioral equipment available is a major factor in shaping a research program. It might be said parenthetically that, just as radioisotope technology opened entirely new fields of research in biochemistry, modern behavioral technology has made it possible to ask and answer questions which were inconceivable just a few years ago. Unfortunately, however, many contemporary investigators attempt to unravel the complexities of behavior with archaic instruments, despite the fact that the tools of 20 to 30 years ago have served their purpose, and despite the great need to exploit the far superior techniques now available.

Let us consider the combination of available equipment for our hypothetical experiment. Such equipment today might consist of solid-state or relay switching-timing circuitry for controlling behavior and recording data. These components may be taken from commercially manufactured operant-conditioning test chambers for rats.[*] Animal rooms adequate for small subjects—pigeons, guinea pigs, rats, or mice—are also available. Given these facilities, we had to select an experimental animal and an apparatus. Dews and Morse (1958) used human subjects in their investigation; and Sidman, (1955) used rats on chronic amphetamine regimens in other behavioral situations. The factors of availability of test equipment and the nature of storage facilities made rats the most appropriate subjects for our initial investigation.

Next we selected a type of behavior that would be susceptible to the effects of amphetamine, one that would most effectively reveal the process under consideration. It was noted above that amphetamine disrupts DRL performance; and it was suggested that it affects any reinforcement schedule involving "timing" or spacing of responses. Therefore, one might expect amphetamine to also affect fixed-interval performance. Since it has already been shown that DRL is particularly susceptible to alteration by amphetamine, it was decided to begin with this schedule and include FI in subsequent investigations.

Antecedent Variables

In most investigations using positive reinforcers, deprivation is a precondition of reinforcement. Two albino rats were selected from a litter pur-

[*] See Appendix II-B

chased from a commercial supplier. *Ad libitum* feeding weights were recorded for a week before beginning deprivation. An 85 per cent body weight deprivation figure was calculated, and the animals were deprived until they reached that level.

Conditioning begins with a magazine training procedure. Magazine training consists of conditioning the animal to approach the place in the experimental chamber where the reinforcer is to be presented. (In this case a small cup presented 0.1 cc. of sweetened condensed milk automatically on an aperiodic schedule.) After 50 to 100 such presentations, the rat approaches the magazine and drinks the sweetened condensed milk as soon as the feeder operates. On the second day, the animal is placed in the situation on a CRF reinforcement schedule. CRF training is continued until the 1:1 performance stabilizes. Following stabilization on CRF, the animals used in the present research were switched to a DRL 17.5-second schedule.

Before continuing to describe the experiment, we might briefly retrace our steps. Initial preparation of the subject consists of food deprivation. If we had deprived the animals more or less than 85 per cent of free-feeding weight, we would surely have seen an altered rate of acquisition of the CRF performance. However, as was pointed out in Chapter 4, mere deprivation by per cent of body weight is not always an adequate control. To control deprivation conditions further, we established a regular feeding cycle. Thus, not only did we maintain body weight constantly, we also maintained a constant period ($22\frac{1}{2}$ hours) since the last feeding. One might expect an interaction between deprivation level and drug dosage, however it is not possible to manipulate deprivation when chronic drug administration is involved, as in the present experiment.

Our acquisition data revealed two interesting phenomena that changed over the course of the first few sessions on CRF. Figure 7.5 presents a sample CRF acquisition curve during the first, second, and third training sessions. During part of each session a positive acceleration occurred; the record for the latter portion of the period is negatively accelerated. The negative acceleration is a consequence of satiation (see Chapter 4). The animals were run long enough so that the amount of food subsequently consumed was excessive. In this case we were not particularly concerned about satiation, since we very rapidly shifted from a CRF to a DRL schedule. The effect of changing from CRF to DRL was to reduce the total number of reinforcements obtained over the course of the session. In this way the satiation effect, which had proved a slight problem in the first several sessions, was eliminated. An alternative solution might have been to reduce the magnitude of food reinforcement.

On examining the positive acceleration during the first few minutes of the session, we were confronted with a phenomenon not previously discussed. It is not particularly unusual for the performance during the first few minutes of an experimental session to differ from the stable performance

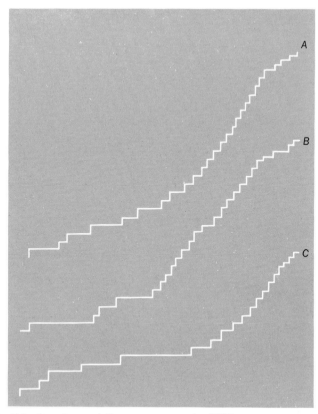

Fig. 7.5 Sample cumulative response records of CRF performance illustrating variability in warm-up early in the session before reaching a steady state.

throughout the larger portion of the session. The initial shift from no responding to CRF or from one schedule to another is associated with a brief transition state. This transition phenomenon has been called a *warm-up effect*. Examination of the sample CRF records in Fig. 7.5 will show that the warm-up effect changes systematically over successive occasions. This is not to say that it necessarily disappears altogether; it does, however, reach a steady state after a number of successive periods.

It would be unwise to discard data obtained during the warm-up period, but it is appropriate simply to treat them as independent information. To include them with the more stable data on performance obtained during the remainder of the session might lead to confusion when the additional variable of a drug is added.

For example, in dealing with the effects of phenothiazine drugs on CRF performance reinforced by intracranial stimulation, one would have to consider the warm-up effect very carefully. Drugs absorbed at different rates can

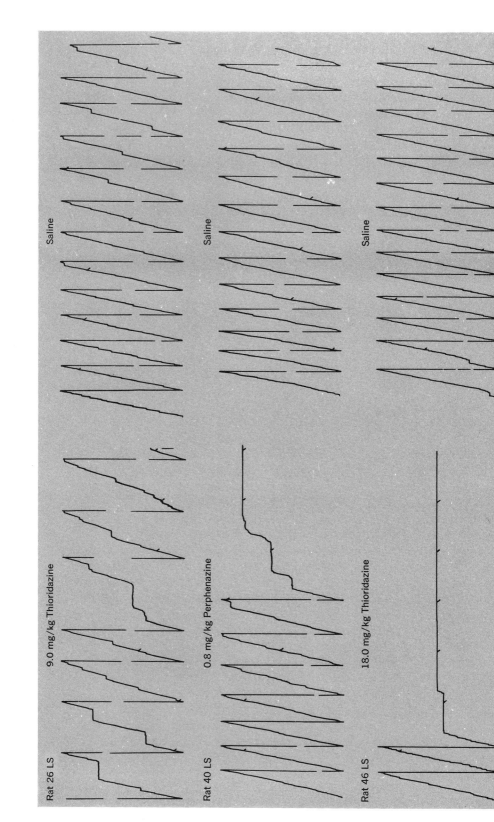

differentially alter performance during the first portion of a session. If the investigator omits successive control sessions in which subjects receive saline, pausing during the first portion of a session could very easily be interpreted as drug-induced variability in warm-up.

Figure 7.6 presents an example of cumulative records illustrating the variability in pausing during the first portion of a session following phenothiazine administration. The top record shows considerable pausing under the influence of 9.0 mg/kg thioridazine, while a sample record for the related phenothiazine derivative, perphenazine, reveals little or no change in pausing early in the session. The saline control records on the right half of the figure clearly indicate that the pausing was drug-induced, probably as a consequence of different rates of absorption of the two drugs.

Antecedent Stimuli

During transition to the DRL schedule, the satiation problem encountered during CRF acquisition often recurs. Over the last few minutes of the session, the lever-pressing rate decreases, or responding may cease entirely. This may initially be interpreted as better performance, since the animal is doing a better job of spacing its responses. However, it is not so much a matter of better timing as of the indirect effect of satiation. To eliminate this problem in the present case we took advantage of another phenomenon discussed in Chapter 4, namely, stimulus control. A visual discriminative stimulus was presented while the DRL 17.5-second performance was being reinforced. During all other times when the discriminative stimulus was not presented, the DRL performance went unreinforced. The control records in Fig. 7.7 present sample cumulative records of DRL performance on a 17.5-second interval in which three-minute blackout periods were interspersed between S^D periods. It can be seen that a stable rate of responding was consistently maintained, whereas a complete cessation of responding might have occurred without such discriminative control.

Fig. 7.6 Sample cumulative records illustrating the effects of thioridazine and perphenazine on lever-pressing reinforced by posterior hypothalamic electrical stimulation in the rat. The records on the right are baselines following saline treatment for each subject. The records on the left show the effects of 9.0 mg/kg and 18.0 mg/kg of thioridazine and 0.8 mg/kg of perphenazine. Notice the long pauses in the top record, with the peak effect coming about three quarters of the way through the session. The onset of the perphenazine is very sudden and produces nearly total cessation, as does 18.0 mg/kg of thioridazine. (Thompson, Pliskoff, and Hawkins, 1962, unpublished)

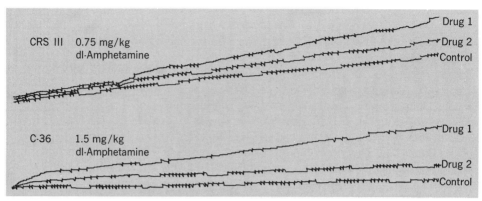

Fig. 7.7 Cumulative records of DRL performance for Rats CRS-3 and C-36. (Schuster and Zimmerman, 1961, p. 328, Fig. 5)

Selection of an appropriate visual stimulus for discriminative control was not altogether arbitrary. Particular properties and sensitivities of the rat's receptors were considered. One could hardly expect this animal's visual acuity to be the same as the pigeon's, for example. Therefore, a "light on-light off" discrimination was chosen instead of a more difficult wavelength or saturation discrimination. Closely related to receptor sensitivity is the nature of the particular temporal properties of the receptor stimulated. If we had chosen, for example, to stimulate intestinal contraction and had used stimuli arising from such contraction as a discriminative stimulus, we would have had to use a much longer duration of stimulation to obtain a comparable degree of stimulus control. Similar consideration must be given in adjusting intensity and duration of stimulation affecting different receptors, whether they are tactual, visual, auditory, or of some other modality.

Session length, another consideration not yet dealt with is extremely important in avoiding satiation artifacts. Session length is particularly important early in training when the number of reinforcements tends to be larger, and there is more variability in response rate. One cannot expect performance during a session in which the animal receives 30 reinforcements in 10 minutes to closely resemble performance during a session in which the same animal receives 15 reinforcements in 60 minutes. For the purpose of the present experiment, session length was fixed at one hour on the basis of the observation that an adequate sample of behavior at a relatively stable level of performance could be obtained over that period of time.

Response Variables

The next problem of design in the present experiment had to do with response variables. One must always inquire into the operant level of any "new" operant used. We were fortunate in dealing with the lever-pressing response, because its operant level is relatively high and the characteristics well known. Since CRF was not the ultimate performance desired, we did not measure initial operant level in this experiment. Had CRF been the final performance, we would surely have paid greater attention to the initial operant level. Instead, we were primarily concerned with operant level insofar as it enabled us to reinforce the operant we were to deal with as our critical dependent variable.

Yet another consideration in the design of this study was the final stable behavioral baseline. We decided what this baseline should be by examining the literature and by observing the performance of our organism under these experimental conditions. We looked at the work of Dews and Morse (1958) and Sidman (1955) and discovered that the behavioral baseline we thought we wanted required spacing of responses. After examining the performance of our subject on a CRF schedule, it occurred to us that spacing requires an animal to "time" when it is shifted from a CRF to a DRL schedule. Even at short intervals, the initial responses during a session occur in bursts. An animal ceases responding for some length of time shorter than the interval, then emits a burst of response, "probing" so to speak. As the schedule becomes more stable, such probes tend to be minimized, and interresponse time adjusts to the appropriate interval.

A second problem related to response variables is topography of response. In this case, our primary topographical concerns were with the duration, force, and patterning of responding rather than the form. As long as the frequency was high enough to get the initial response to occur, we were not particularly concerned with it; however, the frequency of the ultimate baseline performance *was* of concern, since this would covary systematically with interresponse time (IRT) distributions.

Reinforcer Variables

One more group of variables considered in designing this piece of research was the reinforcer to be used with the amphetamine. How did we settle on a specific positive reinforcer? Initially, our decision was made on the basis of the work of others, and of our own experience with positive and negative reinforcers. Since several other projects underway in the laboratory effectively involved the use of sweetened condensed milk as a positive reinforcer with rats, our access to basic parametric information regarding magnitude of reinforcement, deprivation conditions, etc., suggested that this reinforcer would be appropriate for use with the DRL schedule. Although sweetened condensed milk has the disadvantage of producing local satiation, we were able to overcome this effect.

Once we had decided to use food as a reinforcer, another very important consideration was the magnitude of reinforcement. Obviously, if an animal had been permitted to drink 5 cc. sweetened condensed milk for every re-inforcement, satiation would have occurred in the first few minutes of the session. To solve this problem, preliminary studies with a variety of amounts of sweetened condensed milk were conducted. The amount that permitted us to obtain a stable baseline of performance throughout the 60-minute session was the volume and concentration used in the final portion of the experiment. Selection of the schedule was of course crucial. As we will see shortly when we examine the actual performance of the subjects, the DRL schedule is highly sensitive to the effects of amphetamine.

Experimental Results

In the first series of experiments, the two albino rats were conditioned to perform daily on a DRL 17.5-second schedule. Lever-presses spaced at least 17.5 seconds apart were reinforced with 0.1 cc. sweetened condensed milk. A three-minute blackout period followed a fixed number of reinforcements so that from two to five blackout periods occurred during each daily one-hour session. After the DRL baseline performance had stabilized, as indicated by the interresponse time distributions, isotonic saline was administered intraperitoneally five minutes before the beginning of subsequent sessions. A number of saline trials were conducted primarily to find out if the administration of a physiologically inert agent would have any effect on the DRL performance. As can be seen in the upper portion of Fig. 7.8, the saline baseline performance was distributed around 17.5 seconds. After enough data had been gathered to indicate that the distribution of interresponse times could reliably be said to range immediately around 17.5 seconds, a schedule of amphetamine administration was begun.

The first procedure involved intraperitoneal administration of 1.0 mg/kg *dl*-amphetamine five minutes before the beginning of each session. The second row of bar graphs in Fig. 7.8 illustrates the change in the IRT distribution during the first seven to 11 sessions of amphetamine administration as compared with saline trials plotted above them. It is quite clear that the mean of the distribution shifted toward the lower frequency and, as indicated by the hatched bars, the number of reinforcements decreased markedly. After continued daily amphetamine administration, the IRT distributions tended to move once more toward the longer latencies. This effect can be seen in the lower two bar graphs in Fig. 7.8, particularly for Animal A-1, where the mean was approximately 17.0 seconds.

From examining these data, one is inclined to say first of all that with repeated administration the animal tends to compensate for, or in some way adjust to, the effects of the drug. That is, initially the response rate increased, but after repeated administration it appeared to decrease, as indicated by the shift in the IRT distribution toward the longer interval during the last training trials. Certain sympathomimetic effects of amphetamine have long

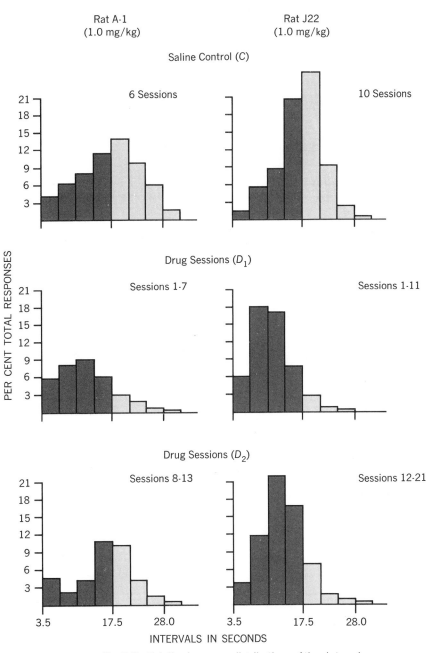

Fig. 7.8 Relative frequency distributions of time intervals between successive lever-pressing responses averaged over: (C), control sessions; (D₁), the first half, and (D₂), the second half, of the chronic drug regimen. Shading indicates reinforced responses. Left distributions, Rat A-1; right distributions, Rat J-22. (Schuster and Zimmerman, 1961, p. 327, Fig. 1)

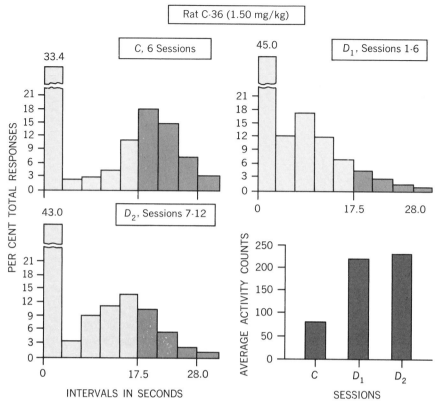

Fig. 7.9 Relative frequency distributions of time intervals between successive lever-pressing responses averaged over: (C), control sessions; (D_1), the first half, and (D_2), the second half, of the chronic drug regimen. Shading indicates reinforced responses. Bottom curve presents averaged activity counts from the same subject over the same period of time. (Schuster and Zimmerman, 1961, p. 328, Figs. 2, 3)

been known to decrease with repeated administration (Tormey and Lasagna, 1960). The present data also seem to indicate such a behavioral change (described in Chapter 2 as drug tolerance) after repeated administration. It may be that the observed decrement in drug effect with repeated administration did not necessarily reflect physiological tolerance but a behavioral adaptation to the stimulant effects of the drug. Such an interpretation has been proposed by Dews (1962). Does the development of tolerance to chronic administration of *dl*-amphetamine depend on the specific situation? In order to investigate the behavioral specificity of this amount of tolerance, a second study was undertaken.

In the second experiment, three albino rats performed on the same DRL 17.5-second schedule used in the first experiment. On alternate days the animals were placed in a standard photoelectric cell activity chamber for 15 minutes. The amount of activity in the 15-minute sessions was measured by

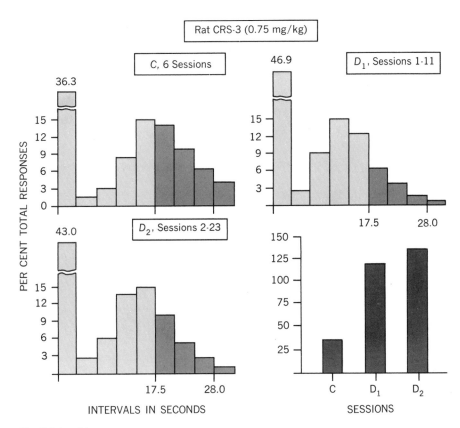

Fig. 7.9 (cont.)

the number of times the animal's movement interrupted the photocell circuit. Saline was administered five minutes before the DRL sessions and 15 minutes before the general activity sessions. After each animal's behavior stabilized in both situations, intraperitoneal *dl*-amphetamine (0.75 or 1.5 mg/kg) was substituted for the saline and was continued until no further changes in the DRL performance were observed.

In this way, it was possible not only to examine the development of tolerance to the effects of amphetamine on DRL performance but also to observe more general, unconditioned activity in which the consequences of increased rates of behavior were entirely different from those in the DRL situation.

Figure 7.9 presents averaged IRT distribution and averaged activity counts for two animals under control conditions (C indicates the saline control sessions, D_1 the first half of the drug regimen, and D_2 the second half of the drug regimen). With *dl*-amphetamine injection, the IRT distribution (D_1) showed a marked increase in the frequency of short IRT's compared with that in the saline control distributions (C). The modal value of the IRT distributions shifted toward the reinforced IRT's during the last half of the drug regimen (D_2). These results seem to corroborate the findings in our first study. In contrast, the general activity level of these animals remained consistently elevated over the entire course of the drug regimen.

It therefore seems that animals do indeed develop specific behavioral tolerance dependent on consequences of their behavior. In the case of general activity, there is little or no tendency for tolerance to develop, and this has been corroborated by other investigators (Tormey and Lasagna, 1960). On the other hand, the DRL performance is markedly affected. Pressing the lever with high frequency has the effect of reducing the total number of reinforcements. If, however, the animal adjusts its performance so that it is able to space its responses despite the effects of the drug, then the number of reinforcements remains the same.

Before interpreting these data, it was necessary to assess the interaction of the DRL interval length with administration of amphetamine. In order to investigate this effect, rats were trained on a multiple reinforcement schedule consisting of two DRL's: a short one (18 seconds), and a longer one (36 seconds). Once again, the primary dependent variable was the interresponse time distributions. Figure 7.10 presents averaged frequency distributions of IRT's for two rats from six predrug saline control sessions. Note that the distributions in both components of the multiple schedule have modal values approximately at the interval appropriate to receive the maximal number of reinforcements. Figure 7.10 also presents distributions from the first, second, third, and fourth quarters of the *dl*-amphetamine sessions. As previously, *dl*-amphetamine was administered (1.0 mg/kg) five minutes before the session. Finally, in a series of six sessions, the animals received isotonic saline and IRT distributions were compiled, as indicated in C_2 at the bottom of Fig. 7.10.

In the initial *dl*-amphetamine sessions, the distributions for both DRL components increased markedly in frequency of short IRT's as compared with saline control. The maximal drug effect occurred during the second quarter of the drug sessions D_2. However, the distributions from both components shifted progressively toward the reinforced IRT intervals from D_2 to D_3 to D_4. These data seem to confirm the observed relation in the earlier study.

If we look carefully at Fig. 7.10, we find that the use of the multiple schedule tells us something about differential effects depending upon the length of the interval. *dl*-Amphetamine administration in D_1 resulted in a slight differential effect on the two components. The initial shift of the DRL 36 distribution toward shorter IRT intervals was more pronounced than the initial shift to the DRL 18 distribution; and the differential control by the

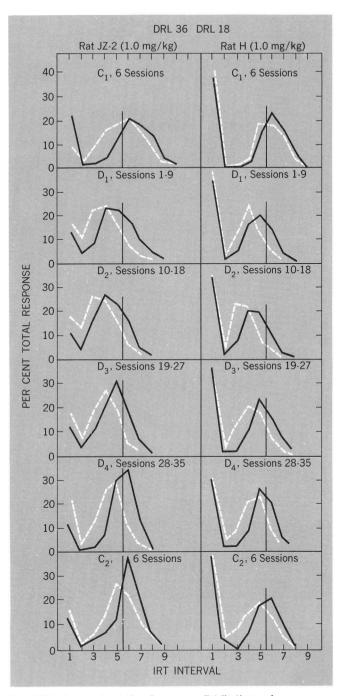

Fig. 7.10 Averaged relative frequency distributions of IRT's for Rat JZ-2 (left column) and Rat H (right column) from predrug saline control sessions (C_1); from the first, second, third, and fourth quarters of the *dl*-amphetamine sessions (D_1, D_2, D_3, D_4, respectively); and from postdrug saline control sessions (C_2). Broken line refers to 36-sec. DRL; solid line refers to 18-sec. DRL. (Zimmerman and Schuster, 1962, p. 501, Fig. 5)

two schedules was not eliminated. During the progressive return of the distribution toward a higher IRT interval, the initial differential was not eliminated; instead, the two distributions shifted back at approximately the same rate.

In other words, the initial differential effect of the drug on the two components with respect to reinforcement ratio was maintained over the drug regimen, even though the behavior of both components shifted toward baseline behavior and the absolute number of reinforcements obtained per session increased. When the drug was discontinued (C_2), performance returned to normal without any overcompensation, and reapproached the predrug level (C_1).

A rather interesting phenomenon was revealed in another animal conditioned on the same multiple schedule. Whereas the subjects described previously exhibited a typical distribution with the modal value being exactly or approximately at the IRT value, one animal never attained this degree of accuracy. Although the distribution from the two components was well separated, the modal value of the DRL 18 distributions occurred at 24 to 27 seconds rather than at 18 seconds, which is two class intervals higher than the earliest IRT interval in which responses were reinforced. The modal value of the DRL distribution occurred right at the DRL value as expected. When this animal was placed on a chronic drug regimen (*dl*-amphetamine, 0.60 mg/kg), the IRT distribution shifted toward the shorter intervals as expected. Figure 7.11 presents relative frequency distribution for this animal for the predrug saline, drug, and postdrug saline sessions. With initial *dl*-amphetamine administration (D_1), the distributions from both components increased and the frequencies of short IRT's were comparable to the distributions for saline controls (C_1). The initial administration of the drug shifted from DRL 18 distribution *more* than the DRL 36 distribution. The modal value of the DRL 18 distribution shifted to the earliest IRT interval in which a response was reinforced. Over the next nine sessions of drug administration (D_2, D_3, D_4), a slight return toward the control values occurred in the DRL 36 distribution, whereas little change occurred in the DRL 18 distribution. The DRL 18 distribution did not return to its earlier "atypical" value during the postdrug saline sessions (C_2), nor did any further changes occur during the 12 postdrug saline sessions.

In the course of this series of experiments we have delved into a variety of facets of the behavioral tolerance problem. Lest we lose sight of the topic under consideration, the DRL-amphetamine tolerance phenomenon might be placed in the larger context of drug-behavior interactions discussed in the introduction to this chapter. The specificity of the development of tolerance to the DRL-maintained behavior is certainly not predictable from either single-dose behavioral studies or physiological tolerance experiments. The initial effect of amphetamine on DRL and "spontaneous motor activity" was increased frequency of occurrence. However, repeated administration of the same dosage of amphetamine was associated with a diminution of the fre-

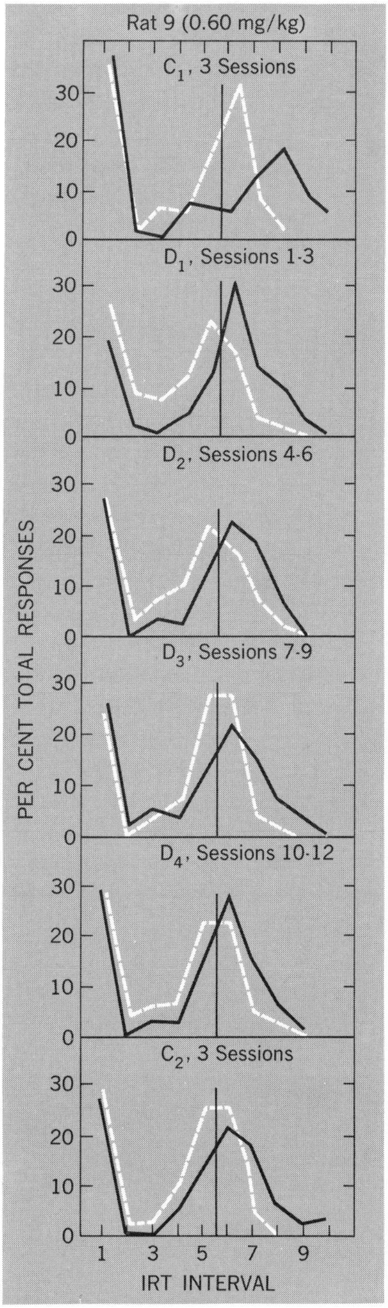

Fig. 7.11 Averaged relative frequency distributions of IRT's for Rat 9 from predrug saline control sessions (C_1); from the first, second, third, and fourth quarters of the dl-amphetamine sessions (D_1, D_2, D_3, D_4, respectively); and from postdrug saline control sessions (C_2). Broken line refers to 36-sec. DRL; solid line refers to 18-sec. DRL. (Zimmerman and Schuster, 1962, p. 503, Fig. 7)

quency of occurrence of DRL-maintained behavior, while photocell activity was essentially unchanged.

When the consequences of increased frequency of occurrence of behaviors in the photocell activity situation are compared with those in the DRL-maintained situation, an important difference becomes apparent. Though amphetamine administration is associated with increased number of crossings, this in no way alters the probability of reinforcement. However, increased lever-pressing under DRL contingencies diminishes the probability of reinforcement. Thus, when the effect of the drug has no consequences in terms of probability of reinforcement, it seems that tolerance may not develop. If, on the other hand, the effects of the drug are to reduce reinforcement probability, behavioral tolerance does develop.

DRUG SELF-ADMINISTRATION

The second research program to be described grew out of the large body of pharmacological literature on drug dependence and a re-examination of drug self-administration from a behavioral standpoint. It is well established that organisms that have become physically dependent on opiate drugs can be returned to a relatively drug-free state through abstinence from the drug (Himmelsbach, 1942; Krueger, Eddy, and Sumwalt, 1941–3; Tatum, Seevers, and Collins, 1929). However, despite the disappearance of the physical signs that occur during the withdrawal period, the tendency to continue consuming the drug is often unaltered. While the factors controlling such behavioral dependence are unknown, experienced clinical investigators have suggested the importance of the environmental conditions under which the patient was addicted, the environmental conditions under which he experiences withdrawal, and the environmental conditions to which the postaddict returns (Wikler, 1953; Nyswander, 1956).

If we reflect for a moment on the problem of drug self-administration, it becomes clear that behavioral as well as pharmacological analyses are in order. Self-administration is, by definition, a behavioral event; and presumably introducing an active drug into the bloodstream has stimulus consequences. An organism emits some behavior that leads to the consequence of getting an opiate into the bloodstream. This analysis bears considerable resemblance to the paradigm applied to lever-pressing behavior reinforced by food presentation. If this paradigm fits the case of drug self-administration, an array of environmental factors known to alter other types of operant behavior can be examined in an effort to determine their effects on drug-reinforced behavior.

A reasonable initial experiment might involve an attempt to show that drug self-administration can be conditioned in much the same way that food-reinforced behavior can be conditioned. As in the preceding experimental program, we must begin by asking questions about the facilities available, and the kind of preparation and the animal most suitable for the purpose. In this case, the basic problem is to find a satisfactory method of automatically dispensing or administering drugs to animals. Headlee, Coppock, and Nichols (1955) and Weeks (1962) have described methods for automatic intraperitoneal and intravenous injection in rats. Werdegar, Johnson, and Mason (1965) Schuster (1962), and Niemann, Schuster, and Thompson (1962) have described methods for the chronic venous or arterial catheterization of restrained monkeys; Deneau, Yanagita, and Seevers (personal communication) have developed a method permitting intravenous infusion in partially restrained monkeys; and Thompson (1965) has designed an apparatus permitting infusion in unrestrained monkeys.

We had used the primate restraining chair in previous behavioral and pharmacological research, and had developed a method of remote infusion of drugs into a monkey's internal jugular vein. We therefore chose the monkey for our experimental animal and a surgically introduced, chronically indwelling, internal jugular catheter for our method of drug administration. We then had to decide on a reinforcer. Since morphine has been the standard drug for evaluation in all addiction research, it was clear that any initial effort must begin with that drug. Thus, the reinforcing event would be the infusion of a morphine sulfate solution into the internal jugular vein via the chronic catheter.

Antecedent Factors

Food deprivation is a necessary antecedent to reinforcing a lever-pressing response with food. Similarly, deprivation of morphine was initially thought to be a necessary antecedent to reinforcing an operant with morphine. However, morphine deprivation is experimentally meaningless until morphine dependence is established. The pharmacological literature indicates that 30 days of morphine administration four times daily produces physical dependence in nearly all monkeys (Tatum, Seevers, and Collins, 1929; Irwin, 1954). Therefore we infused morphine automatically through the chronic catheter into the jugular vein four times daily before attempting to condition the animal.

Current Stimulus Conditions
and Response Factors

After the 30-day period, a white stimulus light and a telegraph key lever were introduced. The white light was illuminated every six hours for 15 minutes. If the monkey closed the telegraph key switch, he was infused with morphine and the light was extinguished for another six hours. However, in order to maintain physical dependence while the animal acquired the new behavior, morphine was automatically infused if 15 minutes passed without a response. The deprivation period was maintained constant at six hours. The stimulus conditions are defined as the presentation of a white light that set the occasion for lever-pressing. Thus, the white light was a discriminative stimulus and the response was lever-pressing.

Reinforcement Contingencies

This reinforcer is unique in that increasing the magnitude of reinforcement can be quite dangerous for the animal. Therefore, we were initially careful to limit the total amount of drug the animal could self-administer. For the first two weeks the amount infused was the same as it had been during the 30-day addiction period (1 mg/kg). A complicating factor is the development of tolerance. That is, it is known that after repeated administrations of morphine, a higher dose is required to produce the same physiological effect. To compensate for the development of tolerance, the dose per infusion was doubled after two weeks of self-administration. After one week on the self-administration regimen, the animal was self-administering before the end of 15 minutes in the S^D. After two weeks, it was self-administering all the time, and the length of time from the onset of the S^D to the occurrence of the response was decreasing. At this point it was clear that the animal was becoming very proficient at self-administering morphine, and that additional information about the properties of drug self-administration would be in order.

One variable of general interest controlling most operant behaviors is reinforcer deprivation. What happens if an animal is deprived of the drug for periods longer than six hours? What happens if, by blocking the action of morphine, a state of deprivation is induced pharmacologically? In order to answer these questions, we felt it was desirable to have access to behavior more sensitive to deprivation conditions than that used in the previous experiment.

Of the various reinforcement schedules studied, FI and FR schedules (Ferster and Skinner, 1957) were among the more labile indicators of deprivation operations. The FI schedule has been studied extensively, and it is known that, under increased deprivation conditions, more responses tend to be emitted early in the interval (that is, the scallop is shallower). There is a quantitative relation between the hours of food deprivation and the number of responses in the FI. The FR schedule is also sensitive to deprivation conditions, but in a different way. For the most part, when FR responding occurs, it occurs at the same rate regardless of deprivation conditions. However, with increasing deprivation the postreinforcement pause is diminished. Thus, by combining the two schedules, we have the following two measures of deprivation conditions: (1) number of responses in the FI, and (2) latency to the end of the FR. It will be recalled from the discussion in Chapter 5 that in chained schedules different stimulus conditions exist during components of the chain. In this case, a green light was the S^D for the FI; a tone was used during the FR. Thus, the first response after two minutes in the presence of the green light turned on a tone; and 25 responses in the presence of the tone turned off the tone and infused 7 mg. morphine intravenously—an FI2-FR25 chain.

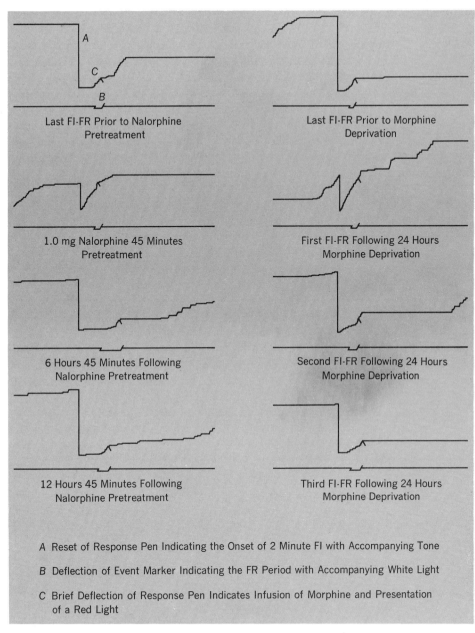

Last FI-FR Prior to Nalorphine
Pretreatment

Last FI-FR Prior to Morphine
Deprivation

1.0 mg Nalorphine 45 Minutes
Pretreatment

First FI-FR Following 24 Hours
Morphine Deprivation

6 Hours 45 Minutes Following
Nalorphine Pretreatment

Second FI-FR Following 24 Hours
Morphine Deprivation

12 Hours 45 Minutes Following
Nalorphine Pretreatment

Third FI-FR Following 24 Hours
Morphine Deprivation

A Reset of Response Pen Indicating the Onset of 2 Minute FI with Accompanying Tone

B Deflection of Event Marker Indicating the FR Period with Accompanying White Light

C Brief Deflection of Response Pen Indicates Infusion of Morphine and Presentation
   of a Red Light

Fig. 7.12 Representative cumulative response records of
FI-FR performance following 24 hours of morphine-de-
privation-compared-FI-FR performance 45 minutes after
the intravenous administration of 1.0 mg. nalorphine.
(Thompson and Schuster, 1964, p. 89, Fig. 1)

After the FI-FR chain had stabilized, the animal was deprived of the opportunity to self-administer the drug for 24 hours. Then the stimuli associated with morphine self-administration were reinstated and the manipulandum made available. The number of responses in the FI increased to approximately 10 times the baseline, and the latency-to-completion of the FR decreased markedly. Figure 7.12 presents sample cumulative records of chained FI-FR performance before 24 hours of morphine deprivation (baseline), after 24 hours of morphine deprivation, and for two subsequent self-administration periods. The deprivation effect was clearly reflected in the FI-FR response output. After the baseline had been re-established, another attempt was made to manipulate the degree of deprivation by treating the animal with a morphine antagonist, nalorphine hydrochloride, prior to the opportunity for morphine self-administration. Figure 7.12 also presents cumulative records of FI-FR performance paralleling those for 24 hours of deprivation. Once again, it was found that the number of responses in the FI period increased markedly and that the latency-to-completion of the FR period decreased comparably. In other words, it appears that the FI-FR chain is a sensitive measure of drug deprivation, whether deprivation is accomplished by abstinence or by pharmacological antagonism.

In view of these findings, the next logical step was to diminish the deprivation effect by pretreating the animal with morphine before self-administration. A series of sessions were run in which the animals received 7.0, 14.0, or 21.0 mg. morphine 45 minutes before the next FI-FR period. The effect of this pretreatment is illustrated in Fig. 7.13. It can be seen that a functional relation exists between the pretreatment dosage and characteristics of subsequent FI-FR behavior.

Morphine self-administration thus seems to be subject to behavioral analysis and to be affected by deprivation operations in the same way as other operants. The morphine-reinforced FI-FR chain was found to be a stable but sensitive instrument for measuring deprivation effect. However, a host of other questions now arise. How does drug self-administration affect other

Fig. 7.13 Representative cumulative response records of FI-FR performance following 45 minutes pretreatment with 7.0, 14.0 and 21.0 mg. of morphine, I.V. 1. Last FI-FR prior to morphine pretreatment. 2. 45 minutes pretreatment with 7.0, 14.0, and 21.0 mg. morphine. 3. 6 hours, 45 minutes following morphine pretreatment. 4. 12 hours, 45 minutes following morphine pretreatment. A—Reset of response pen indicating the onset of two-minute FI with accompanying tone. B—Deflection of event marker indicating the FR period with accompanying white light. C—Brief deflection of response pen indicates infusion of morphine and presentation of a red light. (Thompson and Schuster, 1964, p. 91, Fig. 2)

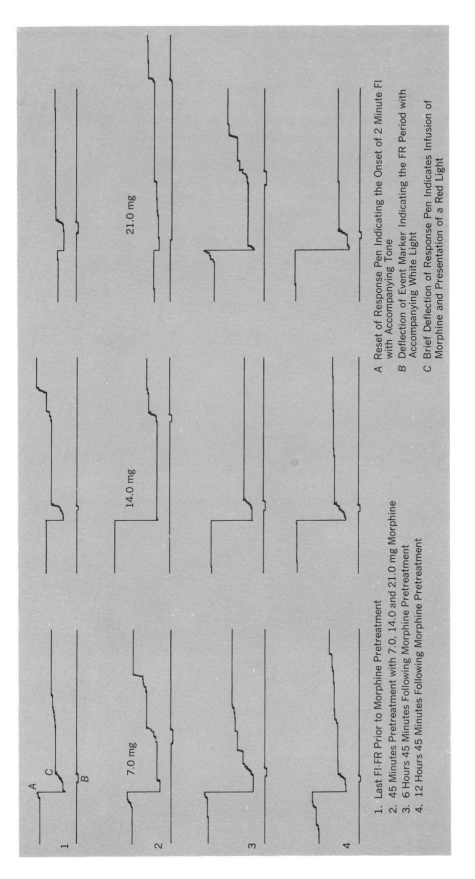

7.0 mg

14.0 mg

21.0 mg

A Reset of Response Pen Indicating the Onset of 2 Minute FI with Accompanying Tone

B Deflection of Event Marker Indicating the FR Period with Accompanying White Light

C Brief Deflection of Response Pen Indicates Infusion of Morphine and Presentation of a Red Light

1. Last FI-FR Prior to Morphine Pretreatment

2. 45 Minutes Pretreatment with 7.0, 14.0 and 21.0 mg Morphine

3. 6 Hours 45 Minutes Following Morphine Pretreatment

4. 12 Hours 45 Minutes Following Morphine Pretreatment

behavior? Does it impair the animal's ability to emit behaviors necessary for maintenance? How do stressful conditions alter the tendency to self-administer? How does abstinence affect other concurrent behaviors? What is the significance of other stimuli associated with the acquisition of morphine? Can experiments like the ones described tell us anything about the development of tolerance? How readily is this conditioned behavior extinguished?

The animals used in the preceding experiments were in the experimental environment 24 hours a day for months at a time. However, their behavior was under experimental control for less than an hour a day. During the remaining 23 hours, the animals performed other unmeasured acts that resulted in food and water acquisition and presumably removed irritating or painful stimuli (e.g., itches, pressure from the restraining chair). It seemed wasteful not to exploit this behavior experimentally.

In an effort to do just that, food and shock-avoidance periods were interspersed between the four drug-reinforced behavior periods. Each six-hour cycle consisted of four shock-avoidance periods, four food periods, and one drug-reinforced FI-FR period. The sequence of these periods was as follows: food, shock, food, shock, FI-FR drug period, shock, food, shock, food. There was a minimum of eight and a maximum of 32 minutes between the various periods.

The food period consisted of five successive FR's of 35 responses. If the animal failed to complete the five ratios, the food period was automatically terminated after eight minutes.

The shock-avoidance periods were presented for a maximum of eight minutes, or until the animal received five shocks. The shock schedule comprised a 10-second warning clicker presented on a variable time schedule with an average interval of 60 seconds. Responses made between the warning-stimulus presentations had no consequences. Responses made during the warning-stimulus turned off the clicker and prevented the 0.5-second electric shock. The 1.5 ma. electric shock was delivered through eight stainless steel electrodes mounted on the inside of the subject's leather waist belt.

This complex schedule was the vehicle for answering some of the aforementioned questions. Performance for the various reinforcers remained stable over long periods (see Fig. 7.14). When we were confident that a steady state had been attained, we wondered what the effect of morphine deprivation would be on other performances necessary for self-maintenance.

Figure 7.15 presents the changes in food-reinforced and shock-avoidance behaviors during a 48-hour abstinence period. As can be seen, there was a progressive reduction in the tendency to work for food; and the shock-avoidance latencies increased. Following the first drug infusion after 48 hours of abstinence, the food-reinforced behavior returned immediately, and the shock-avoidance latencies began to decrease toward the preabstinence baseline. An examination of the baseline behaviors both before and after abstinence periods reveals that the dependent animal's behavior is not adversely affected

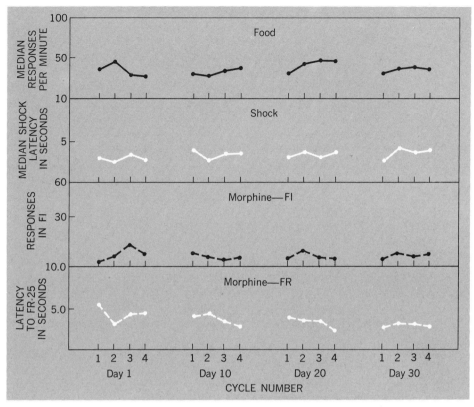

Fig. 7.14 Baseline performance on food-reinforced, shock-avoidance, and FI-FR drug-reinforced behaviors, over a period of 30 days. (Thompson and Schuster, 1964, p. 92, Fig. 3)

by the presence of the drug, but by its absence. Thus, the animal's ability to perform tasks necessary for self-maintenance seemed to be enhanced by the presence of the drug, and impeded by its absence. The possibility remains that this may be a dose-dependent phenomenon, and that performance would deteriorate at the higher doses administered in the course of tolerance development.

Several sessions in which shock was discontinued were then run; there were others in which shock intensity was increased. Changes in the tendency to self-administer were not evident in either case. In an effort to determine the effects of stimuli associated with morphine infusion, a red light was presented during the period of drug administration.

In one experiment, a 48-hour abstinence period was instituted. Disruption of eating and of shock-avoidance behavior ensued, as was observed previously. Thereupon, the self-administration procedure was reintroduced; but

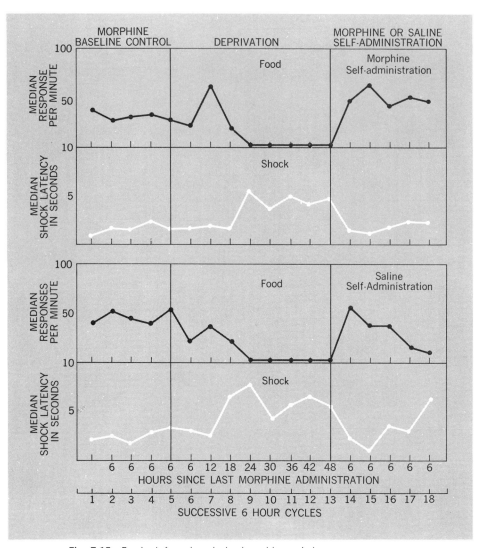

Fig. 7.15 Food-reinforced and shock-avoidance behaviors under conditions of morphine baseline control, 48 hours without the opportunity to self-administer morphine, followed by (upper graph) return to morphine baseline control procedure, or (lower graph) return to baseline condition with saline substituted for morphine self-administration. (Thompson and Schuster, 1964, p. 92, Fig. 4)

saline was substituted for morphine in the infusion pump. The red light previously associated with morphine infusion was presented as usual. A placebo effect occurred in which the animals began to work for food and avoid shock immediately after receiving the first saline infusion. However, this improved performance showed progressive disruption as time without the drug increased (Fig. 7.15). Other subjects were deprived of the drug and received only the red light after the FI-FR chain. Since physical dependence is known to terminate in approximately 30 days, self-administration should also cease if its maintenance is based entirely on physical dependence. It was found that animals were still working on the FI-FR chain 60 days after withdrawal. Clearly, the stimuli associated with drug reinforcement came to have potent discriminative and reinforcing properties in and of themselves.

What will happen to the animal's performance as the dose grows progressively higher during the development of tolerance? Can one expect other behaviors to deteriorate? Several animals were conditioned to self-administer morphine and to work for food on an FR schedule under visual stimulus control. The animals could regulate their own doses of morphine per opportunity by completing a greater number of ratios. A maximal number of infusions was set to avoid dangerous overdosing. As tolerance developed, the number of self-administrations per opportunity increased. Figure 7.16 presents a record of the total milligrams per day received by such regulated self-infusion. It can be seen that the dosage increased progressively for approximately 60 days, then leveled off. Little change in dosage occurred during the 30 days after this "maintenance" level had been reached. Records of the number of food reinforcements per opportunity kept throughout this period reveal that food-reinforced behavior was extremely stable (Fig. 7.16). The only significant variations from the food baseline occurred following apparatus failure in the feeding device, and following a large change in concentration of the morphine solution. The effect of doubling the concentration was to overdose for several days, which produced a reduction in postdrug food-reinforced responses as compared with predrug responses. Therefore, it appears that increasing morphine dosage does not interfere with other behavior as long as dosage is appropriate to the level of tolerance developed.

By rearranging the program so that the subject can obtain food on an FI30-second schedule immediately before and immediately following morphine reinforcement, we can get some idea of the interaction between degree of morphine tolerance and food-reinforced performance. Figure 7.17 shows sample cumulative records of FI-1 food-reinforced lever-pressing on the 10th day, 20th day, and 40th day of self-administration of 0.5 mg/kg of morphine. On the 41st day, the dosage per infusion was doubled; the top record shows the performance on the 41st day. Notice that over the first 40 days, the number of FI's completed decreases, and regularity of the FI's in the period prior to morphine self-administration deteriorates. Following morphine self-administration, the performance is quite normal. On the 41st day (when the dosage was doubled) the premorphine self-administration performance was nearly like the normal baseline.

These data suggest that as tolerance develops over the 40-day period, the reinforcing properties of food decrease over the 6-hour period between successive morphine administrations. As soon as the drug is infused, food re-

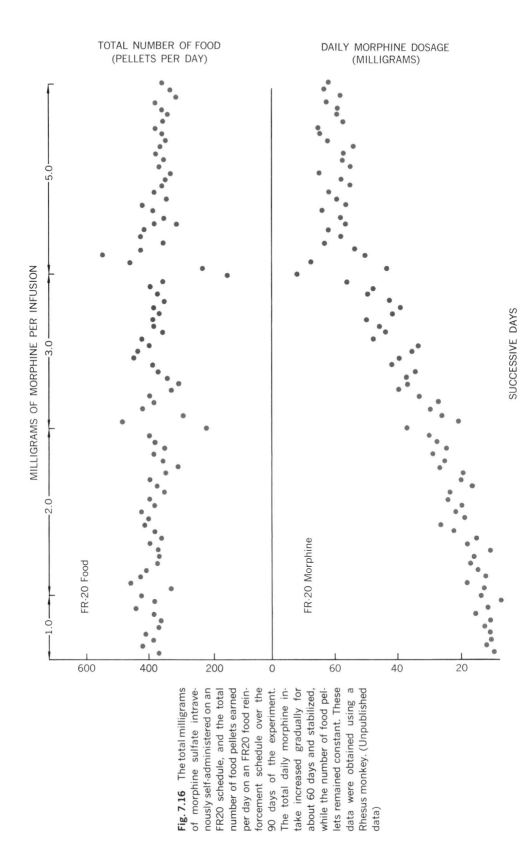

TOTAL NUMBER OF FOOD
(PELLETS PER DAY)

DAILY MORPHINE DOSAGE
(MILLIGRAMS)

MILLIGRAMS OF MORPHINE PER INFUSION

SUCCESSIVE DAYS

FR-20 Food

FR-20 Morphine

Fig. 7.16 The total milligrams of morphine sulfate intravenously self-administered on an FR20 schedule, and the total number of food pellets earned per day on an FR20 food reinforcement schedule over the 90 days of the experiment. The total daily morphine intake increased gradually for about 60 days and stabilized, while the number of food pellets remained constant. These data were obtained using a Rhesus monkey. (Unpublished data)

gains its normal reinforcing properties. When the dosage is doubled, food reinforcement retains its strength throughout the interadministration interval. Thus, one of the ways in which morphine tolerance interacts with food-reinforced responding is by diminishing the relative reinforcing properties of food.

Let us now reconsider some of the decisions that went into designing this series of experiments. It will be recalled that a chronic, indwelling catheter was inserted into the animals' internal jugular vein to permit remote infusion of morphine. Why was the drug introduced intravenously rather than by some other route? The primary advantage was the immediacy of the effect; if the drug had been administered intraperitoneally or through a nasopharyngeal tube into the stomach, there would have been a delay of at least 10 to 15 minutes between the animal's response and any discriminable consequences. It is known that any delay between the occurrence of an operant and its reinforcement weakens the reinforcing properties of the stimulus (Hull, 1943; Ferster, 1953). Therefore, bringing the reinforcing consequence closer to the response by intravenous drug administration increased the effectiveness of the reinforcer.

Another consideration that shaped the design of these experiments was whether initially the animal should be addicted automatically or whether he should be permitted to addict himself. The basis of this decision was twofold. First, the classical experiments of Seevers and coworkers had utilized the 30-day procedure, which has been the model for later experiments. Second, as a matter of expediency we guessed the period required to establish dependence by complete self-administration would be longer than the one required to establish physical dependence automatically.

Another series of experiments with monkeys which had never received morphine prior to implantation of the venous catheter indicated that prior establishment of physical dependence is not necessary for morphine to be an effective reinforcer. Schuster and coworkers (1967) have shown that monkeys will sustain responding on a VI-1 reinforcement schedule in dosages as low as 0.01 mg/kg per infusion. Discontinuation of morphine administration at this dosage produces no gross signs of withdrawal. Recent studies with drugs that do not produce physical dependence in animals having no prior experience with the drugs further support the assertion that drugs may be effective reinforcers without prior treatment with those compounds. Deneau, Yanagita and Seevers (1964) have reported that cocaine is an effective reinforcer; and more recently Schuster (1967) has studied reinforcing effects of various dosages of two stimulants, fencamfamin and SPA. Figure 7.18 presents a dose-effect curve for SPA illustrating that the reinforcing effectiveness increases as a function of dosage to a maximum of 0.1 mg/kg/per infusion, then drops off sharply.

Similar results have been obtained by Pickens and Thompson (1967a, 1968) with *d*-amphetamine and cocaine, using rats as subjects. Rats with

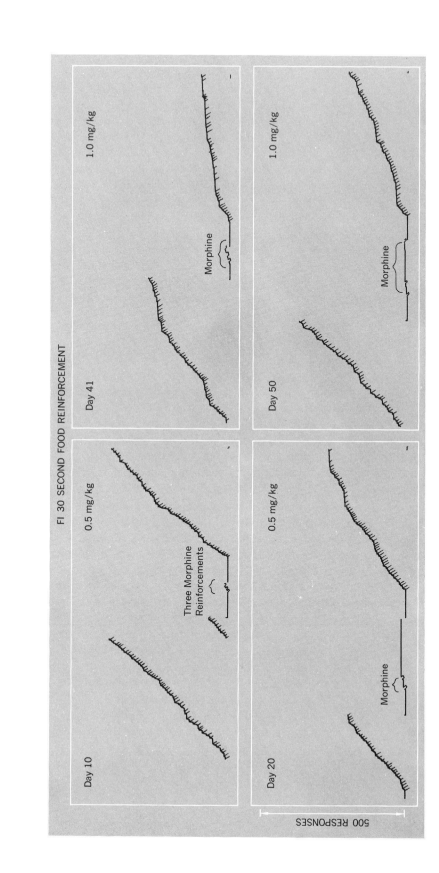

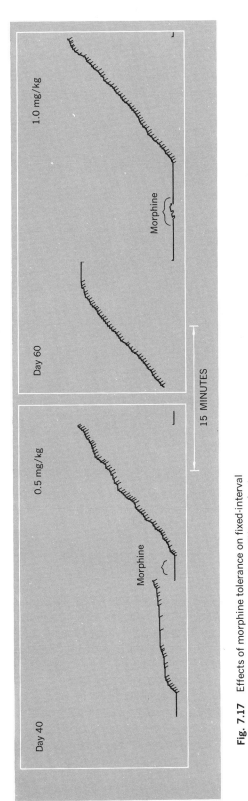

Fig. 7.17 Effects of morphine tolerance on fixed-interval food-reinforced performance in monkeys. Fifteen minute food-reinforcement periods were programmed immediately before and after the opportunity to self administer morphine: for the first 40 days, the dosage per infusion was 0.5 mg/kg. From the 41st to 60th days, the dosage was doubled. Notice that the food-reinforced performance before receiving the drug deteriorates over the first 40 days as tolerance to that dosage develops. When the dosage was doubled, the reverse relationship was observed. (Thompson, unpublished)

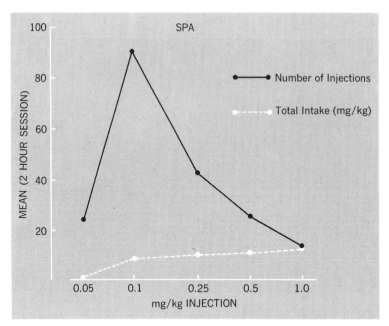

Fig. 7.18 Self-administration of SPA by a Rhesus monkey. Mean number of injections and total drug intake as a function of dosage/injection. (Schuster, unpublished)

chronic jugular catheters were provided with the opportunity to self-administer various dosages of *d*-amphetamine and cocaine. Neither drug produces physical dependence, though both are said to lead to development of tolerance. Figure 7.19 shows the effects of magnitude of *d*-amphetamine reinforcement (expressed as mg/kg/infusion) on frequency and patterning of drug-reinforced responding. There is an inverse relationship between magnitude of *d*-amphetamine reinforcement and number of response-produced infusions per hour; however, the total amount of drug per hour was relatively constant (mean of 0.54 mg/kg per hour).

Similar results have been obtained using cocaine, with an inverse relation between reinforcement magnitude and response rate, though the amount of drug received per hour is, again, relatively constant (mean of 6.8 mg/kg/ per hour). Figure 7.20 shows the relation between the size of a fixed-ratio schedule required per cocaine reinforcement and response rate, and the mean number of reinforcements per hour. There is a direct relation between size of the FR and response rate, and the total hourly infusions remaining constant across all ratios (mean of 7.1 mg/kg/hour).

The interaction between magnitude of cocaine reinforcement and value of a fixed ratio schedule can be seen most effectively in the sample cumula-

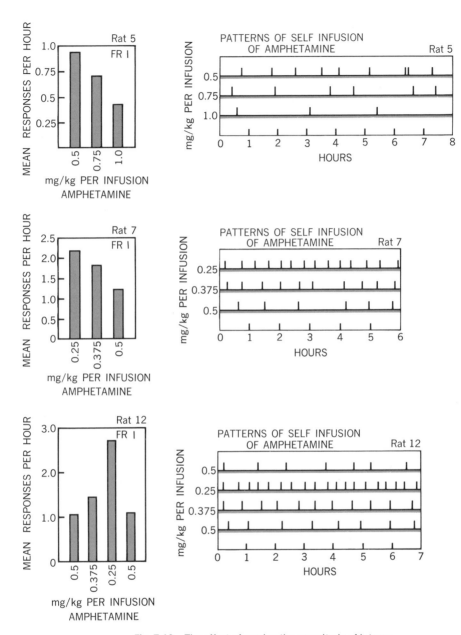

Fig. 7.19 The effect of varying the magnitude of intravenous amphetamine reinforcement on response rate and patterning by rats. There was an inverse relation between rate and reinforcement magnitude. (Pickens and Thompson, 1967)

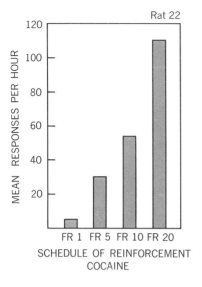

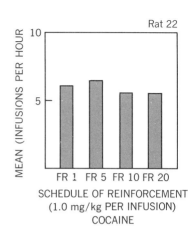

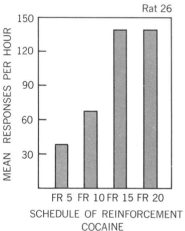

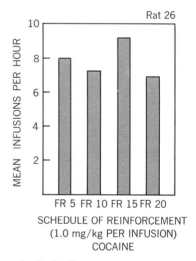

Fig. 7.20 The effect of varying the value of a fixed-ratio schedule of intravenous cocaine reinforcement on response rate and number of cocaine reinforcements per hour. There was a direct relation between ratio value and rate, but a relatively constant number of infusions per hour. (Pickens and Thompson, 1967)

tive records presented in Fig. 7.21. Within the range of reinforcement magnitude 0.5 to 1.5 mg/kg/infusion, ratios are regular, with constant running rates and regularly spaced pauses between successive runs. The maximum ratios maintained varied with the magnitude of reinforcement—FR20 at 0.5 mg/kg/infusion, FR60 at 1.0 mg/kg/infusion and FR80 at 1.5 mg/kg/infusion. Increasing ratio size above that level produced an entire cessation of responding. Thus it would seem that while previous establishment of physical dependence *can* influence the reinforcing properties of drugs, it is not a necessary condition. Indeed, for certain dosages of morphine, and with some stimulants, other variables seem to be of great importance.

The length of morphine deprivation (six hours) was somewhat arbitrary. The standardized procedure used in the addiction screening program at the University of Michigan involves administration of potentially addictive agents every six hours. This regimen has been found most effective in establishing the dependence liability of most drugs. It might have been equally interesting to utilize varying deprivation periods, much as was done in the 24-hour abstinence test. For example, the effects of 6, 12, 24, 48 hours, etc., of deprivation on the FI-FR performance would certainly provide valuable baseline information on the functional relation between amount of deprivation and propensity to work for the drug.

How were the stimuli and manipulanda selected? Standardized jeweled reflector stimulus lights were used in conjunction with a commercially available restraining chair. Obviously, many other kinds of stimuli might have been employed. The basis of the decision to use this particular equipment was (1) that the apparatus was readily available, facilitating replication, and (2) the stimuli were readily discriminable for this organism. The monkey has good color vision and can easily learn to discriminate the five standard colored lights (red, yellow, blue, green, white) provided with the restraining chair. The manipulanda (a telegraph key and a pull-chain) were selected for the same general reasons. They are commercially available, and they minimized response generalization. The animals seldom operated the incorrect manipulandum.

A practical consideration in working with monkeys is that manipulanda must be durable. The heavy-duty telegraph keys used were satisfactory, although a properly protected, cast-mounted microswitch lever is far more satisfactory in this respect. Related to the selection of manipulanda is the problem of response discriminiability. Because the excursion of a telegraph key is relatively short, it is difficult to determine when the response has been made. In order to facilitate this discrimination, the chair was equipped with a feedback relay which operated with a clearly audible click whenever the telegraph key was closed. This tended to accelerate conditioning, since the animal could more readily discriminate occurrence of the response.

An aspect of the operant as a unit of analysis that has changed in recent years is the size of behavioral units that can be brought under experimental control. In these studies, we began by sampling behavior for a few minutes at a time, four times daily. The remainder of the organism's behavior was beyond the pale of experimental analysis. As a matter of fact, some of the more interesting facets of drug dependence have to do with the interaction of self-administration and other behaviors. Therefore, in subsequent replications, we employed systematic modifications of the basic procedure in order to sample other behaviors that led to entirely different consequences.

And as the studies progressed, it was found that repeated samples of behavior could be taken 24 hours a day with the intersample interval ranging

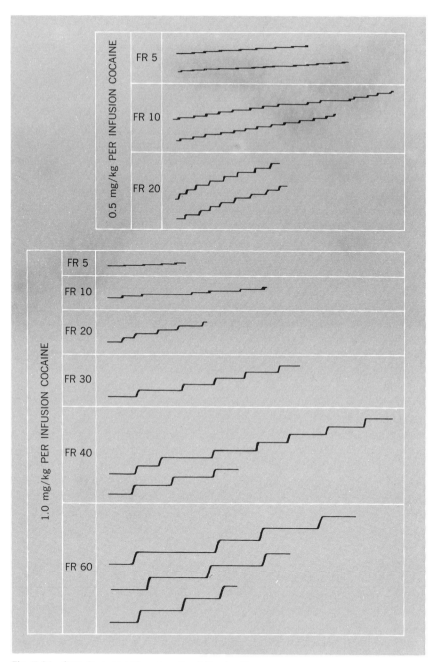

Fig. 7.21 Sample cumulative records of fixed ratio performance of one rat at all fixed-ratio values, maintained by various magnitudes of cocaine reinforcement. For each reinforcement magnitude, increasing the ratio above the values indicated produced a cessation of responding. Similarly decreasing reinforcement magnitude led to ragged performance and cessation of responding. (Pickens and Thompson, 1968)

Rat 22

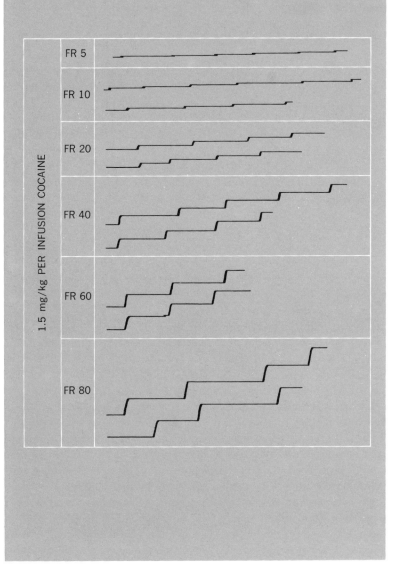

from 8 to 32 minutes. In other words, we brought under experimental control large and continuous segments of the organism's total behavioral repertoire for getting food and water and for avoiding shock, as well as for procuring morphine.

Selection of the reinforcement schedules, of the stimuli, of the duration of each component in the complex multiple schedule, etc., was somewhat arbitrary in every case. Yet these decisions were not as arbitrary as they may seem. As was described in Chapter 4, the heart of effective experimental analysis is systematic replication. In this case, the data obtained from the first few subjects led to partial replication of the FI-FR procedure in subsequent experiments. The data obtained following the addition of food and shock to the complex schedule were used to modify the procedure employed when water was added. The size of the FR leading to food was adjusted according to the properties of the animal's behavior. It was found that two to five days were required to condition a monkey to a highly stable FR35 performance which was ultimately settled upon as our baseline.

The length of the FI and magnitude of the FR in the FI-FR chain were determined by starting with a low FR and building up to FR25. This procedure provided a sample of ratio performance large enough to give us reliable data on latency-to-completion of the FR. The FI duration was arbitrarily picked, then adjusted until a characteristic scallop was obtained. Some animals exhibited less scallop than others; however, the general properties of FI performance prevailed.

In surveying this rather complicated series of experiments, we see that what began as a simple demonstration of conditioned morphine self-administration quickly blossomed into an array of options of experimental manipulations. To the reader unfamiliar with techniques of behavioral control, the path through the maze of manipulations and devices may seem capricious; however, as we have shown above, this impression is an illusory one. The series of manipulations evolved from the data themselves; each experiment was followed by adjustments of procedure, and succeeded by another experiment based on the findings of the preceding one. Thus, each experiment led to further refinements of procedure, etc. This matrix of experiments yielded a body of knowledge and an extremely powerful instrument for further analysis of the interaction between pharmacological and behavioral variables in drug dependence.

The significance of enviornmental variables controlling drug self-administration should be obvious by now. Drug infusion assumes the status of a reinforcing stimulus. Deprivation of morphine alters probability of morphine-reinforced behavior. The relative degree of deprivation also determines the tendency for the organism to emit other behaviors (e.g., food-reinforced and shock-avoidance behaviors). Thus, the presence or absence of morphine modifies behavior, but the way in which behavior is modified depends upon the environmental contingencies maintaining that behavior. In addition, environmental conditions controlling concurrent behaviors or the consequences of other behaviors may also alter the effects of the drug. Studies with low magnitudes of morphine reinforcement and with SPA, fencamfamin, *d*-amphetamine, and cocaine reinforcement, reveal that physical dependence is not a necessary condition for behavioral dependence. Interactions between the magnitude of reinforcement and value of a fixed ratio schedule of cocaine reinforcement were observed as well. Obviously, a great deal of work needs to be done to establish the parameters of the array of variables involved. The program discussed provides a basic vehicle for examination of these parameters. The host of questions rendered answerable by the use of this approach is an indication of its power.

SUMMARY

In the preceding pages two research programs illustrating drug-behavior interactions have been explored at length. These investigations represent first approximations of experimental analysis of the role of behavioral variables in two disparate drug-behavior phenomena. To the extent that the reader has begun to understand the relationship between the principles outlined in Chapters 4 and 5, and the role those principles played in designing these investigations this discussion will have been worthwhile.

Our major point is that the behavioral actions of a drug may be influenced by the interaction of that drug with any of the variables known to control operant behavior. These include all of the antecedent variables (e.g., deprivation conditions), the current stimulus circumstance, the properties of the response, and the response consequences (e.g., reinforcement). It should be clear that the sorting out of environmental influences in drug-correlated behavioral changes can be a very complex task. But when one deals with complex subject matter, complex methods are often required.

8

Predicting Behavioral Actions of Drugs in Humans

The principal impetus for the development of the field of pharmacology is the need to find drugs effective in treating human disease states. This was certainly true for the early development of behavioral pharmacology. For several obvious reasons it is impossible to use humans as test subjects for initial determinations of the effects of new drugs. Until the toxicity of a new compound is known, administration to a human would be unwarranted. Further, the pharmaceutical chemist produces thousands of new chemical compounds yearly; thousands of test subjects are needed to investigate the pharmacological properties of these agents. Finally, pharmacological measurement procedures frequently demand experimental surgery and a degree of environmental control incompatible with humanitarian principles.

For these reasons pharmacologists use infrahuman subjects for investigations of new chemical compounds. The essential problem is to select an appropriate species of test subject, and appropriate measurements, so that we can predict whether a new chemical agent possesses any clinically desirable pharmacological action. This is the problem facing the behavioral pharmacologist when he is asked to evaluate new chemicals to determine whether they produce behavioral changes that would warrant administration to humans for their further study.

The discovery of most drugs currently used to treat psychological disorders has been serendipitous. We can only hope that as behavioral pharmacology develops, systematic predictive procedures will come to replace "chance" discovery of therapeutic agents. To further this end we shall consider some of the problems and pitfalls of the various approaches to the preclinical evaluation techniques now being used in behavioral pharmacology, and suggest a constructive alternative.

SEQUENTIAL PROCESS OF DRUG EVALUATION

Let us assume that a pharmaceutical chemist has given us a newly synthesized compound to study. How would we begin to evaluate the pharmacological actions of this substance? The usual procedure is to begin with gross determinations and to conduct finer analyses only if the compound appears to possess any worthwhile pharmacological actions. These techniques have been termed "screening" procedures, the sequence of tests being analogous to finer and finer sieves. Drugs that pass through the sequence of screening are then considered for clinical evaluation in man.

Establishment of the Dosage Producing Acute Lethal Toxicity

The first step in testing a new compound is to learn whether reasonable doses of the drug possess any biological activity. The grossest test of a drug's biological activity is to determine the lethal dosage. A common procedure is to determine the drug's acute lethal toxicity by administering orally a range of dosages of the test compound to mice or rats. The subjects are observed at certain fixed time periods to determine mortality at each of the dosages. In this manner it is possible to determine the LD-50 oral dosage of a compound in a particular species. The LD-50 dosage is defined as that dosage which causes death in 50 per cent of the test subjects (see Chapter 2).

Observation of subjects frequently provides suggestions for further exploration of the biological actions of the test compound. For example, central nervous system activity would be suggested by changes in the level of locomotor activity, and by the presence of muscle tremors, ataxia, and convulsions. Standardized procedures for observing test subjects have been developed for this purpose (Irwin, 1964; Norton, 1962; Brown, 1959).

On the basis of the information thus derived it is possible to determine

(1) whether clinically practical quantities of the drug possess any biological activity, and (2) the dosage range appropriate for further evaluations of pharmacological effects.

The choice of an appropriate species for drug evaluation is complex. Ideally, the species should be genetically uniform, readily available, and economical. The species should also be easy to handle and to house. These factors must be balanced against the similarity of the species to man in its physiological response to drugs. It is sufficient to point out here that this problem is not unique to behavioral pharmacology.

Let us assume that our test compound has been found to have an LD-50 at a reasonable dosage, and that observation of the test animals reveals changes indicating that the compound is behaviorally active. Now we must proceed to the next step in the screening sequence.

Approaches to the Design of Preclinical Drug Evaluation Procedures

The general purpose of preclinical evaluation of new compounds is to determine whether any of them may be useful in the treatment of human disease conditions. Further, preclinical evaluation should yield an estimate of a compound's toxicity. Pharmacologists have evolved a variety of approaches for the design of preclinical evaluative procedures; and these approaches are outlined below, with special reference to their significance for behavioral phamacology. A subsequent section will deal with the conception of behavioral toxicity.

The Experimental Production of Homologous Pathology: The ideal procedure for predicting the effect of a drug on a given disease in man would be to produce a homologous disease state in test subjects and then to evaluate compounds on the basis of their ability to alter either the etiological conditions producing the disease or its incapacitating symptoms. For example, test subjects may be inoculated with particular lethal pathogenic bacteria, whereupon subjects pretreated with the test drug could be compared to untreated control animals as to the percentage of survivors in each group.

Such an approach demands that we understand, and be in a position to control experimentally, the generative factors of the disease condition. This approach also assumes that no qualitative differences exist between man and the experimental subjects with regard to their responses to the test compound. Of course, this supposition must be empirically verified; if we are successful in doing so, our procedure may have predictive validity for evaluating new chemical agents for the treatment of the same disease state in man. Unfortunately, the etiological factors of human psychological disorders are largely unknown. It is therefore impossible, at present, to utilize this approach to employ infrahuman subjects in evaluating the potential efficacy of new compounds in the treatment of man's psychological disorders. If the etiological factors responsible for a given form of behavioral disorder are ever isolated, this approach may become feasible.

Experimental Production of Analogous Symptoms of Pathological States: A second approach to the problem of preclinical drug evaluation involves the use of test subjects in which the *symptoms* of a disease have been produced. In this case, drugs are evaluated in terms of their ability to prevent or alleviate symptoms. Emesis (vomiting), for example, is one of the incapacitating symptoms of a variety of illnesses. In order to screen new drugs for their potential antiemetic activity, it is necessary to develop techniques for producing emesis in test subjects. Several such techniques have been developed (Borison and Wang, 1953). Since, apomorphine reliably produces emesis in dogs, test compounds could be evaluated for their ability to block apomorphine-induced emesis.

The production of analogous symptoms in test subjects has one major limitation, namely, the assumption that the symptoms produced in the test subject are controlled by the same mechanisms that are responsible for similar symptoms in man. If this assumption is not valid, however, a preclinical evaluation of drugs may not predict correctly the effects of such drugs on the same symptom in man. It has been amply demonstrated, for example, that a drug showing potent antiemetic activity by blocking apomorphine-induced emesis may not be effective in blocking emesis associated with motion sickness (Borison and Wang, 1953). In this instance, we are able to resolve such seeming discrepancies because of our knowledge of the underlying mechanism that controls this symptom. Apomorphine elicits emesis by stimulating the chemoreceptor trigger zone in the medulla, which in turn stimulates the vomiting center. Drugs, therefore, may block apomorphine-induced emesis either by blocking its effect on the chemoreceptor trigger zone or by blocking the actions of the chemoreceptor trigger zone on the medullary vomiting center. If the drug's action is on the chemoreceptor trigger zone, then it will effectively prevent emesis only when vomiting is elicited via this mechanism; when the vomiting center is stimulated directly, the same compound will be ineffective. Thus, it is necessary to employ at least two techniques for the preclinical evaluation of antiemetic activity; these techniques must correspond to the two principal mechanisms controlling the symptom.

The misuse of the analogue approach in behavioral pharmacology has been detrimental to the development of this science, since it has falsely simplified true problems. Applied glibly to infrahuman test procedures, catch labels for symptoms of psychological disorders in man have implied not only analogous behavior but identical mechanisms in test subjects and man. It should not be surprising, therefore, that such techniques have not proven to be valid predictors of the effect of a drug on man. One such procedure has been the Skinner-Estes method for producing experimental "anxiety." Clearly, anxiety is a state that can result from a variety of psychological antecedents. A search for drugs that will alleviate this incapacitating condition is very important. However, it is naïve to assume that drugs effective in alleviating the suppression of lever-pressing (conditioned suppression) will be effective in treating all kinds of anxiety in a human being. This assumption obviously rests on yet another dubious premise: that anxiety is a state controlled by only one set of variables.

Phenotypically similar behaviors hypothesized to be based on anxiety are differentially affected by drugs. For example, Geller and Seifter (1960, 1962) have shown that lever-pressing behavior suppressed by electric shock punishment is selectively increased in frequency by certain drugs; however, these same drugs have not been found to increase the lever-pressing rate when the behavior was suppressed by a stimulus preceding an unavoidable shock. These results seem discrepant only if one assumes that the suppression of both behaviors is based on a common anxiety state and that it is with this process that drugs interact. Clearly, the precise behavioral contingencies determine the effects of pharmacological agents. Kelleher and Morse (1964) provide a detailed analysis of conditioned suppression.

Standard Drug-Correlational Approach: Drugs of demonstrated clinical value in the treatment of diverse behavioral disorders can be used as *standards* to evaluate newly synthesized chemical compounds. The standard drugs are evaluated in infrahuman subjects to determine some of their more easily measured pharmacological actions. Test procedures that show differential effects among known drugs with different therapeutic applications are selected for use as a test battery. This test battery is then used to predict whether a new compound possesses any clinical applications, and to determine the area of such application. The results of the clinical evaluation of compounds selected by these test procedures can be used to assess the predictive validity of the test battery.

It should be stated explicitly that the test procedures initially chosen for a test battery need not have any face validity. That is, there need be no apparent topographical similarity to the behavioral disorders for which the drug may be clinically prescribed. Chlorpromazine has been extremely successful in diminishing the atavistic behavior of disturbed psychiatric patients; but this drug has also been successful in diminishing the scratching behavior of mice which have received mescaline intradermally. If it can be shown that the ability of drugs to block the mescaline-induced scratching of mice is correlated with their antipsychotic activity, we will have a valid test for such drugs.

Obviously, the "mescaline-scratch" test does not have any face validity; it may nonetheless be a valuable preclinical drug-evaluation procedure. Chlorpromazine is known to have some antihistaminic actions that may be related to its ability to block the mescaline-induced scratching. However, its antihistaminic actions may be unrelated to its therapeutic efficacy in controlling psychotic behavior. The use of a screening procedure based on an irrelevant action of a standard drug (e.g., the antihistaminic activity of chlorpromazine) may lead to erroneous predictions.

The question of how one goes about selecting the components of a test battery naturally occurs. The process is obviously not one of random sampling. We have previously discussed the problems associated with the homologous and analogous behavioral approaches in the development of screening procedures for behavioral pharmacology. A more systematic approach to the initial selection of test items would be based on a functional analysis of behavior.

The Selection of Preclinical Drug-Evaluation Procedures Based on a Functional Analysis of Operant Behavior

The selection of behavioral test procedures should begin with the functional analysis of behavior. Such an analysis for operant behavior has been presented in Chapters 4 and 5, in which the principal variables controlling operant behavior were described. In Chapter 6, we applied this analysis of behavior to the problem of understanding the behavioral mechanisms of drug action. In this section we shall use this analytic approach in discussing how to select revelant classes of operant behavior for inclusion in a drug-screening battery. Such classes of behavior, it will be remembered, are not defined topographically, but rather by the variables controlling them (see Chapters 4 and 5).

Our first task is to select standard drugs with proven efficacy in a variety of clinical applications. These standards should then be subjected to intensive analysis in order to determine their differential effects on a variety of classes of operant behavior. Analysis not only affords us a means of selecting the classes of behavior that differentiate these agents, it may also suggest their behavioral mechanisms of action.

Table 8.1 reviews the principal variables defining the classes of operant behavior. It would, of course, be absurd to suggest that a single investigator could implement a battery of behavioral tests representing each of these classes of behavior. This task is amplified by the necessity to study drug effects on behavior generated by a variety of parameters within each of these classes. However, such a research program is necessary if the differential effects of standard drugs are to be fully described. Examples of this type of research were presented in Chapter 7.

For purposes of drug screening, it may be possible to eliminate certain procedures that fail to discriminate among drug classes. Further, we might find several tests that will yield the same information, in which event we could decrease our battery size by discarding all but one of them. Ultimately, of course, the procedures to be retained in the test battery are those that are found to predict the behavioral effects of new chemical compounds in man.

A valid criticism of the usual use of the standard drug-correlational approach is that it leads to the discovery of new drugs that are highly simi-

Table 8.1   SEQUENTIAL PRESENTATION OF VARIABLES KNOWN TO CONTROL
OPERANT BEHAVIOR

I. Antecedent Variables
   a. Deprivation of a positive reinforcer
   b. Presentation of a negative reinforcer
   c. Withdrawal of a positive reinforcer

II. Current Stimulus Circumstances
   a. Unidentified stimuli
   b. Discriminative stimuli
   c. Receptors stimulated

III. Properties of Behavior
   a. The operandum
   b. Response topography

IV. Reinforcement
   a. Primary vs. conditioned
   b. Positive vs. negative
   c. Scheduling of contingencies

Sequential presentation of variables known to control
operant behavior. In designing a research program to
determine the behavioral effects of drugs each class of
variables should be considered, much as one considers
drug dosages, treatment time, route of administration,
etc.

lar to the standard drugs in their pharmacological actions. We have witnessed
in the past decade the "discovery" of scores of new drugs with a chlorpro-
mazine-like activity because chlorpromazine itself has been used as a standard drug for screening new chemical compounds. If the criterion for sending
a drug from the laboratory to the clinic for evaluation is its similarity to
chlorpromazine, we can hardly expect to find new drugs with different
clinical applications. It is for this reason that drugs effective in the treatment
of psychotic depressions, for example, were accidentally discovered because
of the clinical observation of an incidental effect of iproniazid in the treatment of tubercular patients.

It is difficult to resolve this dilemma. Clearly the pharmacologist must
have criteria for selecting, from thousands of new chemical compounds
shown by his screening tests to have diverse effects, those that should be
subjected to clinical evaluation. One can, therefore, rationalize the practice
of introducing new psychotherapeutic drugs into the clinic on the basis of
their similarity to standard drugs by expressing the hope that they may be
more potent and have less severe undesirable side effects.

The discovery of truly new types of psychotherapeutic drugs has been
left largely to chance, and we would like to suggest a more rational alternative to this practice—a procedure predicated on an understanding of the
ways in which drugs may affect behavior. The understanding of drug's interaction with behavior is based on a knowledge of the variables governing

behavior; and the isolation of the principal variables governing the behavior of infrahumans has led to the investigation of human behavior within the same conceptual framework. Such investigations suggest that many of the variables isolated by an analysis of infrahuman behavior control the behavior of humans in comparable ways. It may therefore be possible to demonstrate homologous relationships between the behavior of infrahumans and humans that are based upon functional rather than topographical similarity. It cannot be emphasized too strongly that we are not suggesting the development of infrahuman models with only phenotypic similarity to human behavior, but rather the establishment of truly genotypic models based on common defining features.

The development of these homologues requires the concurrent exploration of infrahuman and human behavior within the same conceptual framework. It could be argued that current limitations in our knowledge of human behavior preclude the use of this approach for selecting drugs with new behavioral actions. This is not necessarily the case, since the validity of a predictor can be verified concurrently with the development of a predictive battery (Meehl, 1965). The establishment of common drug effects on certain infrahuman and human behaviors has two results: (1) it adds to our ability to use infrahuman testing to predict the effects of a drug in humans, and (2) it suggests the homologous relation of these classes of behavior.

This approach has certain limitations. First, to the extent that unknown, genetically linked biochemical abnormalities control the human behavior under study, we will be unable to establish infrahuman behavioral homologues. Second, to the extent that the human species possesses certain unique classes of behavior, it will be impossible to develop infrahuman homologues.

Many writers now believe that certain psychotic disorders result from genetically linked biochemical abnormalities combined with specific kinds of early conditioning histories (Meehl, 1962). Clearly, any approach basing its predictive efforts *solely* on either environmental *or* biochemical influences will fail to predict clinical efficacy of new drugs for treating such disorders. One experimental approach has been to breed selectively for behavioral abnormality, with an effort to isolate the relevant biochemical and behavioral variables *post hoc.*

An alternative tactic involves ontogenetic manipulation of the biochemical integrity of the organism while concurrently subjecting the animal to various early conditioning experiences. The latter approach is typified by efforts to selectively alter the precursors and metabolic products of epinephrine, norepinephrine and serotonin, combined with specific conditioning procedures, to produce lasting behavioral changes (Kulkarni, Thompson, and Shideman, 1966; Abuzzahab, Thompson, and Shideman, 1965). Ultimately, of course, isolation of the biochemical abnormality in humans will provide the basis for creating homologous biochemical conditions in infrahuman subjects.

As to the second limitation, the existence of unique species differences in behavior is of importance to the behavioral pharmacologist only insofar as such uniqueness is central to the abnormal human behavior. Obviously, a great many behavioral differences can be demonstrated to exist among organisms. However, it is only when the factors responsible for the maladaptive behavior have no infrahuman homologue that this is a limitation. It remains to be seen whether such differences exist.

The development of preclinical drug-evaluation procedures based on a functional analysis of behavior may have another important implication to the extent that such procedures yield valid predictions about new drugs. That is, they confirm the phylogenetic continuity of the variables controlling behavior. Ultimately, usefulness of this approach in the selection of screening techniques must be empirically demonstrated; and it is to be hoped that this is the direction in which behavioral pharmacology will develop.

BEHAVIORAL TOXICITY

A second area of application of behavioral techniques to drug screening is the use of such techniques to assess the behavioral toxicity of drugs.

All drugs can have deleterious effects if they are administered at a wrong dosage, via an inappropriate route, or under wrong conditions. However, most clinically useful drugs exert an effect that is primarily desirable, entailing relatively few damaging changes. When the frequency and/or degree of such injurious effects are high, a drug is considered relatively toxic; a drug qualifies as having relatively minor toxicity if the frequency and degree of damaging effects associated with its use are low.

Often, toxic effects are manifested in some biological system other than the system that is the target of drug treatment. For example, atropine may be administered to diminish gastric secretions but it may also cause tachycardia. Iproniazid was given to tubercular patients until it was found to produce behavioral excitability and agitation. Some chemical agents have been developed specifically *because* of their toxicity, e.g., insecticides and chemical warfare substances. In such cases, the primary desired effect is either death or a graded alteration of some normal biological function.

Toxic drug effects may be structural, biochemical, or functional (Zbinden, 1963). Drug-related macroscopic and microscopic alterations of tissues or organs detectable by standard techniques are called *structural*. The term *biochemical toxicity* is restricted to drug-induced organ changes that are routinely detected by chemical methods and unaccompanied by marked anatomical changes. Certain other drug effects that are not necessary to the desired action, but may, under different circumstances, constitute an important therapeutic effect, are called *functional toxicity* if no known anatomical or biochemical basis can be identified. Such functional toxic effects are very often reversible.

Behavioral toxicity is a special case of functional toxicity. Broadly speaking, when a behavioral change associated with drug administration exceeds the normal limits of individual variability, the condition can be called behavioral toxicity. If an animal which had previously ingested fixed amounts of food on a more-or-less regular feeding cycle begins to ingest food continuously while under the influence of a drug, the drug's effect on feeding behavior may be considered toxic. Animals treated with alcohol are relatively ineffective at emitting responses necessary for obtaining positive reinforcers and terminating negative reinforcers.

Both such drug effects can appropriately be called behaviorally toxic. They also constitute examples of functional toxic effects, because we are unable to identify a specific anatomical or biochemical basis for the hyperphagia or for the alcohol-altered behavior. More specifically, behavioral toxicity must be defined in terms of the prevailing environmental conditions. If behavioral changes associated with drug administration are inappropriate under the existing environmental conditions (i.e., as compared with baseline behavior in the absence of the drug), the drug effects are behaviorally toxic. A given drug may be therapeutic for one organism under a given set of conditions but toxic to another organism under other conditions. For example, a depressed psychotic patient may attempt to commit suicide following reserpine administration, while another patient exhibiting assaultive-agitated behavior may behave more normally while receiving the drug. One effect is obviously toxic (i.e., lethal) and the other therapeutic.

Clinical psychopharmacology and clinical toxicology make use of many terms to describe the toxic effects of drugs. Atropine psychosis, psychic amphetamine dependence, and impaired ability to concentrate while under the influence of diphenylhydantoin are common clinical examples of toxic side effects. Widely used behaviorally active drugs, as well as insecticides and industrial products, produce "psychological" changes described subjectively by terms like agitation, anxiety, confusion, dizziness, drowsiness, euphoria, irritability, lightheadedness, restlessness, tiredness, and weakness. While it would be highly desirable to be able to screen drugs for behavioral toxicity in the infrahuman laboratory, it is clearly impossible to employ infrahuman methods to study such subjective phenomena. Indeed, so long as the criteria of toxicity are based on such concepts, analysis of behavioral toxicity at a basic-science level must proceed independently, and with only indirect reference to clinical toxicity.

We must hope that the data evolving from the behavioral pharmacology laboratory regarding basic behavioral toxicity will eventually be related to clinical problems. However, our purpose here is to outline several approaches to the analysis of behavioral toxicity in infrahuman subjects. Since relatively little research has been specifically directed to this problem, we will emphasize potential programs of analysis rather than review the scanty literature.

Convulsions, hypnosis, paralysis, and death are usually outside the range of concern of *behavioral* toxicity. Particular interest is invested in behavioral changes that will have serious and possibly irreversibly deleterious effects (e.g., cessation of escape or avoidance behavior, inability to perform simple visual or auditory discriminations, motor incoordination rendering the organism incapable of procuring positive reinforcers). Under toxic drug conditions, the organism may subject itself to lethal noxious stimuli, may be injured or killed because of failure to make a discriminated response, or may starve.

A second group of toxic behavioral changes results from the organism's exposure to substances having an array of toxic biochemical, physiological, and structural effects when moderate to high doses of a drug are administered, but only functional effects when lower doses are given. Heavy metals, phenolic compounds, strychnine and picrotoxin, anticholinesterase insecticides and "nerve gases," and chlorinated hydrocarbons have been reported to produce toxic behavioral changes. Sensory distortions, muscular weakness, tremors, and hypermotor activity frequently accompany exposure to low doses of these agents. If the dosage is low enough, and the duration of exposure is brief, such effects may be largely reversible; however, higher doses and long term exposure may produce irreversible damage, usually with identifiable structural changes in the nervous system.

Thus, behavioral toxicity is of specific interest (1) insofar as it can reflect the "side effects" of an agent that has a desirable therapeutic action, or (2) when the agent is believed to be toxic in a variety of ways and behavioral changes are among the more subtle indices of early poisoning.

The analysis of the behavioral side effects of drugs is no different from the analysis of the primary behavioral actions of a drug. The investigation of such untoward effects often reveals behavioral mechanisms of action that may not be immediately apparent from the primary therapeutic action. The approach previously developed, is based on a functional analysis of behavior, and provides a suitable framework for the analysis of the diversity of the effects of a drug. The behavioral mechanisms of such side effects may be revealed by specific investigations for alterations in stimulus control, changes in the response form or pattern, the response frequency and force, as well as the kind and contingencies of consequences.

Known or suspected toxins frequently have diverse and profoundly deleterious effects at high dosages. Long before these biochemical, physiological, or structural changes become apparent, the toxicity may be manifested behaviorally (e.g., Medved, Spynu, and Kagan, 1964).

By carefully selecting behavioral procedures for analysis when studying a given class of toxins, the investigator may be able to detect toxicity that would otherwise remain undetected, at least until serious irreversible damage had taken place. Moreover, such behavioral procedures can provide suggestions for further analysis of other mechanisms of action. An example is the behavioral toxicity of the insecticide DDT. Rats were trained in an S^D-S^Δ tone discrimination near the auditory threshold (so that the S^D rates

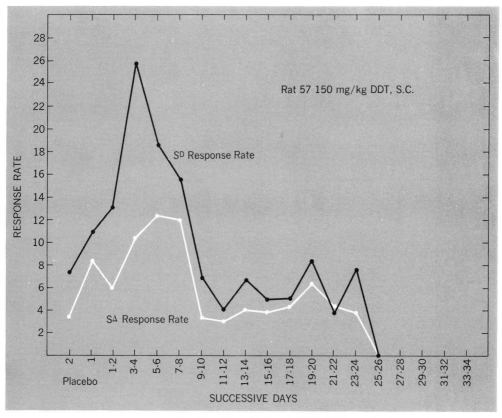

Fig. 8.1 The effects of DDT (150 mg/kg/day) subcutaneously, on an auditory discrimination in the rat. The response rate in the presence of a tone (S^D) and nontone (S^Δ) are compared over 26 days of DDT treatment. The S^D rate increased markedly, before progressively deteriorating. (Thompson and Lilja, 1964, Fig. 2)

were approximately two to three times the S^Δ rates) on a VI-1 food-reinforcement schedule. Then the animals were subjected to a chronic subcutaneous regimen of 50 mg/kg or 150 mg/kg of DDT daily, and sessions of S^D-S^Δ discrimination were continued. Figure 8.1 presents the rates during two days of placebo treatment followed by 26 to 35 days of DDT treatment. The S^D rates increased markedly in animals treated with 150 mg/kg, indicating enhanced auditory discrimination (Thompson and Lilja, 1964).

It should be obvious that the study of behavioral toxicity of drugs is simply an extension of the procedures used for the screening of new compounds. Both functions may be served by the same procedures, and in this manner it is possible to assess not only a new compound's therapeutic efficacy but its potential behavioral toxicity as well.

9

Strategy and New Directions for Research in Behavioral Pharmacology

This book is an outgrowth of the conviction that significant developments in drug-behavior research can only come about through increased intradisciplinary sophistication and tolerance by investigators in both fields. It is based on the additional premise that a systematic descriptive research tactic can be applied equally well to pharmacological and behavioral phenomena. We have attempted to develop such a descriptive research tactic for the experimental analysis of drug-behavior interactions. Of the problems that occupy large portions of research time and effort, we have emphasized those areas most extensively studied within this framework. There remain, however, several pharmacological principles and experimental models, by-and-large ignored by behavioral pharmacologists. We would like to suggest certain pharmacological approaches, outlined in Chapter 2, with specific reference here to behavioral pharmacology.

Drug Interactions: Pharmacologists frequently investigate drug interactions as a means of suggesting the site and mechanisms of drug action. Drug antagonism (Cook and Weidley, 1957; Brown, 1963) and potentiation of behavioral actions (Carlton, 1962) have received some attention, although the general exploitation of drug interactions in behavioral pharmacology has been minimal. The fact that this type of research is technically demanding and time consuming may partially account for the paucity of data in this area. Lack of familiarity with drug interactions and their significance is a more likely reason psychologists have failed to pursue this avenue of investigation.

Site of Action: When examining drug-behavior data, pharmacologists often ask, "Does the drug produce its behavioral effect because of actions on the peripheral or central nervous system?" Since most behaviorally active drugs exert both peripheral and central actions, this question is of fundamental importance to the neuropharmacologist. There are several approaches to this problem. One drug may be used to block the peripheral effects of the test drug, and a drug that possesses the same peripheral actions but does not penetrate the blood-brain barrier can be used as a control. For example, Villarreal, Schuster, and Domino (1966) demonstrated that arecoline suppresses fixed-ratio responding in rats for food reinforcement. This disruption is antagonized by atropine but not methylatropine. The peripheral actions of arecoline are blocked equally well by atropine and methylatropine. The central actions of arecoline are selectively blocked by atropine but not by methylatropine (which does not cross the blood-brain barrier). This indicates, therefore, that the actions of arecoline on fixed-ratio behavior are due to its central nervous system effects rather than to its peripheral effects. This is one example of the role that behavioral pharmacology can play in delineating the site of drug action.

Structure-Function Relations: The search for relations between chemical structure and pharmacological action has also been of major concern to pharmacologists. Such relations between structure and behavioral activity have been explored for the phenothiazine derivatives (Cook and Kelleher, 1962) but have not been systematically pursued with other classes of compounds. To the extent that fundamental behavioral processes can be found to covary with changes in chemical structure, this could be an extremely valuable line of research.

The Problem of Units of Analysis: While certain aspects of the two disciplines are already experimentally productive, other basic concepts separating them remain unresolved. One of the major stumbling blocks to communication among neurochemists, neuropharmacologists, and behavioral pharmacologists is the absence of common units of analysis. It is difficult, for example, to express any simple relation between the operant as a unit and an evoked cortical potential. The neuropharmacologist can discuss the evoked potential with a neurochemist in terms of ionic concentration fluxes. The neurochemist can communicate with the physical chemist concerning the forces regulating ionic changes. Continuity of units permits such communication and aids mutual analysis of problems. No such common units are shared by behavioral pharmacology and neuropharmacology.

From our present vantage point, it would appear that if there is a solution to this problem, it lies in further analysis of processes at the areas of greatest proximity between the two disciplines. Those who ask to have specific steps to the solution of this problem spelled out for them are really asking for an a priori answer to an empirical question. As the analytical tools of both disciplines become increasingly refined, the probability of discovering areas of interjacency will increase. This goal is dependent on the concurrent autonomous development of each of these areas, which should generate findings of inherent value in each domain.

Subjective Drug Effects: Conspicuously absent in this text has been any reference to the subjective effects of drugs. This is not wholly attributable to our stated exclusion of the vast clinical psychopharmacology literature. Rather, it reflects a basic methodological requirement of intersubjective testability. Most subjective evaluations of drug effects are interpreted as indications of mental changes rather than as changes in verbal behavior occasioned by the drug. Such mental events are uniquely accessible to the subject and cannot be confirmed by other observers. Our position is not one of isolated academic polemics then, but reflects our adherence to the fundamental requirements of any science.

This issue is of particular contemporary relevance because of increasing public and governmental interest in drugs producing sensory distortions and associated behavioral changes (e.g., LSD-25, mescaline, psilocybin). The occurrence of sensory distortions associated with drug administration is of interest to the behavioral pharmacologist only insofar as the distortions are reflected in behavioral changes. Presumably any drug with such profound subjective effects as those attributed to LSD-25 and related drugs must have associated behavioral changes. Investigators specifically interested in these drugs might profitably attempt to develop objective procedures for studying the sensory and behavioral changes commonly described as hallucinations, mystic and ecstatic experiences, "the great truth phenomenon," etc. It should be borne in mind that we are not questioning the possible therapeutic efficacy of such drugs nor the possibility that they may indeed alter sensory input; but we do question the proposed methods of analyzing these effects and the kinds of assertions based on such analyses.

Classification of Behaviorally Active Drugs: Various schemas for classifying behaviorally active drugs have been suggested but, as Chapter 3 shows, none have proven very useful to the behavioral pharmacologist. It is not our purpose to present a new classification schema, but to suggest the framework for *empirically deriving* a classification of behaviorally active drugs. This framework is based on the ways in which drugs interact with the variables controlling behavior. Thus, certain drugs may be classified together if they produce common effects on behavior that is suppressed by extinction, on the functional relation between deprivation conditions and behavior, or on behavior controlled by interval reinforcement schedules. The development of such a taxonomic scheme will result from systematic exploration of the variables outlined in Table 8.1.

EMOTION, MOTIVATION, AND BEHAVIORAL PHARMACOLOGY

In the past 50 years, the dominant approaches to an understanding of maladaptive human behavior have emphasized the "motivational" bases of behavior. It has been presumed that underlying "emotional disorders" are responsible for maladaptive behavior. As the reasoning goes, any treatment that effectively changes maladaptive behaviors must act on the underlying "motivational" and/or "emotional" mechanisms. Some of the inadequacies of this general approach have been discussed in several contexts throughout this book, but these problems have not been dealt with explicitly in detail. Our purpose here is to examine an exemplary group of behaviors shown to be modifiable by drugs, and very often said to be based on internal motivational conditions. This example will serve to illustrate the basic problems, with explanations of drug effects based on hypothesized motivational-emotional mechanisms; it will also elucidate the general tactical foundations of descriptive behavioral pharmacology.

One of the principal clinical applications of behaviorally active drugs is the control of aggressive and destructive behavior in psychiatric patients; and the ways in which various types of aggressive behavior are altered by drugs have consequently been the subject of numerous infrahuman investigations. However, because of the great diversity of behaviors generically described as aggressive, the validity of making direct comparisons of drug effects across types of aggressive behavior becomes questionable. In order to evaluate in a meaningful way any study of the effects of a drug on a particular type of aggressive behavior, it is essential that we understand the type of behavior under consideration, and the variables that control it. The basic scheme for the classification of behavior outlined in Chapter 5 provides a useful framework for this analysis of aggressive behavior.

The term "agonistic behavior" encompasses a broad class of responses—attack, threat, appeasement, and flight, among others. Aggressive behavior is a subclass of agonistic responses, usually limited to threat and attack (Verplanck, 1957). Much of the ambiguity associated with discussions of aggressive behavior arises because the term is frequently used to refer to responses that *accompany* threat and attack without, perhaps, being necessary parts of such behaviors.

A rat will bite and gnaw at the lever in a conditioning chamber during extinction of a food-reinforced response, and a monkey will bite a hard rubber tube placed in front of it, although these behaviors have no contingent relation to reinforcement (Hutchinson, Azrin, and Hake, 1966). (See Fig. 9.1.) If another animal is available, the biting will be directed at the second animal, and fighting will ensue. Similarly, fighting cocks will learn to emit operant responses that lead to the presentation of a visual image of another fighting cock (Fig. 9.2). The subject exhibits a characteristic unconditioned aggressive threat in the presence of the image of the intruding male; and

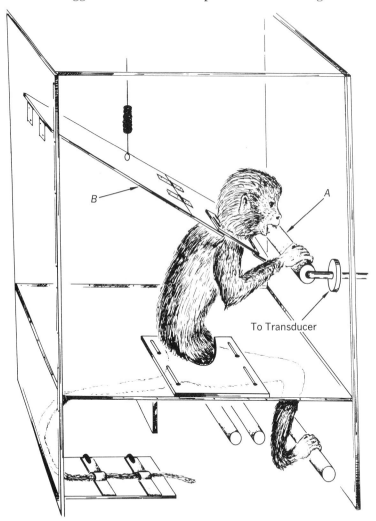

Fig. 9.1   Device for measuring aggressive biting responses in the squirrel monkey. A hard rubber tube (A) is connected via tubing to a pressure transducer to detect biting responses elicited by painful tail-shock. (Hutchinson, Azrin, and Hake, 1966, p. 234, Fig. 1)

the conditioned operant behavior that leads to the aggressive-threat behavior might also be considered aggressive behavior.

A moment's reflection reveals that it would be truly remarkable if any given behaviorally active drug affected these several "aggressive" behaviors in comparable ways. It should be obvious that the diversity of factors controlling these behaviors could be sufficient to produce quite different results. Whatever effects might be obtained could be interpreted only if we understood the variables controlling a particular class of responses. By specifying how a given class of aggressive behavior is measured and what major variables control it, the analysis of drug effects begins to take on meaning.

Unconditioned Aggressive Behavior

Reflex Aggressive Responses: Presentation of a painful stimulus to an array of animals elicits a relatively simple and stereotyped attack directed at any other animal in immediate proximity (O'Kelly and Steckle, 1939; Ulrich and Azrin, 1962; Ulrich, Wolff, and Azrin, 1964). (See Fig. 5.3.) The basic factors controlling such reflexive fighting have been explored in depth by Azrin, Ulrich, and coworkers in an excellent series of experiments (1962–1965). Because of this parametric foundation, we are now in a position to approach more systematically the changes in reflexive fighting associated with drug administration. When the interaction of drug variables with the array of behavioral variables that controls fighting has been explored, earlier findings (e.g., Tedeschi, *et al.*, 1959) should be more meaningful. This exploration will take much the same form as the systematic investigations of mechanisms controlling food-reinforced, variable-interval performance outlined in the preceding chapter.

Similar unconditioned reflexive fighting occurs when animals which have been isolated are placed together. Presentation of any intense stimulus, or mere contact between two such animals, will elicit fighting (Yen, Stanger, and Millman, 1959). Such "isolation-induced" aggressive behavior has been used as a baseline for the analysis of the effects of reserpine and chlorpromazine.

Another class of aggressive responses, somewhat less reflexive, is associated with time-out from positive reinforcement. The notion that the discontinuation or withdrawal of positive reinforcement is associated with aggressive behavior is not at all new. However, there have been no explicit experimental analyses of this relationship until relatively recently. Azrin, Hutchinson, and Hake (1965) clarified matters considerably by subjecting pigeons to brief extinction periods and measuring pecking responses against a stuffed pigeon mounted in the test chamber. Thompson and Bloom (1966) made a similar observation about hooded rats; they also found that there was a consistent relation between "bursts" of the previously food-reinforced lever-pressing

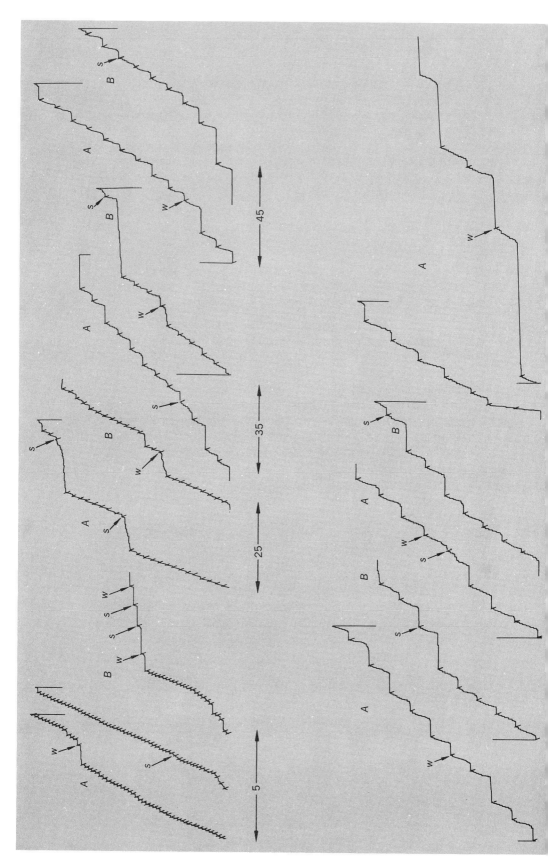

Fig. 9.2 Sample cumulative records for Birds A and B at fixed-ratio values of 5, 25, 35, 45, 55, 65, and 75. All reinforcements were food except those indicated by an arrow and the letters W (water) and S (social). (Thompson, 1964, p. 48, Fig. 2)

early in extinction and the tendency for one rat to attack another (Fig. 5.4). As discussed earlier, these bursts of activity during extinction, which covary with aggressive behavior, have been used to analyze the effects of chlorpromazine, thioridazine, pentobarbital (Thompson, 1961, 1962), and reserpine (Kulkarni, Thompson, and Shideman, 1966). (See Fig. 9.3.)

Aggressive Fixed-Action Patterns: The relatively simple reflexive responses are to be contrasted with complex sequences of threat and attack behaviors elicited by the highly specific stimulus configuration of another orga-

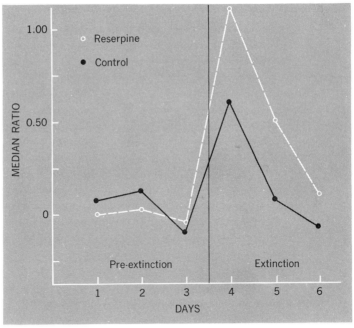

Fig. 9.3 Effect of reserpine on extinction-induced rate increase in the rat. Reserpine, 0.5 mg/kg was administered 18 to 24 hours before the first extinction (Day 4) and again at a dose of 0.1 mg/kg at the same time before the second and third extinctions (Days 5 and 6). Each point represents the median of nine controls on seven reserpine animals. Reserpinized animals exhibit relatively greater rate increase than nonreserpinized subjects. (Kulkarni, Thompson, and Shideman, 1966)

nism. Such fixed-action patterns are highly stereotyped, are observable in most members of the species, and tend to occur as unitary sequences of responses. The complex unconditioned display and attack behaviors of Siamese fighting fish (Walaszek and Abood, 1956; Abrahamson and Evans, 1954) have been employed to study the actions of drugs. The selective disruption of aggressive behavior patterns, as opposed to generalized alteration of a great diversity of behaviors, is crucial for this line of research, but unfortunately such selective alteration has not been adequately demonstrated.

Conditioned Aggressive Behavior

Classically Conditioned Aggressive Behavior: It has been shown that certain aspects of aggressive-display behaviors in fish can, following classical conditioning, be elicited by a previously ineffective stimulus (Adler and Hogan, 1963; Thompson and Sturm, 1965). (See Fig. 9.4.) Certain components of mammalian aggressive behavior can be classically conditioned (Vernon and Ulrich, 1966); and aggressive behavior in Japanese quail has been classically conditioned (Farris, 1966).

One might reasonably expect drugs to have differential effects on classically conditioned aggressive responses and unconditioned behaviors, much as drugs differentially affect other conditioned and unconditioned reflexes. There are obvious advantages to using conditioned aggressive responses rather than aggressive behavior elicited by an unconditioned releasing stimulus. Actual fighting, with concomitant damage and subsequent behavioral change, is more likely with presentation of the unconditioned stimulus. Further, conditioned aggressive behavior would, in all likelihood, be more susceptible to alteration by drugs than would unconditioned aggressive behavior (i.e., the conditioned behavior would be more labile and sensitive). Finally, it is possible to study the effects of drugs on the acquisition and extinction of conditioned aggressive behavior, while unconditioned behavior tends to occur at its optimal level on almost the first presentation of the unconditioned stimulus.

Operant-Conditioned Aggressive Behavior: When an aggressive response is strengthened by the consequences of that response, it is appropriate to say that it has been reinforced. A dominant animal which attacks a more submissive animal, thereby gaining access to food or the opportunity to mate, is reinforced for the aggressive behavior, increasing the likelihood of recurrence of that behavior. Reynolds, Catania, and Skinner (1963) have shown that it is possible to reinforce a food-deprived pigeon for emitting aggressive responses by following such behavior with food presentation.

Under some conditions, operants that are not face-valid aggressive can be strengthened by providing the opportunity to engage in other aggressive behavior. For example, Myer and White (1965) found that some hooded rats would learn a T-maze when reinforced by the opportunity to kill mice. These findings are related to work by Thompson (1963) and Thompson and

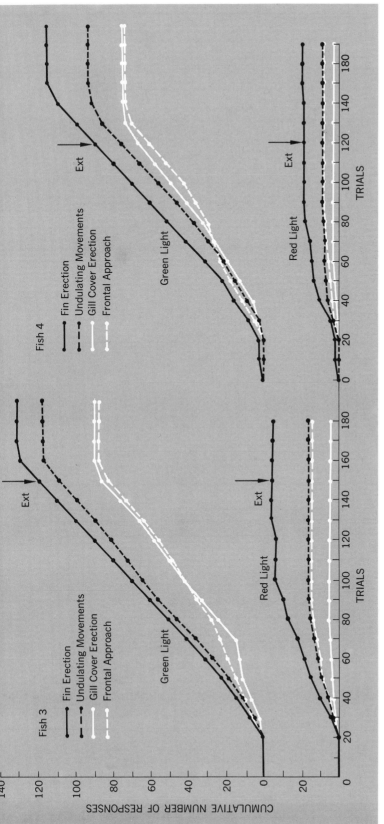

Fig. 9.4 Discriminative classical conditioning of four components of a previously unconditioned aggressive display in male Siamese fighting fish. The fish were trained in blocs of ten trials in which a green light was presented, followed by a mirror (unconditioned stimulus), or a red light that was never followed by the unconditioned stimulus. The unconditioned display responses to the subjects' mirror images included fin erection, undulating movements, gill cover erection, and frontal approach. (Thompson and Sturm, 1965, p. 403, Fig. 6)

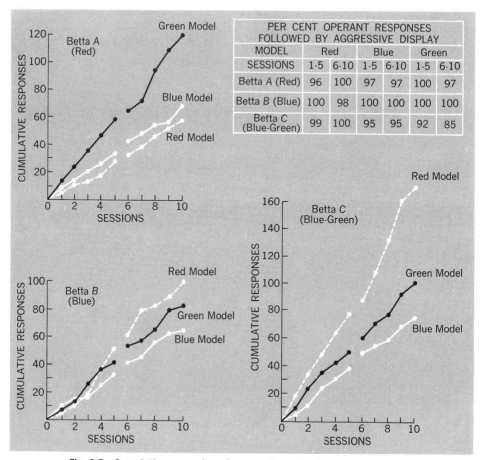

Fig. 9.5 Cumulative records of operant swimming responses reinforced by the presentation of a model of another male Siamese fighting fish. The reinforcing effectiveness of the model was found to vary with the coloration of the model as it related to the color of the subject. The table inset indicates the percentage of model presentations followed by aggressive display. (Thompson and Sturm, 1965, p. 343, Fig. 2)

Sturm (1965), who found that male Siamese fighting fish would learn to emit an operant reinforced by the presentation of a model or the mirror image of another male Siamese fish, during which period the subject would engage in aggressive-display behavior (Fig. 9.5). Azrin, Hutchinson, and McLaughlin (1965) found that squirrel monkeys will learn to emit an operant response that leads to the opportunity to bite a hard rubber ball during presentation of a stimulus previously associated with painful electric shock.

To the best of our knowledge, none of the operant behaviors maintained by the opportunity to engage in attack or threat behavior, and none of the aggressive responses that have been maintained by other reinforcers have been used as behavioral baselines for drug studies.

This very brief examination of one of the more common types of "emotional" behavior modified by drugs reveals that applying a single name to all of such behaviors implies an underlying simplicity, which is misleading. Further, an understanding of the causes of the several types of aggressive behavior is not advanced by reification; nor does attributing further hypothetical properties to the presumed internal motivational state increase our knowledge of the basic condition. Indeed, pursuit of a unitary motivational basis of all aggressive responses is an act of faith—an act of faith tending to generate ineffective research. If a common denominator of a given class of emotional behavior exists, it should become apparent through the analysis of variables controlling the behavior. If the data fail to reveal a unitary basis, we at least have an understanding of some of the factors with which drugs may interact to alter the responses under consideration. Thus, this approach does not deny the existence of emotional or motivational states, but directs attention to the measurable antecedent of such states and the associated behavioral changes.

Critics of this descriptive approach to behavioral effects of drugs find it superficial, "know nothing," and grossly oversimplified. Descriptive behavioral pharmacology *is* superficial to the extent that it deals exclusively with observables; it is "know nothing" to the extent that it does not claim to know anything that can't be replicated by independent observers; and it is oversimplified to the extent the world is simple. Advocates of this admittedly modest approach are content to add descriptive links to the body of knowledge relating drugs to behavior. The power of this tactic derives from the concurrent discovery of new relations while strengthening established relations by systematic replication.

APPENDIX *1*

Pharmacological Section

Students unfamiliar with pharmacology frequently ask several questions of a very practical nature: (1) How does one go about calculating drug dosages and preparing drug solutions? (2) Where can I find a description of methods of administering drugs via various routes? (3) What are some key sources of information regarding drugs?

Calculating Drug Dosages

The standard procedure for expressing drug dosage is in milligrams of drug per kilogram of the animal's body weight. For example, if a 250 gram rat received 7.5 milligrams of sodium pentobarbital intraperitoneally, the dosage would be expressed as 30 mg/kg I.P. It may be helpful for the student to learn a simple procedure for converting dosage in mg/kg, into a solution concentration and volume for a particular subject. In this method, a single drug concentration is prepared for all subjects used in a given experiment, and the volume administered is varied according to variation in body weight of individual subjects by the following steps:

1. Calculate in milligrams the total amount of drug the lightest and heaviest animals must receive.

   If, for example, the desired dosage is 5 mg/kg and the subjects range from .200 kg. to .400 kg. the heaviest animal should receive 2.0 mg. and the lightest 1.0 mg.

2. Prepare the solution so that the animal's body weight in kg. can be directly converted into cc.'s of solution.

   The animal weighing .200 kg. should receive .200 cc. and the animal weighing .400 kg. should receive .400 cc. Thus, .200 cc. must contain 1.0 mg. of the drug, and .400 cc. should contain 2.0 mg. To accomplish this, a 5.0 mg/cc solution must be prepared $\left(\dfrac{0.2}{1.0} \text{ or } \dfrac{0.4}{2.0}\right)$.

3. When administering the drug, the volume injected in cc.'s should equal the animal's weight in kilograms (or a simple multiple of it).

   If, rat #46 in the above example weighs .318 kg., it should receive .318 cc. of drug solution.

The student may find it helpful to pursue another example with an entirely different weight range. We might wish to give monkeys ranging in weight from 3.8 to 7.2 kilograms 25 mg/kg of a drug.

1. The lightest animal should receive 95.0 mg. (3.8 kg. × 25 mg/kg) and the heaviest animal should receive 180.0 mg. (7.2 kg. × 25 mg/kg).

2. The animal weighing 3.8 kg. should receive .38 cc. (multiply weights by .10), while the animal weighing 7.2 kg. should receive .72 cc. Thus, .38 cc. must contain 95 mg. and .72 cc. should contain 180. To accomplish this, a 250 mg/cc solution must be prepared $\left(\dfrac{95}{.38} \text{ or } \dfrac{180}{.72}\right)$.

3. When administering the drug, the volume injected in cc.'s should equal one tenth the animal's weight in kilograms. For example, a monkey weighing 4.9 kg. should receive .49 cc. of the drug solution.

Methods for Administering Drugs

Some of the basic principles considered in drug administration were discussed in Chapter 2, however certain practical matters relating to methods of introducing drugs were only alluded to.

Our purpose here is to provide an illustrated description of the actual mechanics introducing the drug via several of the more commonly used routes.

Depending on the route of administration, one of several commercially available instruments will be necessary for introducing a drug into an animal. The basic method consists of inserting a hollow tube or shaft into the intended site of application of the drug. The drug is forced into this area of the body by a manual or motor-operated pump mechanism.

The hollow tubes used for passing the drug to the site of administration are needles, catheter tubing, or combinations of needles and tubing. The most commonly used procedures employ a hypodermic needle in combination with a manually operated syringe. Needles vary in length, diameter, and bevel of the point. All needles are made of rustless metal; they vary in length from 1/2 to 3 inches, and in standard gauge from 27 to 13. The higher the gauge, the smaller the bore of the needle. Longer needles are required for intramuscular injection. Larger diameter needles may be necessary when the skin through which the needle must pass is particularly tough, or if the suspension being administered is especially viscous. Smaller needles are generally used for intravenous administration, although large vessels can receive needles appropriate to the vessel size. The bevel of the needle is either regular or short bevel. Regular bevel needles are almost always used; when entering a very small vessel, however, it may be better to use a short bevel needle.

There are permanent syringes made of Pyrex which is autoclavable, and also disposable instruments of sterile plastic. Most single-injection procedures (e.g., anesthesia, local anesthetic, antibiotic administration) can be done completely satisfactorily with a presterilized disposable syringe. For many purposes, it is as economical to use a disposable syringe only once as it is to clean and resterilize a glass syringe. At least one manufacturer produces disposable glass cartridges prefilled with a drug, or sterile water for injection; a steel plunger mechanism is used for emptying the cartridge.

Syringes, in general, consist of a hollow tube with a tight-fitting plunger. The needle is attached to the end of the syringe opposite the plunger. Several types of needle-syringe attachments are possible; and each has advantages for certain purposes. Some have lock mechanisms, insuring that the needle will always withdraw from the tissue, rather than become disengaged from the end of the syringe. Plain ground glass tips, however, are usually less expensive. Most of the disposable plastic syringes are presterilized. Figure A-1 shows a variety of commonly used syringes. The tuberculin syringe is most widely used with small animals (mice and rats), while the 5 cc. intramuscular and hypodermic syringe is more commonly used in working with larger animals, such as dogs or monkeys.

When drugs are chronically infused via an intravenous drip or a pump, a catheter tube is surgically inserted and tied in a vessel. Three types of tub-

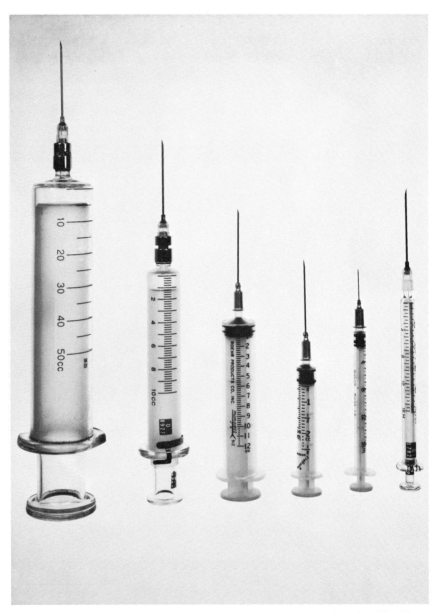

Fig. A.1 Glass and disposable plastic syringes used for drug administration. The 50 cc. syringe on the left is most commonly motor driven, while the other syringes are often hand operated. The sizes in this photograph are from 1.0 cc. to 50 cc.

ing are commonly used: polyethylene, Teflon, and silicone rubber. Polyethylene melts easily and is fairly easy to work with. The material is available in a wide range of outside and inside diameters. Teflon tubing is relatively stiff, kinks very easily, and is generally difficult to work with; its primary advantage is that blood tends not to adhere to the tubing, thus clotting is minimized. Silicone rubber tubing is pliable, has very little clotting tendency and virtually no tissue-irritating properties. In addition, it is autoclavable.

Several types of infusion pumps, permitting intermittent or continuous infusion, are commercially available. They fall into two major categories: (1) Pumps that displace the drug by driving the plunger of a syringe into the stationary barrel, and (2) pumps that force the drug through a pliable tube by pressing along the outside wall of the tube. The former type of pump usually employs a worm gear to drive the plunger at a fixed motor speed.

Another variation on the syringe pump involves driving the plunger by evolving a gas within a fixed enclosed volume behind the plunger. The rate of gas production is determined by the voltage applied to the electrodes in the gas-producing chamber.

The finger or roller type of pump does not actually come into contact with the solution, but rather forces the drug through a pliable tube. Manufacturers make available a variety of pumps that operate on this principle, ranging from small battery-operated pumps to large pumps for larger volumes.

Routes of Administration

Oral: Figure A-2 shows a rat being given an oral dose of a drug. A long, large gauge hypodermic needle (e.g., #14) is given a ball tip. This can be

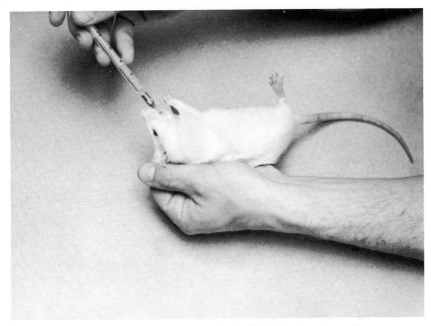

Fig. A.2 Technique for orally administering drugs to a rat.

accomplished by cutting off the tip of a needle and forming a ball of solder on the tip, making certain that the lumen of the needle is unobstructed. The four- to five-inch shaft of the needle is curved approximately 20°. The experimenter holds the rat in one hand, to restrict head and leg movement. The ball tip of the needle is gently inserted into the animal's mouth, over the tongue, and pushed gently downward. Once in the esophagus, there should be little or no resistance, and the drug can be slowly expelled from the syringe into the stomach. If the animal gags or coughs, the fluid may be entering the lungs. Obviously, further injection could be very dangerous to the animal, so the needle should be immediately withdrawn.

Subcutaneous: In depositing a small volume of a drug solution under the skin, it is necessary to restrain the animal adequately before attempting to inject the drug. Figure A-3 shows a rat being held down on a table—one hand holds the jaws closed; the other remains free for inserting the needle. Once the animal is restrained, the skin on the back is pinched between the

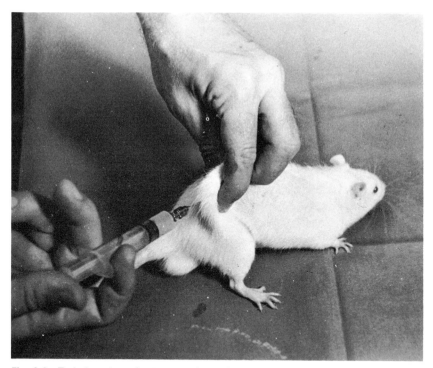

Fig. A.3 Technique for subcutaneous drug administration in the rat. The loose skin on the back is pinched between thumb and first two fingers of one hand, and needle is inserted under the skin between the fingers and thumb. Ordinarily the animal's head would be restrained by wrapping it in a towel; or the experimenter would use a gloved hand to avoid having the animal turn around and bite during the injection.

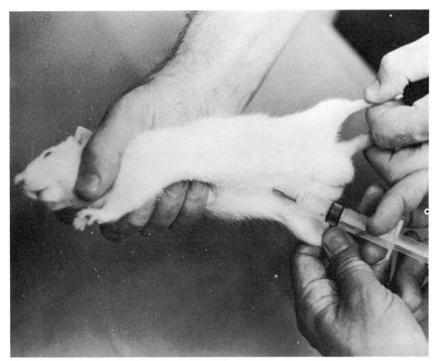

Fig. A.4 Technique for intraperitoneal administration in the rat. The subject's head is restrained and the abdomen stretched taut. The needle is inserted off the midline approximately halfway between the bottom rib and pelvis at a 45° angle.

thumb and index finger. The experimenter then grasps the barrel of the syringe, inserts a 20 to 25 gauge needle under the skin with a rapid thrust, quickly depresses the plunger, and withdraws the needle. Since subcutaneous administration is usually painful, it is of some importance that the injection itself be executed rapidly, and the needle withdrawn quickly.

Intraperitoneal: Figure A-4 shows a rat receiving an intraperitoneal drug injection. There are several common methods of restraining the animal. In this photograph, a rat's legs are held apart so that the subject's abdominal wall is stretched taut. A short needle (1/2 inch) is inserted in the lower abdomen with a quick, straight thrust. (Before depressing the plunger, withdraw slightly to make certain that the tip of the needle is not in a blood vessel or in a fluid-filled cavity such as the intestine or bladder.) 24 or 25 gauge needles are usually satisfactory for work with rats.

Intramuscular: Usually, intramuscular injections are given to larger animals—cats, monkeys, or dogs—although rats and mice can be given I.M. injections as well. Figure A-5 shows a monkey receiving an intramuscular injection of a drug solution. A suitably large muscle mass is found (in the

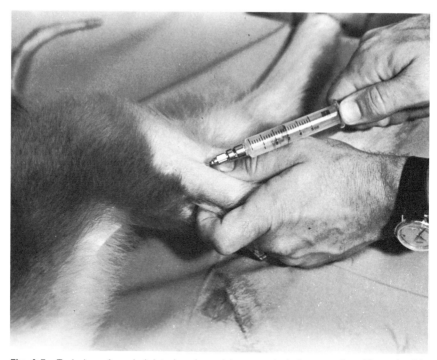

Fig. A.5 Technique for administering drugs intramuscularly to a monkey. The animal is well restrained and the site of administration has been shaved and scrubbed with alcohol. The needle is inserted at a 45–90° angle with a rapid thrust. In this figure, negative pressure is being placed on the syringe to establish that the needle is not in the lumen of a blood vessel.

monkey, usually the gluteus maximus), and squeezed firmly between the thumb and first two or three fingers of the left hand. The needle (20 to 25 gauge) is inserted with a thrust, deep into the muscle mass. Slight negative pressure is then applied to the plunger to determine whether the tip of the needle is in a blood vessel. If so, the needle is withdrawn and reintroduced in another location. If not, the plunger is depressed rapidly and the needle withdrawn. With a large animal, it is often desirable to have an assistant hold the limb of the animal while the drug is being administered.

Intravenous: Figure A-6 shows a monkey receiving an intravenous injection of a drug. The hair has been shaved from the skin of the area covering the vein and the skin has been scrubbed with an alcohol sponge. A tourniquet is placed proximal to the site of intended injection, and the vein is allowed to distend and become readily visible. If the vein is small, it may be desirable to use a scalp vein needle (#25) which can be inserted into very minute vessels. Larger veins can be approached directly with a standard needle attached to the syringe.

The flat bevel of the needle should be facing up when the lumen of the vein to be entered is relatively large in relation to the needle. If the vein is small, and the lumen is thought to be approximately the same size as the outside diameter of the needle, entry should be made with the bevel facing downward. In the former case, insertion through the skin is faster, and less painful. However, if the vein is too small, the needle may only partially enter the lumen or pass directly through. Reversing the bevel has the advantage of causing the flat bevel to slide along the inferior wall of the vessel rather than passing through.

The needle is inserted under the skin first, then, with a second very short thrust, introduced into the lumen of the vein with a slight downward pressure. The needle should be kept as closely parallel to the vein as possible when making the second insertion; and the thumb should be placed on the plunger of the syringe, maintaining a very slight negative pressure. When the needle is in the lumen of the vein, blood should come freely back into the syringe. Then, holding the barrel securely, slowly depress the plunger.

If a bubble begins to develop under the skin at the tip of the syringe as

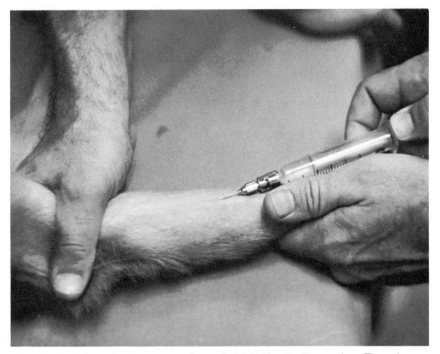

Fig. A.6 Technique for intravenous drug administration to the monkey. The vein was palpated, then the area was shaved and scrubbed. The blood return has been occluded proximal to the site of administration causing the vein to distend. The needle is kept as closely parallel to the vessel as possible, and inserted first under the skin, then into the vessel. Location in the vessel is established by free movement of blood back into the syringe as negative pressure is applied.

you inject, indicating that the needle tip is outside the vein and the drug is being injected into the perivascular tissue you should stop immediately, withdraw the needle, and attempt to reintroduce it further up the limb or change to a different vein.

Sources of Pharmacological Information

The Pharmacopeia of the United States (U.S.P.), The United States Pharmacopeial Convention, Mack Publishing Co., Easton, Pa. A periodically revised compendium of medicinal substances of demonstrated therapeutic value, providing standards of therapeutic usefulness; prescribing tests for identity, quality, and purity of drugs; and insuring uniformity in physical properties and active constituents of drugs. Information provided: recommended human dosage ranges and routes of administration, chemical name and structure, synonyms, preparations, assay procedures, solubility properties, and general distinguishing physical characteristics. Now in the 15th revision.

National Formulary (N.F.), American Pharmaceutical Association, Washington, D.C. The N.F. establishes and proclaims standards of official drugs and unofficial preparations used for medicinal purposes; the latter differ from official drugs primarily in proportions and unimportant therapeutic characteristics. This standard differs from the *Pharmacopeia* in that the criteria for including drugs are not only therapeutic efficacy, but also extent of use. Since it is primarily designed for use by pharmacists, information of value in compounding prescriptions is emphasized.

New Drugs, American Medical Association Council on Drugs, formerly *New and Non-official Drugs* (N.N.D.), American Medical Association, Chicago, Ill., 1965. An annual publication containing descriptions of drugs proposed for human use in the diagnosis, prevention, or treatment of disease. Descriptions are limited to drugs available in the United States that have been, for the most part, introduced within the last ten years. *New Drugs* does not "approve" or "accept" drugs, but rather attempts to present an authoritative and objective evaluation of therapeutic agents, primarily for the use of physicians. Information provided: nonproprietary name, commercial name, chemical or biological identity, actions and uses, limitations, adverse reactions and contraindications, dosages, and routes of administration, preparations, and known sources of supply.

Drug Dosage in Laboratory Animals: A Handbook, C. D. Barnes and L. G. Eltherington, University of California Press, Berkeley, Calif., 1965. A handbook of pharmacodynamic and toxicologic dosage information covering intravenous, intraperitoneal, intramuscular, subcutaneous, and oral routes of administration of representatives of major drug groups. Data are presented for mice, rats, guinea pigs, rabbits, cats, dogs, and monkeys. Drug responses are classified according to toxicity data, primary and secondary uses. Median lethal dosages (LD-50's) and minimum lethal dosages (MLD's) are expressed in milligrams per kilogram of body weight. This is undoubtedly the most valuable, practical reference source for experimenters concerned with actions of drugs in infrahuman mammals.

Psychopharmacological Agents, Vols. I and II., M. Gordon, Academic Press, N.Y., 1964. These two volumes of this key reference work describe the history, synthesis, pharmacological activity, *in vivo* distribution and metabolic rate, analytical methods, and clinical application of the major behaviorally active drugs. Each chapter deals with a different class of drugs and was written by the discoverer or developer of that class of agents. These books are without question the most exhaustive and authoritative source of information regarding the medicinal chemistry of behaviorally active drugs.

APPENDIX 2
Behavioral Section

CUMULATIVE RECORDS

Throughout this book, records of the behavior of various animals are presented graphically as cumulative response records. To interpret this information meaningfully, the reader must know how to read such records. All commercially manufactured cumulative recorders operate in basically the same way, although paper feed rates and response-step sizes may vary. Recorders have three basic parts: (1) a constant-rate paper feed which drives the paper from a roll inside the recorder over a drum; (2) a response-step pen, which writes from the bottom to the top of the paper, moving upward by fixed increments as each response is made; and (3) an event-marker pen, which simply moves a fixed distance whenever an event occurs, then returns to its previous position. Since the paper moves at a constant speed, and since each response causes the response-step pen to move upward one discrete step, the resulting record looks like a series of stair steps. The response-step pen is also capable of making another mark, a diagonal slash that usually indicates the presentation of a reinforcer.

Figure A-7 schematically indicates the three basic parts of a cumulative recorder. Notice that the response pen returns to the bottom of the chart automatically when it has reached the top of the paper, leaving a straight line across the chart. When the pen rapidly drops from the top to the bottom of the paper, or when it is automatically returned to the bottom of the chart on an electrical command from control equipment, it is said that the pen has *reset.* Frequently the response-step pen is reset at the end of every stimulus period, or after reinforcement on a chained schedule. In this way, the reset of the pen can facilitate demarcation of various experimental procedures, thus making the record more readable.

The response-step size on most cumulative recorders is small enough so that the stair-step appearance of the records is not apparent except on detailed scrutiny. Some commercially available recorders require 500 steps to cross the chart paper, making individual responses difficult to distinguish. However, the properties of the cumulative records in which we are most often interested are not individual responses, but rather larger behavioral units. Scallops, over-all rate changes, rate changes from one stimulus period to another, etc. are of greater concern than the step-to-step changes. As we shall see, when data of the latter order of magnitude are of primary concern, other methods of recording are required.

Figure A-8 presents a sample cumulative record in which responses are indicated both cumulatively and as discrete events on the baseline. The advantages of the cumulative record are immediately apparent. The event-

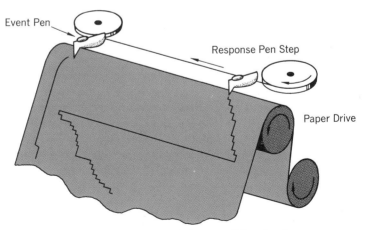

Fig. A.7 Schematic diagram of the essential parts of a cumulative recorder.

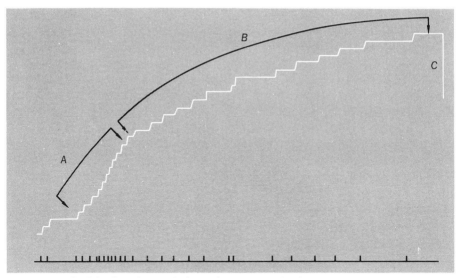

Fig. A.8 Sample cumulative and events records of lever-pressing responses, illustrating the advantage of a cumulative record for immediate access to response rate. During the period designated A, rate was relatively constant; negative curvature during B reveals progressively decreasing rate such as might be obtained during satiation or extinction. The pen resets at C.

marker permits one to discern that the rates for the periods marked A and B differ. However, the fact that the rate was relatively constant during A and negatively accelerated during B isn't as obvious. Finer analysis of the A period indicates a slight positive acceleration in the cumulative record. This information could only be detected by measuring the distance between successive responses on the events record, and plotting them graphically. This is a relatively simple case, and has been magnified for detail.

Figure A-9 presents three schematized cumulative response records of performance on three intermittent reinforcement schedules. In this case the details of individual steps are not discernible because much larger samples of behavior are under consideration. The top record (1) is characteristic of fixed-ratio performance. Typically, there are two response-rate conditions during well-established fixed-ratio responding: (A) virtually no responding during the *postreinforcement pause*, alternating with a *running rate* (B), characteristic of a particular animal under given experimental conditions. Reinforcement is indicated by the diagonal slash (C). The second record (2) is typical of well-trained fixed-interval performance. Instead of the rather discrete rate change from the postreinforcement pause to the running rate, a more gradual increase over the interval occurs, with the maximum rate in evidence at the time of reinforcement. The positively accelerated record is called a *scallop* (D), and varies considerably with deprivation conditions and drug effects. The third record in Fig. A-9 illustrates characteristic performance on a DRL schedule. Response rate is zero (E), or approximately zero, during the interval, with one or two responses occurring after the interval has elapsed.

The examples presented in Fig. A-9 were called "typical." They should be described more accurately as abstractions from many records of "idealized" performance: all variables were under excellent control, and the behavior had stabilized. Often, early in training or following a change in an experimental procedure, alterations in the properties of the cumulative record occur. Figure A-10 presents two examples of such changes. The upper record (1) shows fixed-ratio performance following a relatively large increase in ratio size. *"Knees"* (a) and *pausing* (b) tend to occur under such condi-

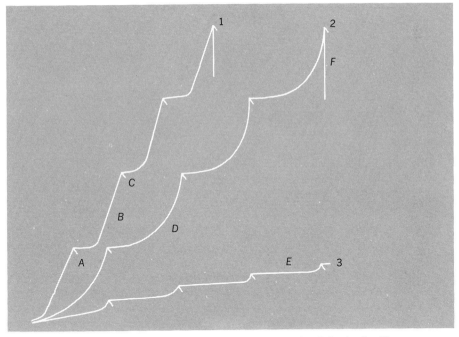

Fig. A.9 Sample cumulative records of fixed-ratio (1), fixed-interval (2), and DRL (3) performance. The characteristic postreinforcement pause can be seen at A, alternating with a high running rate (B). Reinforcement is indicated by the diagonal slash of the pen (C). Gradually increasing rate during the interval on an FI schedule produces smooth scallops such as that indicated at D. The pen resets at F. On a DRL schedule, no responses are emitted during the interval producing a flat curve (E), and a single response occurs at the end of the interval.

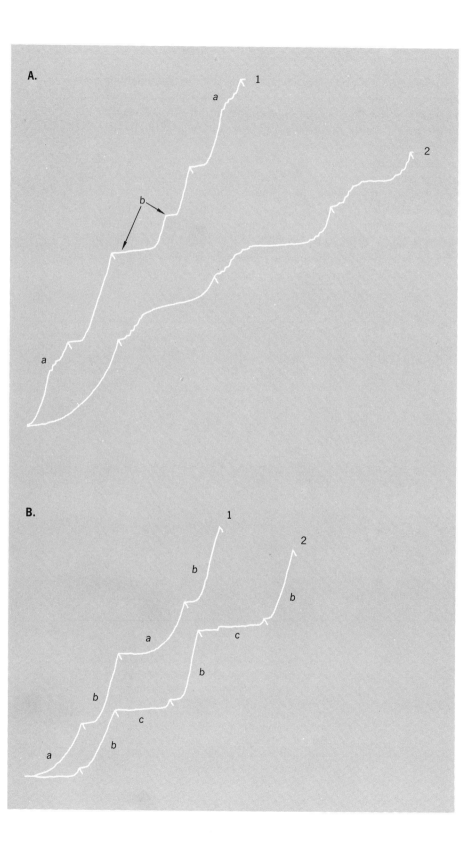

tions; the changed performance is described as "strained." *Strained ratios* may also be in evidence under the influence of certain drugs, possibly indicating the way in which the drug alters behavior.

The second record (2) of fixed-interval performance might have been obtained from an animal which had previously been trained on a ratio schedule, or possibly a previously stabilized interval performance under the influence of *d*-amphetamine. There is very little pausing after reinforcement —in fact, the animal exhibits a small postreinforcement pause and begins to approach a running rate again, suggestive of ratio performance.

Under more complex experimental conditions, changes from one component of a schedule to another are revealed most dramatically by changes in the cumulative record. The upper record in Fig. A-10 presents multiple FI-FR performance. Notice that the scallop characterisitc of fixed-interval performance occurs during periods marked 1; and postreinforcement pause, followed by a constant high rate, occurs during ratio periods (2). Selective drug effects on these two performances might be revealed by changes in one or the other, like those illustrated in the simple schedule case in Fig. A-9. The second record (2) in Fig. A-10 presents multiple FR-DRL, with the FR periods marked 3 and the DRL periods indicated with a 4. This example clearly shows alternative periods of essentially no responding, and high rates.

APPARATUS INFORMATION

The development of a refined behavioral science has been made possible to a considerable degree by the availability of more precise automated instruments for the control and measurement of behavioral events. The proliferation of electromechanical and electronic devices for analyzing behavior has entirely altered the range of possible behavioral research. This technological development has taken place mainly within the last decade, making many of the instruments used in the behavioral laboratories of the early 1950's almost obsolete today.

While it is beyond question that no amount of elaborate and expensive apparatus will generate a creative and sound research program, it is equally true that judicious selection of a limited range of appropriate equipment can vastly extend the research potential of a sound and inventive investiga-

Fig. A.10 A—Sample FR and FI cumulative records showing common irregularities. Record 1 shows periods of negative curvature with coarse grain, called "knees" (a). At other times, pauses occur part way through the ratios (b). Record 2 shows FI performance that might occur on transition after a history of FR. Knees early in the interval are followed by pausing, and positive acceleration toward the end of the interval. B—Sample cumulative records of multiple FI-FR (1) and DRL-FR (2) performances. The FI periods are indicated (a) while the FR's are designated (b). The DRL's on record 2 are marked (c).

tor. Such equipment is as valuable an adjunct to behavioral pharmacology as are electrophysiological and biochemical instruments to the other areas of drug research. Since many readers may be unfamiliar with behavioral programming, measuring, and recording equipment, we present below a brief discussion of some kinds of equipment commercially available.

The basic physical components required in a behavioral testing situation are a controlled environment (usually enclosed), an operandum to measure the occurrence of responses, antecedent stimulus presentation devices, and reinforcement devices.

Test chambers for rats, pigeons, and monkeys are readily available from various manufacturers. Figure A-11 presents a typical operant-conditioning test chamber for rats, with the liquid- food-reinforcing device situated behind the test compartment, and two stimulus lights and a lever situated in the chamber. The test chamber for pigeons illustrated in Fig. A-12 has a removable instrument panel. Two keys (which may be illuminated with dif-

Fig. A.11 A typical rat operant-conditioning chamber equipped with a lever, stimulus lights and liquid feeder. (Courtesy of The Ralph Gerbrands Co., 8 Beck Road, Arlington, Mass.)

Fig. A.12 An operant-conditioning chamber for the pigeon. The removable instrument panel contains two response keys and a feeder suitable for delivering grain reinforcement. (Courtesy of The Lehigh Valley Co., Inc., Fogelsville, Pa.)

ferent colors from the rear of the chamber), and a loud speaker are mounted on the instrument panel, along with a grain hopper. A restraining chair test chamber for a Rhesus monkey is presented in Fig. A-13. The animal is restrained in a Lucite cockpit that can be adjusted for monkeys of different sizes and weights. The cockpit rests on slides that permit the animal to be pulled out of the test compartment. Mouth-operated food and water operanda and a multiple visual stimulus device are also mounted on the chair.

One of the more widely used devices for assessing the behavioral effects of drugs is a photocell locomotor activity chamber. Figure A-14 illustrates a commercially available chamber in which six photocells and an adjustable floor make it possible to study activity patterns in a variety of small animals.

There are a great many specialized devices, some designed as part of larger programming systems, other self-contained. Figure A-15 illustrates a sequential-response apparatus, self-contained for both control and recording, designed for use with rats. This particular apparatus requires that the animal respond in a certain sequence to four identical and potentially reinforced sites placed 90° apart around the circumference of the test chamber.

It may sometimes be experimentally desirable to remove an operandum from an experimental test chamber and reintroduce it on a later occasion. A variety of retractable levers for accomplishing this are available; one is

Fig. A.13 A restraining chair with accompanying apparatus and sound-resistant enclosure for studying operant behavior in Rhesus monkeys. The chair is constructed of heavy Lucite and is equipped with a telegraph key lever, mouth-operated food and water dispensers, as well as a visual stimulus presentation panel. (Courtesy of Foringer & Co., Inc., Rockville, Md.)

illustrated in Fig. A-16. This particular lever is motor driven and has an accompanying control panel that is compatible with the various relay-switching systems produced by several behavioral equipment manufacturers.

The defining operation in operant behavior is reinforcement; and there are a great many reinforcement devices. These may form a part of commercially available or custom-made chambers, or they may be built in. One of

Fig. A.14 A photoelectric cell locomotor activity measuring device (ACTOPHOTOMETER) for the rat. (Courtesy of Metro Scientific, Inc., 141 Old Country Road, Carle Place, N.Y.)

Fig. A.15 A rat sequential response apparatus requiring that the subject respond on a specified sequence to four identical and potentially reinforced sites situated 90° apart. (Courtesy of The Wisconsin Instrument Company, 817 Stewart Street, Madison, Wis.)

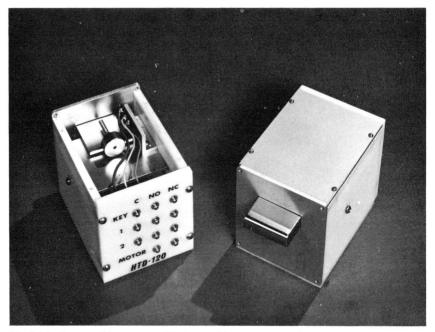

Fig. A.16 A motor-driven retractable lever, with an accompanying control panel. (Courtesy of Hawley Training Devices, Inc., 9616 Roosevelt Way N.E., Seattle, Wash.)

the most common negative reinforcers is electric shock, which is usually scrambled, i.e., grid floor bars that alternate positive and negative electric charges at rapid short intervals. Devices for food reinforcement are usually solenoid or motor driven; they advance a compartment containing the food to such a position that the reinforcer is deposited within the subject's reach. Figure A-17 illustrates three widely used, commercially available feeders.

The arrangement of contingencies among an organism's behavior, antecedent stimulus conditions, and reinforcing consequences is the major job of automated behavioral test equipment. Such devices, now called "programming equipment," are the heart of any apparatus for the experimental analysis of behavior. The first equipment used for this purpose was based on relay- and timer-switching circuitry—basically logic systems. Very little knowledge of electronics is required to operate most of the commercially available relay-timer switching apparatus.

Figure A-18 illustrates a relay rack with clip-on modular control panels. The panels are used to determine the contingencies controlling stimulus presentation, response recording, and response consequences. In recent years, similar behavioral programming systems based on solid-state components have been developed. Proper use of solid-state behavior-control apparatus usually requires more knowledge of electronics. It is seldom as feasible to "wire-as-you-go," following the practice common in some laboratories with

A.

Fig. A.17 Automatic food-dispensing devices for use in operant conditioning A—Pellet feeder for rats, solenoid-operated B—Liquid feeder, solenoid-operated C—A universal feeder to dispense irregularly shaped objects, including food. (Courtesy of: (A), (B) The Ralph Gerbrands Co., 8 Beck Road, Arlington, Mass.; (C) Davis Scientific Instruments, 11116 Cumpston Street, North Hollywood, Calif.)

B.

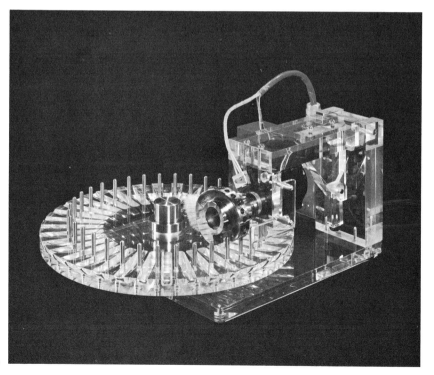

C.

Fig. A.18 Typical arrangement of relay-timer switching apparatus for controlling behavioral contingencies. (Courtesy of Medical Audio Visual Department, Walter Reed Army Institute of Research, Washington, D.C.) AMS # 10240.

relay modules; more careful preplanning of programs is required before the program is actually wired. Solid-state modules are often more compact and reliable, and are invariably quieter. Figure A-19 presents closeup photographs of two lines of solid-state modular programming equipment; these are among the models that can quite readily be translated into behavioral contingencies.

Figure A-20 illustrates another line of solid-state programming equip-

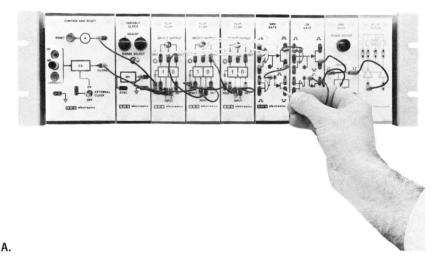

A.

B.

Fig. A.19 Two commercially available solid-state logic systems for programming behavioral contingencies. (Courtesy of: (A) BRS Electronics, 5451 Holland Drive, Beltsville, Md.; (B) Massey-Dickinson Co., Inc., 151 Bear Hill Road, Waltham, Mass.)

ment; while this line is not specifically designed for behavioral application, it can be used for that purpose. Obviously, the further the original purpose of such apparatus is from behavioral application, the more initial time and interface effort is required to translate behavioral problems into machine language and back into behavioral language again.

Once the behavioral contingencies have been provided for, certain kinds of information about the relations of those contingencies to the behavior generated is recorded. For example, the experimenter usually records the number of responses and reinforcements, and the number and kind of other events (e.g., stimulus presentations, unreinforced responses, etc.). Digital

Fig. A.20 A solid-state logic system not specifically designed for controlling behavioral contingencies, but usable for that purpose. (Courtesy of Control Logic Inc., 3 Strathmore Road, Natick, Mass.)

counters are used to indicate number of responses, and these are available in both relay-logic and solid-state-logic programming systems (Fig. A-21). The number of responses or events during successive time intervals may need to be recorded on paper tape by means of printout counters (Fig. A-22).

In most operant-conditioning experiments, a complete graphic record is

Fig. A.21 Bank of decimal counters compatible with relay-timer programming equipment. (Courtesy of Foringer & Co., Inc., Rockville, Md.)

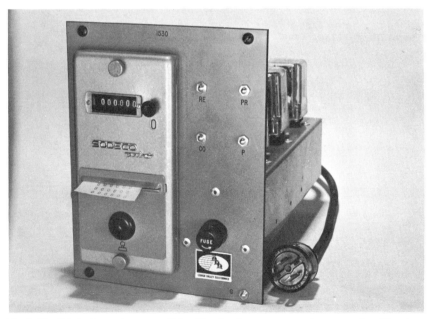

Fig. A.22 Printout counter compatible with relay-timer programming apparatus. (Courtesy of The Lehigh Valley Co., Inc., Fogelsville, Pa.)

A.

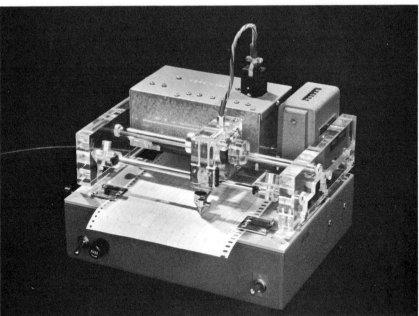

B.

Fig. A.23 Three widely used cumulative recorders coming in a variety of response-step sizes and paper speeds. The recorder on the left is directly compatible with some solid-state logic equipment as well. (Courtesy of: (A) Ralph Gerbrands Co., 8 Beck Road, Arlington, Mass.; (B) Davis Scientific Instruments, 11116 Cumpston Street, North Hollywood, Calif.; (C) Scientific Prototype Mfg. Corp., 615 W. 131 Street, N.Y., N.Y.)

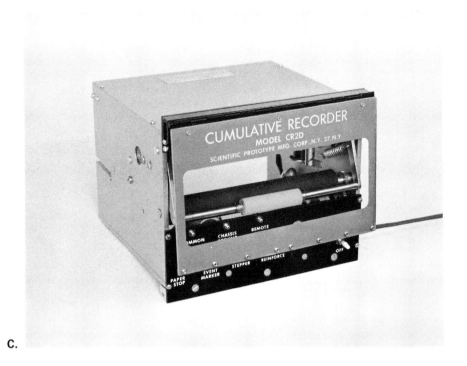

C.

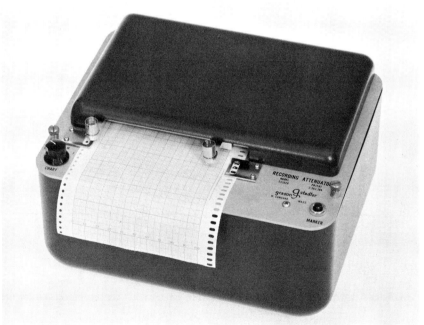

Fig. A.24 A recording attenuator for both recording and controlling stimulus intensity, as in the Bekesy or Weiss-Laties titration procedures. (Courtesy of Grason-Stadler, Inc., West Concord, Mass.)

Fig. A.25 A punched tape device for programming behavioral contingencies, or recording. This model is designed for use with solid-state binary logic systems. (Courtesy of BRS Electronics, 5451 Holland Drive, Beltsville, Md.)

usually expressed as cumulative responses. Figure A-23 presents three widely used cumulative recorders. In experiments that involve the titration procedure (as opposed to those requiring a cumulative record of responses), they are expressed in terms of a physical intensity variable that is either increased by a clock or decreased by a response. An attentuating recorder, also serving to vary the magnitude of the stimulus, is used to record this information (Fig. A-24).

With the introduction of solid-state logic modules for behavioral programming, other computer developments have begun to filter down to behavioral scientists. One such technological advance involves the use of punched paper tape and electromagnetic tape recording and programming devices. Devices of this type can be used to record incoming information on multiple channels, or to program behavioral contingencies as a readout from the prepunched paper tape or preprogrammed magnetic tape. Two commercially available tape devices, compatible with solid-state behavioral programming systems, are illustrated in Fig. A-25.

Glossary

Absorption   The movement of a drug from the site of administration to a particular tissue or fluid compartment, usually understood to be the blood plasma. Absorption is said to be complete when the drug concentration in the blood equals the concentration at the site of administration.

Abstinence syndrome   A set of signs and symptoms of illness that ensues when chronic treatment with certain drugs, especially the opiates and barbiturates, is discontinued.

Addiction liability   The probability that a drug will be abused by humans in such a way that physical and behavioral dependence will result.

Adjusting reinforcement schedule (Adj)   A complex reinforcement schedule in which the size of each successive ratio is determined by some characteristic of immediately preceding performance (e.g., a pause of longer than 30 seconds).

Adrenergic   A term referring to the epinephrine-mediated neuroeffector transmission of postganglionic sympathetic nerve fibers (except for the nerves to sweat glands and certain blood vessels).

Aggregate toxicity The LD-50 for a drug administered to animals in groups, which is lower than the LD-50 of matched controls housed individually.

Agitated A clinical term used to designate excessive behavioral activity, irritability, and/or anxiety.

Alkaloid A term applied to various naturally occurring basic, organic, nitrogenous compounds, usually of plant origin.

Alpha receptors Adrenergic receptors concerned primarily with excitatory responses, and most sensitive to epinephrine.

Analgesic A drug that blocks or diminishes pain.

Anorexia In clinical work, the term anorexia refers to diminished appetite. Experimentally, anorexia is characterized by a reduction in food intake.

Antagonism A situation in which the combined effect of two drugs is less than the effect of either drug alone.

Antecedent operation The manipulation of a variable prior to putting the subject in an experimental environment (e.g., food deprivation).

Anticonvulsant A drug that diminishes either the threshold for elicited convulsions or the frequency and intensity of spontaneous convulsions.

Antidepressant A clinical term referring to drugs that ameliorate symptoms of psychiatric depression without producing euphoria or hyperexcitability.

Ataxia Incoordination of striate muscular action.

Avoidance, discriminated Operant behavior reinforced by termination of a conditioned negative reinforcer (e.g., termination of a tone preceding shock).

Avoidance, Sidman Operant behavior reinforced by postponement of a forthcoming unconditioned negative reinforcer, without an exteroceptive warning stimulus (e.g., a shock that will be presented unless a response is made, each response postponing the next shock for 20 seconds).

Baseline, behavioral The terminal stabilized operant behavior under specified conditions; it can serve as a steady state from which to measure the reversible effect of an experimental manipulation (e.g., drug administration).

Behavior The observed movement of an organism or its parts within a spatio-temporally defined frame of reference.

Behavioral dependence (habituation) A state of an organism characterized by the disposition to self-administer a drug with considerable regularity. Behavioral dependence may also involve physical dependence, but not necessarily. Humans who are behaviorally but not physically dependent on a drug are called *habituated*.

Behavioral toxicity Functional drug toxicity in which behavioral changes that exceed the normal limits of variability occur; these changes may have serious, and possibly irreversible, deleterious consequences (e.g., cessation of escape behavior, cessation of eating).

Beta receptors Adrenergic receptors primarily concerned with inhibitory functions; these receptors are most responsive to isopropyl arterenol.

Biotransformation The transformation of a drug with a specific biological action into an inactive form, or to a form with different effects. The term detoxification, sometimes used synonymously with biotransformation, is a misnomer.

Blocking agent A drug that antagonizes the action of another drug, or nerve stimulation, at synaptic or neuroeffector junctions.

Bradycardia Diminished heart rate; synonymous with *brachycardia*.

Central nervous system (CNS) active   A drug exerting a major influence on functions in the brain and spinal cord is said to be central nervous system active. The term is sometimes erroneously used synonymously with *behaviorally active.*

Chained schedule of reinforcement (chain)   A reinforcement schedule in which responding in the presence of one discriminative stimulus produces a second discriminative stimulus; and responding in the presence of the second stimulus leads to unconditioned reinforcement. The contingencies for reinforcement during each stimulus period are defined by a simple schedule (e.g., FR, FI, VR, VI). Chain FI-1 FR10 would mean that the first response after one minute in the presence of one stimulus would produce a second stimulus, in the presence of which 10 responses would lead to unconditioned reinforcement.

Cholinergic   All preganglionic nerve transmission, and all postganglionic parasympathetic transmission, certain postganglionic sympathetic transmission (sweat glands, blood vessels), and all innervation of striate muscles are mediated via acetylcholine and are therefore called *cholinergic.*

Clonic spasms   An involuntary series of alternate contractions and relaxations of striate muscles.

Complex reinforcement schedule   A reinforcement schedule involving both ratio and interval contingencies. Complex schedules are of the following types: (1) schedules in which ratio and interval contingencies remain constant regardless of the subject's behavior (e.g., conjunctive schedules), and (2) schedules in which ratio or interval values vary as a function of the organism's previous behavior (e.g., adjusting).

Components (of schedules)   Individual segments of a sequential, compound, or complex schedule defined by a single or multiple contingency, with or without a distinctive exteroceptive stimulus (e.g., the FR1 component of a chain FR1-FI10 schedule).

Compound reinforcement schedules   Reinforcement schedules in which two or more simple schedules are programmed sequentially or concurrently (e.g., chained, tandem, multiple, mixed, concurrent schedules).

Conditioned reflex   (1) A reflex consisting of a conditioned stimulus and a conditioned response established by the repeated presentation of the conditioned stimulus in approximate temporal contiguity with the unconditioned stimulus. The response elicited by the unconditioned stimulus (the unconditioned response) comes to be elicited by the conditioned stimulus. (2) A classically conditioned (Pavlovian) reflex.

Conditioned (secondary) reinforcer (S^r)   A stimulus that comes to have reinforcing properties through repeated presentation in close temporal contiguity with an unconditioned reinforcer.

Conditioned response (CR)   The response elicited by a conditioned stimulus in a conditioned reflex.

Conditioned stimulus (CS)   The stimulus that comes to elicit a conditioned response through repeated pairing with an unconditioned stimulus, in a conditioned reflex.

Conditioned suppression   The diminished frequency of occurrence of a positively reinforced ongoing operant in the presence of a stimulus that had previously been paired with shock. Also called a conditioned emotional response (CER).

Conditioning, Type R Operant, or instrumental, conditioning. The strengthening of an operant by following the occurrence of the operant with a reinforcing stimulus. The letter R is used to indicate that the controlling stimulus is correlated with a response rather than with a stimulus.

Conditioning, Type S Classical or Pavlovian conditioning. The establishment of a new reflex by the pairing of a previously ineffective stimulus (CS) with an unconditioned stimulus, the new reflex consisting of the CS and a conditioned response. The letter S indicates that the controlling stimulus is correlated with a stimulus and not with a response.

Contingencies for reinforcement (1) The temporal requirements and/or number of responses that will produce reinforcement. (2) A reinforcement schedule.

Continuous reinforcement (CRF) A nonintermittent reinforcement schedule in which each response is followed by reinforcement. (Same as an FR1 schedule.) Also called a regular reinforcement schedule.

Cortical activation A shift in the electrical activity of the cerebral cortex from the 10/sec. alpha rhythm to 1 to 3 per second rhythms. Such changes can be produced by environmental stimulation or by injecting the reticular activating system with epinephrine.

Cross tolerance The development of tolerance to a drug that is related to but not identical with a drug that has actually been administered. Thus, organisms treated with morphine will be found to have developed tolerance to the related drug, meperidine, although they have never been given meperidine.

Cumulation The accumulation of a drug or the effects of a drug owing to readministrations of the substance before it has been entirely excreted, or before the effects of previous doses have disappeared.

Cumulative record A graphic record of operant behavior in which responses move a pen vertically by discrete steps along a strip of paper that advances at a constant rate. The slope of the line corresponding to cumulative responses is proportional to response rate. When the pen reaches the top of the paper, it resets to the bottom.

Delayed conditioned reflex A classically conditioned reflex in which a delay of five seconds or longer occurs between the onset of the conditioned stimulus and the presentation of the unconditioned stimulus.

Depletion Disappearance of an endogenous substance from tissue or fluid-compartment stores, usually produced by drug administration (e.g., depletion of serotonin from hypothalamic cellular stores following reserpine treatment).

Depolarization Collapse of electrical potential differences across nerve-cell membranes as a consequence of irritation or electrical excitation of the cell membrane.

Depression (1) A decrease in normal cell functioning. (2) A drug-induced behavioral depressant effect evidenced by diminished motor activity following drug administration. (3) A term used clinically to designate a state characterized by diminished motor activity and a mood of dejection.

Deprivation Withholding a reinforcing stimulus for some period prior to attempting to use that stimulus as a reinforcer. The term commonly refers to food deprivation, but it can apply to drug deprivation when a drug is a reinforcer, or to visual stimulus deprivation when that is a reinforcer.

Direct replication Duplication of a procedure as exactly as possible in an effort to reproduce an experimental result.

Discrimination learning (1) The conditioning of an organism to respond selectively with respect to a specific (discriminative) stimulus or set of stimuli. (2) The establishment of stimulus control by reinforcing responses in the presence of one stimulus without reinforcing responses under other stimulus conditions.

Discriminative stimulus (S^D) A stimulus that sets the occasion for reinforced responding.

Distribution The movement of a drug via the bloodstream to various tissues throughout the body; this action implies differential assimilation of the drug by various tissues.

Dosage form The physical state in which a drug is administered.

Dose The quantity of drug administered at one occasion. *Dose* is to be distinguished from *dosage,* which is the amount of drug administered for a given case or condition (totally or during set time periods).

Dose-response The relation between the dose of a drug and the magnitude of the effect achieved, also called the dose-effect relation.

Dose-response curve The curve relating dose of a drug to the effect produced (see graded dose-effect curve and quantal dose-effect curve).

DRH schedule (differential reinforcement of high rates) A complex reinforcement schedule in which reinforcement is forthcoming if a specific number of responses is made within a specified time interval after the last reinforcement. The number of responses and the time interval are set so that the schedule differentially reinforces high rates of responding.

Drive A state of an organism, characterized by increased locomotor activity, in which reinforcement is possible. Drive may be induced by presenting a negative reinforcer or by withholding a positive reinforcer.

DRL schedule (differential reinforcement of low rates) A complex reinforcement schedule in which reinforcement is forthcoming on the occurrence of the first response after a minimum interval. Premature responding starts the interval over. Thus, these contingencies have the effect of differentially reinforcing low rates of responding.

Emotion The generic name for a great many states of the organism produced by an array of manipulations. These manipulations are characterized by changes in the strength of a large number of responses, including numerous smooth-muscle and glandular responses. As a construct, emotion is analogous to drive.

Endogenous agents Compounds produced within the tissues of organisms. Term often defines chemicals that are manipulated or altered, or act on drugs administered for experimental or therapeutic purposes.

Errorless discrimination learning A procedure for establishing stimulus control by consistently reinforcing responding during one stimulus (S^D), and presenting the S$^\Delta$ for such short periods that the organism does not have time to respond during S$^\Delta$. Gradually, the duration of the S$^\Delta$ period is increased, but no responses occur. Thus, "errors" (responses during S$^\Delta$ periods) never occur during conditioning.

Escape, conditioned Operant behavior reinforced by the termination of an unconditioned negative reinforcer (e.g., shock termination).

Excretion The process of eliminating a drug or its metabolites from the body.

Extinction (1) Diminishing the strength of a conditioned reflex by repeatedly presenting a conditioned stimulus and never following it with an unconditioned stimulus. (2) Diminishing the strength of an operant by allowing repeated emissions of occurrences of the operant without following them with the reinforcing stimulus. (3) Extinction schedule (Ext)—A nonintermittent reinforcement schedule in which each occurrence of a response goes unreinforced although there has been some history of reinforcement for that response.

Fate The biotransformations that a drug undergoes, and the mechanisms of its excretion.

Fibrillation A local quivering of muscle fibers, usually cardiac arrhythmia.

FI clock An exteroceptive stimulus that varies with time elapsed since the last reinforcement in a fixed-interval reinforcement schedule.

Fixed-interval schedule (FI) A simple reinforcement schedule in which a response may not be reinforced again until a fixed time interval following the last reinforced response has elapsed.

Fixed-ratio schedule (FR) A simple reinforcement schedule in which reinforcement is forthcoming following occurrence of a fixed number of responses following the last reinforced response.

Fractional escape avoidance Negatively reinforced operant behavior maintained by the postponement of a negative reinforcer that progressively increases in intensity at fixed time intervals; can also be maintained by diminished intensity of an already present negative reinforcer, as a consequence of each response.

Free-feeding weight An animal's body weight under conditions of free access to food (ad libitum feeding conditions) over a period sufficient to obtain a reliable baseline weight.

Free operant An operant placing the organism in a position to re-emit the response immediately following reinforcement, and to be reinforced again— as opposed to maze, runway or other spatially restricted situations where behavior and reinforcement are isolated from each other.

Graded dose-effect The magnitude of effect produced by a drug, which magnitude is believed to reveal a differential sensitivity of portions of the cell to the drug. The curve relating dose and magnitude of graded effect is a hyperbola.

Hallucinogen A drug that produces hallucinations (e.g., mescaline, LSD).

Higher-order conditioning (1) Conditioning in which a previously established conditioned stimulus is used as an unconditioned stimulus to establish a second-order conditioned reflex. (2) Conditioning in which conditioned reinforcers for one schedule are used to establish a second-order schedule. FR5(FR25), for example, signifies that a conditioned reinforcer is presented following every 25 responses, five of which (a total of 125 responses) would lead to unconditioned reinforcement.

Hypnotic A drug that produces anesthesia at high doses but, when administered in lower doses, causes drowsiness, reduced motor activity, and reduced responsiveness to the environment.

Hypomanic Describes a mild state of hyperexcitability in which the patient is easily distracted and is somewhat more active than usual, but exhibits no bizarre or extremely agitated behavior.

Hypotension Lowered blood pressure.

Hypothetical construct   A theoretical construct possessing meaning over and above that contained in the defining operations and observable changes (e.g., the notion of drug receptors). Hypothetical constructs are to be distinguished from intervening variables, which possess no meaning other than that contained in the defining operations and measurable changes: drive, for example, is defined in terms of hours of food deprivation and resulting behavioral changes.

Injection   (1) The process of administering a drug by introducing it across a skin membrane into subcutaneous, muscular, peritoneal, or vascular space. (2) A sterile solution prepared by a pharmaceutical manufacturer for direct injection.

Instinctive behavior   Approximately equivalent to "innate behavior." A complex sequence of species specific unconditioned responses, relatively fixed in pattern, and repeated from the beginning of the sequence if the behavior chain is interrupted. The term is used less frequently today than some years ago. (See Verplanck, 1957.)

Interoceptive stimuli   Stimuli capable of activating interoceptors—receptors located in smooth muscles, internal organs, body cavity linings, etc.

Interpolated reinforcement schedule (Interpol)   A special type of mixed reinforcement schedule in which a simple schedule is inserted into a longer "background" schedule that is also a simple schedule (e.g., Interpol FR10-FI15 would indicate that a period of FR10's had been inserted into a background of FI15 minutes, without exteroceptive stimuli indicating which schedule was in effect).

Interresponse time (IRT)   The time between successive operant responses. The time elapsed between R_{n-1} and R_n is a measure of the spacing between responses. (See interresponse time distribution.)

Interresponse time distribution   Interresponse time distribution is a measure of the spacing of responses expressed as the relative frequency of intervals elapsed between successive responses (R_{n-1} and R_n).

Intramuscular (I.M.)   A route of parenteral administration in which the solution being administered is injected deep into a muscle.

Intravenous (I.V.)   A parenteral route of administration in which a drug solution is injected directly into a vein by inserting the tip of a hypodermic needle into the lumen of a vein, and expelling the drug solution.

Kilogram (kg.)   1,000 milligrams, or 2.2 pounds. Body weights are usually expressed in kilograms, and drug dosages in terms of milligrams of drug per kilogram of body weight (e.g., 5 mg. of drug per kilogram of body weight [5 mg/kg]).

Latency   (1) Time from onset of a conditioned stimulus (or unconditioned stimulus) until the occurrence of a response. Also called the latent time. (2) The time from the onset of a discriminative stimulus until the occurrence of an operant.

Local drug action   Characteristic of a drug that produces its primary effect at or near the site of administration. Local action is to be distinguished from *systemic action*, which occurs throughout the body.

Magazine training   A procedure for conditioning organisms to approach the food or water magazine as soon as the magazine has operated. This is done by repeatedly presenting some stimulus that is immediately followed by food or water presentation until the organism has learned to approach the magazine as soon as the stimulus sounds. Magazine training is essential to establishing the chain of responses following the operant that leads to ingestion of the reinforcer.

Manipulandum   A hand-operated operandum. A response-detecting device in operant conditioning experiments.

Median effective dose (ED-50)   The dose dividing the population into two equal groups (e.g., the dose at which 50 per cent of subjects fail to avoid a painful electric shock).

Median lethal dose (LD-50)   The dose at which 50 per cent of the subjects die following drug administration.

Metabolism, drug   The biotransformations that drugs undergo in converting from inactive to active forms, and subsequently into other less active or inactive forms that are excreted.

Metabolite, drug   The product(s) of biotransformation following drug administration.

Microgram (μg)   One one-thousandth of a milligram, abbreviated "gamma."

Milligram (mg.)   One one-thousandth of one kilogram, or one thousand micrograms. A milligram is the standard unit for expressing drug dosages.

Monosynaptic transmission   Synaptic transmission in which nerve activity is relayed but once, from presynaptic to postsynaptic neurons. Monosynaptic pathways are found in sympathetic ganglia and in the stretch reflex mechanisms of the spinal cord.

Motivation   See *drive.*

Motor end-plate   A specialized region of muscle fiber coming into close proximity to the motor axon nerve ending.

Motor incapacitation   Incoordination of striate muscular activity, approximately equivalent to ataxia. Usually refers to gross alterations of behavior rather than subtle changes of aspects of striate action (e.g., fine tremors, slight changes in topography).

Multioperant repertoire   A complex program of operants consisting of serial and/or parallel arrangements of three or more simple operants. (See Findley, 1962.)

Multiple reinforcement schedule (mult.)   A compound reinforcement schedule consisting of two or more simple schedules arranged sequentially, each with a distinctive discriminative stimulus, with unconditioned reinforcement on completion of each component.

Muscarinic   A cholinergic receptor antagonized by atropine and which, when stimulated, produces postganglionic parasympathetic actions on the heart, glands, and smooth muscles.

Negative reinforcement   The removal of a stimulus that increases the probability of recurrence of the preceding response (e.g., removal of a painful shock following a lever-press).

Neuroeffector junction   The space between the termination of an axon and a striate muscle or gland.

Neurohumor   An endogenous compound occurring in relatively large quantity at synaptic and/or neuroeffector junctions. Neurohumor is thought to mediate transmission of the action potential of one fiber to the innervated cell (e.g., acetylcholine).

Neuromuscular effect   Change in striate muscular activity attributable to action of a drug at neuroeffector or synaptic sites.

Nicotinic   A cholinergic receptor antagonized by curare and which, when stimulated, produces sympathetic ganglionic and striate muscular stimulation.

Observing response   A discriminative-stimulus-producing response as opposed to a food- or water-producing response. S^D and S^Δ periods alternate. Responses on one operandum lead to food during the S^D period; responses on a second operandum illuminate a dial indicating whether S^D or S^Δ conditions are in effect. Responses on the second operandum are called observing responses.

Operandum   (1) A portion of the environment on which an organism operates to procure reinforcement in an operant-conditioning situation. (2) A device to objectively and unequivocally detect the occurrence of members of a given response class.

Operant   (1) A member of a given class of responses defined by specified contingencies for reinforcement. (2) A given dated occurrence of an operant is called a response instance. Since no two response instances are identical, this term must be distinguished from response class. (3) A type of conditioning in which occurrences of responses are controlled by stimulus consequences (reinforcement).

Operant level (op. l)   (1) The frequency of occurrence of an operant response prior to conditioning. (2) A schedule of reinforcement prior to conditioning in which each response goes unreinforced; such a schedule is used to establish the unconditioned operant level.

Parasympathomimetic   Actions of a drug that mimic either the effects of stimulation of the parasympathetic nervous system or the effects that follow acetylcholine administration.

Parenteral   Any route of drug administration outside the alimentary tract; usually understood to mean subcutaneous, intravenous, peritoneal, intramuscular, or intrasternal injection.

Peroral (P.O.)   Oral route of drug administration.

Physical dependence   A state produced by chronic drug administration in which discontinuation of drug treatment will be followed by a characteristic syndrome of illness (abstinence syndrome). Found especially in connection with opiates and barbiturates.

Placebo effect   A conditioned drug effect that occurs when administration of a new drug, usually an inert vehicle, produces effects qualitatively like the effects of the previously administered active compound.

Polysynaptic transmission   Synaptic transmission involving variable numbers of synapses and interneurons. Most synaptic pathways are polysynaptic.

Postganglionic fiber   Sympathetic and parasympathetic fibers innervating smooth muscles and glands that are receiving efferent impulses in synapses in sympathetic ganglia, or at parasympathetic ganglia located on or near the effector. Sympathetic mediation is adrenergic; parasympathetic mediation is cholinergic.

Potentiation   The effect of two combined drugs when this is greater than the sum of their individual effects.

Preganglionic fiber   Autonomic fibers originating in the dorsal or lateral horns of the spinal cord, synapsing in sympathetic and parasympathetic ganglia. Synaptic transmission is cholinergic.

Pressor response   A rise in blood pressure.

Program (behavioral)   A formal electromechanical procedure for defining and controlling an operant-conditioning experiment. A behavioral program consists of switches, relays, timers, and electronic semiconductors that present antecedent stimuli, detect response occurrences, and control reinforcement contingencies.

Punishment   A stimulus following an operant which decreases the probability of the recurrence of that response.

Quantal dose-effect   The relation of dose to the response of a biological system that is either maximally responsive or fails to respond to the drug at all— also called the all-or-none dose-effect relation. Quantal dose-effect relations are log normally distributed.

Receptor   (1) The portion of protoplasm with which a drug molecule combines to produce the measured effect. (2) A functional entity (intervening variable) in a model of drug action referring to the relation of chemical structure to the measured effect (Ariens, 1964). (3) A transducer that converts mechanical, electromagnetic, or chemical energy into action potentials (physiology and psychology).

Reflex   (1) The correlation of an antecedent stimulus with an elicited response (may be conditioned or unconditioned); e.g., patellar reflex. (2) A reflex response refers to a response elicited by an antecedent stimulus.

Reflex arc   A physiological concept that relates antecedent stimuli to electrophysiological changes in afferent fibers, to initiation of action potentials in association neurons, which in turn excites motor neurons to terminate the chain in a muscular contraction.

Reinforcement schedule   Formal statement of the relationship between temporal events, parameters of an organism's behavior, and the consequences of its behavior.

Reinforcer, positive/negative   A stimulus, the presentation of which (positive) or removal of which (negative) increases the probability of recurrence of the preceding operant response.

Response   (1) A change in some measured aspect of an organism produced by a given dose of a drug (pharmacology). (2) A unit of behavior defined by the variables controlling the behavior. See: *Unconditioned response, Reflex response, Operant response, Response instance, Response class* (psychology)

Response class (operant)   A class of behaviors whose members, though sharing a common controlling reinforcing consequence, may vary considerably topographically.

Response differentiation   The selective reinforcement of components of a complex of operant responses, leading to a well-defined subset of behaviors or to a different set of responses occurring at high frequency. Responses that successively approximate the ultimate behavior which is the goal of conditioning are the reinforced responses.

Response strength   (1) A theoretical construct abstracted from measures such as *response frequency, latency, magnitude,* etc. (2) Usually in operant conditioning, response strength is equivalent to response probability, which is expressed in terms of frequency of occurrence per unit of time.

Route of administration   The pathway by which a drug is introduced into an organism.

Saline   A solution of sodium chloride in distilled water that is isosmotic with red blood-cell plasma.

Schedule effects The actions of a drug that constitute a function, at least in part, of the schedule of reinforcement or a parameter of the reinforcement schedule.

Screening, drug The selective evaluation of the actions of a drug for the purpose of predicting therapeutic and toxic effects. Unless stated otherwise, screening usually refers to preclinical evaluation for clinical efficacy and behavioral toxicity.

S-delta (S^Δ) A stimulus in the presence of which a given operant goes unreinforced.

Sedative A drug that, in low doses, elevates the threshold for irritability in the central nervous system without producing the sleeplike drowsiness associated with hypnotic doses.

Sequential schedule A reinforcement schedule in which component simple schedules are arranged in series (sequentially) rather than concurrently or parallelly (e.g., chained, mixed).

Shaping See *Response differentiation*

Side effects Effects of a drug other than those of immediate clinical relevance; usually refers to undesirable actions that detract from the clinical application of a drug.

Simultaneous conditioning A reflex conditioning procedure in which the conditioned stimulus and unconditioned stimulus are presented at the same time.

Site of action The organ, tissue, or cells in the body with which a drug interacts to produce the measured drug effect.

Solution The name given to drug preparations in which a compound is dissolved in a vehicle, most commonly distilled water, saline, or oil.

Spontaneous motor activity (S.M.A.) Locomotor activity measured by numerous devices (e.g., array of photocells, squares drawn on the floor of an open field, "jiggle cages," running wheels). S.M.A. is often said to be unconditioned, although it can be profoundly affected by the organism's history and the consequences of increased activity.

Spontaneous recovery (1) The occurrence of a previously extinguished reflex at a level well above the extinguished value after a period without extinction or conditioning trials. (2) The occurrence of an operant at some strength after extinction following a period without reinforcement or extinction.

Steady state (behavioral) A condition of behavioral stability in which a highly reliable baseline of operant performance has been reached. On manipulation of an experimental variable, there may be a progressive shift in performance and arrival at a new steady state. The shift is called a *transition state*.

Stimulation (1) An increase in the normal function of cells produced by a drug. (2) Increase in frequency and/or vigor of some ongoing activity following drug administration. (3) The term *stimulated* is used clinically to designate increased motor activity, increased agitation, or euphoria.

Stimulus An aspect of the environment that can be shown to uniquely covary with some specific aspect of behavior.

Stimulus control The extent to which the value of an antecedent stimulus determines the probability of occurrence of an operant response.

Stimulus discrimination A type of stimulus control in which the probability of response is high under one set of stimulus conditions and low under other stimulus conditions.

Stimulus generalization (1) The tendency of a conditioned reflex elicited by a conditioned stimulus located at a given value along a physical continuum to occur at lower strengths in response to stimuli varying along the same continuum. (2) A type of stimulus control in which the probability of responding to stimuli along a continuum, with the discriminative stimulus used to establish stimulus control, is less than the probability of response in the presence of the S^D, although it is greater than zero.

"Structure-activity" relation The relation between specific chemical structures of drugs and specific quantitative and qualitative actions of drugs.

Stupor A clinical condition of being partly conscious or sensible; a condition of insensibility.

Subcutaneous (S.C.) A parenteral route of drug administration in which a drug is deposited beneath the skin by inserting a needle under the skin and expelling the drug solution.

Successive approximation See *Response differentiation*

Summation The combined effects of two drugs when such are equal to the sum of their individual effects.

Suspension A drug preparation in which insoluble drug particles are held in a homogeneous phase by a gum or viscid substance.

Sympathomimetic (1) Actions of a drug that mimic either the effects of stimulation of the sympathetic nervous system, or the effects associated with epinephrine administration. (2) A drug that produces effects like those following epinephrine administration.

Synergism The combined effects of two drugs which are greater than the individual effects, but not greater than the sum of their individual effects.

Systematic replication A procedure of replicating an experiment that involves systematically varying certain aspects of a procedure from an original method. If, in spite of these differences, similar orderliness results, a more generalizable replication has been obtained.

Systemic action Drug action throughout tissues of a given type throughout the body.

Tachycardia Increased heart rate.

Tandem reinforcement schedule (tand) A sequential reinforcement schedule in which two or more simple schedules are arranged in a series, without distinctive stimuli associated with each component, and with unconditioned reinforcement on completion of all components.

Therapeutic index The ratio of LD-50 to ED-50. The larger the therapeutic index, the greater the margin of safety.

Time-out from reinforcement (T.O.) A behavioral consequence consisting of termination of a discriminative stimulus period during which a response will be positively reinforced.

Tolerance A phenomenon in the administration of some drugs in which the dose required to produce a given effect must be increased on successive administrations.

Tonic spasms An involuntary state of continuous striate muscle contraction.

Topography, response The form and pattern of a response as distinguished from a simple physical property of the response, such as its force.

Trace-conditioned reflex A conditioned reflex established by presenting a CS followed by a five-second or longer delay between termination of the CS and onset of the US.

Unconditioned behavior Behavior that occurs in a complete and intact form without prior conditioning.

Unconditioned (primary) reinforcer A stimulus that is effective as a reinforcer for an operant without prior conditioning.

Unconditioned response (UR) A reflex response elicited by an unconditioned stimulus.

Unconditioned stimulus (US) A stimulus capable of eliciting an unconditioned reflex response.

Variable-interval schedule (VI) A simple reinforcement schedule in which reinforcement is forthcoming following the first response after a specified time interval varying around a given mean with a specified range of intervals.

Variable-ratio schedule (VR) A simple reinforcement schedule characterized by the reinforcement of the first response after a specified number of responses following the last reinforcement. The number of responses before reinforcement varies around a given mean with a specified range of responses.

Vehicle The substance in which a drug is dissolved or suspended.

Warm-up effect A transition effect of positive acceleration from low rate to moderate or high rate of responding at the beginning of an experimental session in an operant situation.

Bibliography

Abrahamson, H. A., and L. T. Evans, 1954. "Lysergic acid diethylamide (LSD-25): II. Psychobiological effects on the Siamese fighting fish." *Science*, **120**: 990.

Abuzzahab, F. S., T. Thompson and F. E. Shideman, 1965. "Catecholamines in the brain of the embryonic and newly hatched chick." *The Pharmacologist*, **7**: 2.

Adler, N., and J. Hogan, 1963. "Classical conditioning and punishment of an instinctive response in *Betta splendens*." *Animal Behavior*, **11**: 351.

Ahlquist, R. P., 1958. "Adrenergic Drugs" in *Pharmacology in Medicine*, ed. V. A. Drill. New York: The McGraw-Hill Book Company, Inc.

Amsel, A., and J. Roussel, 1952. "Motivational properties of frustration: I. Effect on a running response of the addition of frustration to the motivational complex." *J. exp. Psychol.*, **43**: 363.

Anrep, G. V., 1923. "Irradiation of conditioned reflexes." *Proc. Roy. Soc.*, London, **94B**: 404.

———, 1920. "Pitch discrimination in the dog." *J. Physiol.*, **53**: 367.

Ariens, E. J. (ed.), 1964. *Molecular Pharmacology* (Vol. I). New York: Academic Press Inc.

Axelrod, J., and J. Reichenthal, 1953. "The fate of caffeine in man and a method for its estimation in biological material." *J. Pharmacol. and exp. Therap.*, **107**: 519.

Azrin, N. H., R. R. Hutchinson, and D. F. Hake, 1965. "Extinction-induced aggression." *Am. Psychologist*, **20**: 583.

———, ———, ———, 1963. "Pain-induced fighting in the squirrel monkey." *J. exp. anal. Behav.*, **6**: 620.

———, ———, and R. McLaughlin, 1965. "The opportunity for aggression as an operant reinforcer during aversive stimulation." *J. exp. anal. Behav.*, **8**: 171.

———, ———, and R. D. Sallery, 1964. "Pain-aggression toward inanimate objects." *J. exp. anal. Behav.*, **7**: 223.

Bain, W. A., 1932. "Method of demonstrating humor transmission of effects of cardiac vagus stimulation in frog." *Quart. J. exp. Physiol.*, **22**: 269.

Barry, H., N. E. Miller, and G. E. Tidd, 1962. "Control for stimulus change while testing effects of amobarbital on conflict." *J. comp. physiol. Psychol.*, **55**: 1071.

Bein, H. J., 1956. "The pharmacology of Rauwolfia." *Pharmacol. Rev.*, **8**: 435.

———, F. Gross, J. Tripod, and R. Meier, 1953. "Experimentelle Untersuchugen über 'Serpasil' (Reserpin), ein neues, sehr wirksames Rauwolfia alkaloid mit neuartiger zentraler Wirkung." *Schweiz, med. Wschr.*, **83**: 1007.

Belleville, R. E., 1964. "Control of behavior by drug-produced internal stimuli." *Psychopharmacologia*, **5**: 95.

Benson, Wilbur M., and Burtrum C. Schiele, 1962. *Tranquilizing and Antidepressive Drugs*. Springfield, Ill.: Charles C. Thomas, Publisher.

Berger, F. M., 1960. "Classification of psychoactive drugs according to their chemical structure and sites of action" in *Drugs and Behavior*, eds. L. Uhr and J. G. Miller. New York: John Wiley & Sons, Inc.

Bernal, J. D., 1958. "Structure arrangements of macromolecules." *Disc. Faraday Soc.*, **25**: 7.

Bindra, D., and H. Anchel, 1963. "Immobility as an avoidance response, and its disruption by drugs." *J. exp. anal. Behav.*, **6**: 213.

———, and J. Mendelson, 1963. "Training, drive level, and drug effects: A temporal analysis of their combined influence on behavior." *J. comp. physiol. Psychol.*, **56**: 183.

Blaschko, H., and T. L. Chrusciel, 1960. "The decarboxylation of amino acids related to tyrosine and their awakening action in reserpine-treated mice." *J. Physiol.*, **151**: 272.

Blough, D. S., 1958. "A new test for tranquilizers." *Science*, **127**: 586.

———, 1956. "Technique for studying the effects of drugs on discrimination in the pigeon." *Ann. N.Y. Acad. Sci.*, **65**: 334.

Borison, H. L., and S. C. Wang, 1953. "Physiology and pharmacology of vomiting." *Pharmacol. Rev.*, **5**: 193.

Bosworth, D. M., 1960. "Ioniazid: a brief review of its introduction and clinical use." *Ann. N.Y. Acad. Sci.*, **80**: 809.

Brady, J. V., 1965. "A comparative approach to the evaluation of drug effects upon affective behavior." *Ann. N.Y. Acad. Sci.*, **64**: 632.

———, 1957. "Comparative behavioral pharmacology" *Ann. N.Y. Acad. Sci.*, **66**: 719.

————, 1955. "Motivational-emotional factors and intra-cranial self-stimulation." *Amer. Psychologist,* **10**: 396.

————, 1959. "Procedures, problems and perspectives in animal behavioral studies of drug activity" in *Psychopharmacology: Problems in Evaluation,* eds. J. O. Cole and R. W. Gerard. Washington, D.C.: National Academy of Sciences–National Research Council.

————, 1958, "Ulcers in 'executive' monkeys." *Scient. Am.,* **199**: 95.

————, and H. F. Hunt, 1955. "An experimental approach to the analysis of emotional behavior." *J. Psychol.,* **40**: 313.

Bridgman, P. W., 1927. *The Logic of Modern Physics.* New York: The Macmillan Company.

Brodie, B. B., and J. Axelrod, 1949. "Fate of acetophenetidin (Phenacetin) in man and methods for the estimation of acetophenetidin and its metabolites in biological material." *J. Pharmacol. and exp. Therap.,* **97**: 58.

————, and P. A. Shore, 1957. "A concept for a role of serotonin and norepinephrine as chemical mediators in the brain." *Ann. N.Y. Acad. Sci.,* **66**: 631.

Brown, B. B., 1959. "Behavioral effects of drugs derivable from observation of intact, normal animals" in *Psychopharmacology: Problems in Evaluation,* eds. J. O. Cole and R. W. Gerard. Washington, D.C.: National Academy of Sciences–National Research Council.

————, 1960. "CNS drug actions and interaction in mice." *Arch. int. Pharmacodyn.,* **128**: 391.

Brown, H., 1963. "d-Amphetamine-chlorpromazine antagonism in a food reinforced operant." *J. exp. anal. Behav.,* **6**: 395.

Bykov, D. M., 1957. *The Cerebral Cortex and the Internal Organs.* New York: Chemical Publishing Company, Inc.

Cares, R. M., and C. Buskman, 1961. "A survey of side-effects and/or toxicity of newer psychopharmacologic agents." *Dis. Nerv. System.,* **22**: 97.

Carlton, P. L., 1962. "Some behavioral effects of atropine and methyl atropine." *Psychol. Rep.,* **10**: 579.

Chance, M. R. A., 1946. "Aggregation as factor influencing toxicity of sympathomimetic amines in mice." *J. Pharmacol. and exp. Therap.,* **87**: 214.

————, 1947. "Factors influencing toxicity of sympathomimetic amines to solitary mice." *J. Pharmacol. and exp. Therap.,* **89**: 289.

Clark, A. J., 1937. "Methods of general pharmacology" in *Handbuch der experimentallen Pharmakologie* (Vol. IV), eds. Heffter, Heubner, and Shuller. Berlin: Carl Springer Verlag.

————, 1933. *The Mode of Action of Drugs on Cells.* Baltimore, Md.: The Williams & Wilkins Company.

Conger, J. J., 1951. "The effects of alcohol on conflict behavior in the albino rat." *Quart. J. Stud. Alcohol.,* **12**: 1.

Cook, L., and A. C. Catania, 1964. "Effects of drugs on avoidance and escape behavior." *Fed. Proc.,* **23**: 818.

————, A. Davidson, D. J. Davis, and R. T. Kelleher, 1960. "Epinephrine, norepinephrine, and acetylcholine as conditioned stimuli for avoidance behavior." *Science,* **131**: 990.

————, and R. Kelleher, 1963. "Behavioral pharmacology." *Ann. Rev. of Pharmacol.,* **3**: 205.

———, ———, 1963. "Effects of drugs on behavior." *Ann. Rev. of Pharmacol.*, **3:** 205.

———, and J. J. Toner, 1954. "The antiemetic action of chlorpromazine, SKF No. 2601-A (RP-4560)." *J. Pharmacol. and exp. Therap.*, **110:** 12.

———, and E. Weidley, 1957. "Behavioral effects of some psychopharmacological agents." *Ann. N.Y. Acad. Sci.*, **66:** 740.

Courvoisier, S., J. Fournel, R. Ducrot, M. Kolsky, and P. Kostxchet, 1953. "Propriétés pharmacodynamiques du chlorhydrat de chloro-3-(dimethylamino-3-propyl)-10 phenothiazine (4560 RP)." *Arch. int. Pharmacodyn.*, **92:** 305.

Dale, H. H., 1914. "The action of certain esters and ethers of choline, and their relation to muscarine." *J. Pharmacol. and exp. Therap.*, **6:** 147.

Dawson, J. F. and W. A. Hiestand, 1955. "Influence of chlorpromazine (Thorazine) on body temperature control in small animals and anoxic resistance." *Fed. Proc.*, **14:** 36.

DeMaar, E. W., and W. R. Martin, 1956. "Effects of chlorpromazine on EEG and its activation." *Fed. Proc.*, **15:** 416.

Deneau, G. A., and M. H. Seevers, 1962, personal communication.

———, T. Yanagita, and ———, 1964. "Psychogenic dependence to a variety of drugs in the monkey." *Pharmacologist*, **6:** 182.

Dews, P. B., 1956. "Modification by drugs of performance on simple schedules of positive reinforcement." *Ann. N.Y. Acad. Sci.*, **65:** 268.

———, 1962. "Psychopharmacology" in *Experimental Foundations of Clinical Psychology*, ed. A. J. Bachrach. New York: Basic Books, Inc., Publisher.

———, 1955. "Studies on behavior. I. Differential sensitivity to pentobarbital of pecking performance in pigeons depending on the schedule of reward." *J. Pharmacol. and exp. Therap.*, **113:** 393.

———, 1955. "Studies on behavior. II The effects of pentobarbital, methamphetamine and scopolamine on performances in pigeons involving discriminations." *J. Pharmacol. and exp. Therap.* **113:** 380.

———, and W. Morse, 1961. "Behavioral pharmacology." *Ann. Rev. of Pharmacol.*, **1:** 145.

———, and W. Morse, 1958. "Some observations on an operant in human subjects and its modification by dextro amphetamine." *J. exp. anal. Behav.*, **1:** 359.

Dorland's Illustrated Medical Dictionary. 1964. Philadelphia, Pa.: W. B. Saunders Company.

Drill, V. A. (ed.), 1958. *Pharmacology in Medicine.* New York: The McGraw-Hill Book Company, Inc.

Ehrlich, P., 1907. "Experimental Researches on Specific Therapy. First Harben Lecture for 1907" in *The Collected Papers of Paul Ehrlich* (Vol. III. Chemotheraphy), ed. F. Himmelweit. London: Pergamon Press, 1960.

Ellison, G. D., and J. Konorski, 1964. "Separation of the salivary and motor responses in instrumental conditioning." *Science*, **146:** 1071.

Estes, W. K., and B. F. Skinner, 1941. "Some quantitative properties of anxiety." *J. exp. Psychol.*, **29:** 390.

Falk, J. L., and W. O. Haas, 1965. "The control and recording of response force." *J. exp. anal. Behav.*, **8:** 195.

Farris, H. E., 1967. "Classical conditioning of courting behavior in the Japanese quail (coturnix xoturnix japonica)." *J. exp. anal. Behav.*, **10:** 213.

Ferster, C. B., 1958. "Control of behavior in chimpanzees and pigeons by time out from positive reinforcement." *Psychol. Monogr.,* **72:** 1. Whole No. 461.

————, 1953. "The use of the free operant in the analysis of behavior." *Psychol. Bull.,* **50:** 263.

————, and B. F. Skinner, 1957. *Schedules of Reinforcement.* New York: Appleton-Century-Crofts.

Findley, J. D., 1959. "Behavior output under chained fixed-ratio requirements in a 24-hour experimental space." *J. exp. anal. Behav.,* **2:** 258.

————, 1962. "An experimental outline for building and exploring multi-operant behavior repertoires." *J. exp. anal. Behav.,* Monogr. Suppl., **5:** 113.

————, 1958. "Preference and switching under concurrent scheduling." *J. exp. anal. Behav.,* **1:** 123.

————, 1966. "Programmed environments for the experimental analysis of human behavior" in *Operant Behavior: Areas of Research and Application,* ed. W. K. Honig. New York: Appleton-Century-Crofts.

————, and J. V. Brady, 1965. "Facilitation of large ratio performance by use of conditioned reinforcements." *J. exp. anal. Behav.,* **8:** 125.

————, B. M. Migler, and ————, 1962. "A long–term study of human performance in a continuously programmed experimental environment." *Space Research Lab. Tech. Report,* Univ. of Maryland, **November.**

Funderburk, W. H., E. E. King, and K. R. Unna, 1953. "Pharmacological properties of benazoles III. Effects of 2-aminobenzothiazoles on the electroencephalogram." *J. Pharmacol. and exp. Therap.,* **108:** 94.

Galviano, V. V., and S. C. Wang, 1955. "Dual mechanism of anti-emetic action of 10 (alpha-dimethyl-aminopropyl)-2-chlorphenothiazine hydrochloride (chlorpromazine) in dogs." *J. Pharmacol. and exp. Therap.,* **114:** 358.

Geller, I., and J. Seifter, 1960. "The effects of meprobamate, barbiturates, d-amphetamine and promazine on experimentally induced conflict in the rat." *Psychopharmacologia,* **1:** 482.

————, and ————, 1962. "The effects of mono-urethans, di-urethans and barbiturates on a punishment discrimination." *J. Pharmacol. and exp. Therap.,* **136:** 284.

Gemmill, C. L., 1958. "The Xanthines" in *Pharmacology in Medicine,* ed. V. A. Drill. New York: The McGraw-Hill Book Company, Inc.

Gilman, H., and D. A. Shirley, 1944. "Some derivatives of phenothiazine." *J. Am. Chem. Soc.,* **66:** 888.

Gollub, L. R., 1964. "The relations among measures of performance on fixed-interval schedules." *J. exp. anal. Behav.,* **7:** 337.

————, and J. V. Brady, 1965. "Behavioral pharmacology," *Ann. Rev. of Pharmacol.* **5:** 235.

Goodman, L. S., and A. Gilman (eds.), 1965. *The Pharmacological Basis of Therapeutics,* New York: Crowell-Collier & Macmillan Company, Inc.

Gunn, J. A., and M. R. Gurd, 1940. "The action of some amines related to adrenaline, Cyclohexylalkylamines." *J. Physiol.,* London, **97:** 453.

Guttman, N., and H. I. Kalish, 1958. "Experiments in discrimination." *Scient. Am.* **198:** 77.

Harlow, H. F., M. K. Harlow, and D. R. Meyer, 1950. "Learning motivated by a manipulation drive." *J. exper. Psychol.,* **40:** 228.

Headlee, C. P., H. W. Coppock, and J. R. Nichols, 1955. "Apparatus and techniques involved in a laboratory method of detecting the addictiveness of drugs." *J. Am. Pharmaceut. Assn.*, **44**: 229.

Hearst, E., 1964. "Drug effects on stimulus generalization gradients in monkeys." *Psychopharmacologia*, **6**: 57.

Hefferline, R. F., B. Keenan, and R. A. Harford, 1959. "Escape and avoidance conditioning in human subjects without their observation of the response." *Science*, **130**: 1338.

Heistad, G. T., 1957. "A bio-psychological approach to somatic treatments in psychiatry." *Am. J. Psychiat.*, **114**: 540.

———, 1958. "Effects of chlorpromazine and electroconvulsive shock on a conditioned emotional response." *J. comp. physiol. Psychol.*, **51**: 209.

———, and A. A. Torres, 1959. "A mechanism for the effect of a tranquilizing drug on learned emotional responses." *U. Minn. Med. Bull.*, **30**: 518.

Himmelsbach, C. K., 1942. "Clinical studies of drug addiction. Physical dependence, withdrawal and recovery." *Arch. int. Med.*, **69**: 766.

Hinde, R. A., 1966. *Animal Behavior.* New York: McGraw-Hill Book Company.

Hoffman, H. S., M. Fleshler, and P. Jensen, 1963. "Stimulus aspects of aversive controls: the retention of conditioned suppression." *J. exp. anal. Behav.*, **6**: 575.

Holland, J. G., and B. F. Skinner. 1961. *The Analysis of Behavior.* New York: McGraw-Hill Book Company.

———, R. L. Klein, and A. H. Briggs, 1964. *Introduction to Molecular Pharmacology.* New York: Crowell-Collier & Macmillan, Inc.

Hollister, L. E., F. P. Motzenbecker, and R. O. Degan, 1961. "Withdrawal reactions from chlordiazepoxide ('librium')." *Psychopharmacologia*, **2**: 63.

Hull, C. L., 1943. *The Principles of Behavior.* New York: Appleton-Century-Crofts.

Hutchinson, R. R., N. H. Azrin, and D. F. Hake, 1966. "An automatic method for the study of aggression in squirrel monkeys." *J. exp. anal. Behav.*, **9**: 233.

Irwin, S., 1954. "Characteristics of depression, antagonism and development of tolerance, physical dependence and neuropathology to morphine and morphine-like agents in the monkey (Macaca mulatta)." Unpublished Doctoral Dissertation, University of Michigan.

Isbell, H., S. Altschul, C. H. Kornetsky, A. J. Eisenman, H. G. Flanary, and H. F. Fraser, 1950. "Chronic barbiturate intoxication: an experimental study." *A.M.A. Arch. Neurol. and Psychiat.*, **64**: 1.

Joyce, D., and A. Summerfield, 1966. "Effects of drugs related to serotonin on water intake and defecation in rats. Implications for behavioral studies." *Arch. Int. Pharmacodyn.*, **161**: 489.

Kadenbach, B., and Lührs, 1961. "Effects of 7-chloro-2-methylamino-5-phenyl-3H-1, 4-benzodiazepin-4-oxide on mitochondria from rat liver and brain." *Nature*, **192**: 174.

Kagan, J., and M. Berkun, 1954. "The reward value of running activity." *J. comp. physiol. Psychol.*, **47**: 108.

Kelleher. R. T., 1966. "Conditioned reinforcement in second order schedules." *J. exp. anal. Behav.*, **9**: 475.

———, and L. R. Gollub, 1962. "A review of positive conditioned reinforcement." *J. exp. anal. Behav.*, Monogr. Suppl., **5**: 543.

———, and W. H. Morse, 1964. "Escape behavior and punished behavior." *Fed. Proc.*, **83**: 808.

Keller, F. S., and W. N. Schoenfeld, 1950. *Principles of Psychology*, New York: Appleton-Century-Crofts.

Kellogg, W. N., and E. L. Walker, 1938. "Ambiguous conditioning, a phenomenon of bilateral transfer." *J. comp. Psychol.*, **26**: 63.

Kintsch, W., and Witte, R. S., 1962, "Concurrent conditioning of bar press and salivation responses." *J. comp. physiol. Psychol.*, **55**: 963.

Kok, K., 1955. "Investigation into the distribution of chlorpromazine and 10-(3' dimethylaminopropyl) phenothiazine (RP 3276)." *Acta Physiol. Pharmacol. Neurol.*, **4**: 388.

Konorski, J., and S. Miller, 1930. "Méthode d'examen de l'analysateur moteur par les réactions salive-motices." *C.r. Soc. de biol.*, **104**: 907.

Krantz, J. C., and C. J. Carr, 1958. *The Pharmacologic Principles of Medical Practice* (4th ed.,). Baltimore, M.: The Williams & Wilkins Company.

Krueger, H., N. B. Eddy, and M. Sumwalt, 1941–43. *The Pharmacology of the Opium Alkaloids*. Washington, D.C.: U.S. Government Printing Office, Suppl. No. 165.

Kulkarni, A., T. Thompson, and F. E. Shideman, 1966. "Effect of reserpine administered during infancy on brain catcholamines and adult behavior in the rat." *J. Neurochem.*, **13**: 1143.

Laties, V. G., and B. Weiss, 1958. "A critical review of the efficacy of meprobamate (Miltown, Equanil) in the treatment of anxiety." *J. chron. Dis.*, **7**: 500.

Lee, R., 1963. "Unpublished studies of the process of conditioning by successive approximations." University of Maryland.

Lehmann, H. E., and G. E. Hanrahan, 1954. "Chlorpromazine." *A.M.A. Arch. Neurol. and Psychiat.*, **71**: 227.

Lemere, F., 1956. "Habit forming properties of meprobamate." *A.M.A. Arch. Neurol. and Psychiat.*, **76**: 205.

Lorenz, K., 1950. "The comparative method in studying innate behavior patterns." *Symp. Soc. exp. Biol.*, **4**: 221.

MacCorquodale, K., and P. Meehl, 1954. "Edward C. Tolman," in *Modern Learning Theory*, eds. W. K. Estes *et al.* New York: Appleton-Century-Crofts.

———, and ———, 1948. "On a distinction between hypothetical constructs and intervening variables." *Psychol. Rev.*, **55**: 95.

McIntyre, A. R., 1958. "Curare and related compounds." in *Pharmacology in Medicine*, ed. V. A. Drill. New York: McGraw-Hill Book Company.

McLennan, H., 1963. *Synapatic Transmission*. Philadelphia, Pa.: W. B. Saunders Company.

Margulies, S., 1961. "Response duration in operant level, regular reinforcement and extinction." *J. exp. anal. Behav.*, **4**: 317.

Marsh, D. F., 1950. *Outline of Fundamental Pharmacology*. Springfield, Ill.: Charles C. Thomas, Publisher.

Medved, L. I., E. I. Spynu, and I. S. Kagan, 1964. "The method of conditioned reflexes in toxicology and its application for determining the toxicity of small quantities of pesticides." *Res. Rev.*, **6**: 42.

Meehl, P. E., 1965. "Detecting latent clinical taxa by fallible quantitative indicators lacking an accepted criterion." *Psy. Res. Report*. Dept. of Psychiatry, Univ. of Minn.

———, 1962. "Schizotaxia, Schizotypy, Schizophrenia." *Am. Psychologist*, **17**: 827.

Mendelson, J., and D. Bindra, 1962. "Combination of drive and drug effects." *J. exp. Psychol.*, **63**: 505.

Michael, J., 1963. *Laboratory Studies in Operant Behavior.* New York: McGraw-Hill Book Company.

Miller, J. W., T. M. Gilfoil, and F. E. Shideman, 1955. "The effects of levallorphan tartrate (Levo-3-tydroxy-N-allylmorphinan tartrate) on the respiration of rabbits given morphine." *J. Pharmacol. and exp. Therap.*, **115**: 350.

Miller, N. E., 1956. "Effects of drugs on motivation: the value of using a variety of measures." *Ann. N.Y. Acad. Sci.*, **65**: 318.

———, and H. Barry, 1960. "Motivational effect of drugs: methods which illustrate some general problems in psychopharmacology." *Psychopharmacologia*, **1**: 169.

———, and S. S. Stevenson, 1936. "Agitated behavior in rats during experimental extinction and a curve of spontaneous recovery." *J. comp. Psychol.*, **21**: 205.

Myer, J. S., and R. T. White, 1965. "Aggressive motivation in the rat." *Animal Behavior*, **13**: 430.

Nachmansohn, D., 1950. "Studies on permeability in relation to nerve function. I. Axonal conduction and synaptic transmission." *Biochem. et. biophys. acta.*, **4**: 78.

———, and I. B. Wilson, 1951. "The emzymic hydrolysis and synthesis of acetylcholine." *Advanced in Enzymol.*, **12**: 259.

Niemann, W. H., C. R. Schuster, and T. Thompson, 1962. "A surgical preparation for chronic intravenous infusion of Rhesus monkeys." Lab. Psychopharma. Tech. Rpt. Series, Rpt. No. 62-39, Univ. of Maryland, September.

Norton, S., 1962. "Use of other behavioral techniques for evaluating depressant drugs." in *Psychosomatic Medicine*, eds. J. H. Nodine and J. H. Moyer. Philadelphia, Pa: Lea & Febiger.

Notterman, J. M., 1959. "Force emission during bar pressing." *J. exp. Psychol.*, **58**: 341.

———, and D. E. Mintz, 1965. *Dynamics of Response.* New York: John Wiley & Sons, Inc.

Nyswander, M., 1956. *The Drug Addict as a Patient.* New York: Grune & Stratton, Inc.

O'Kelly, L. I., and L. C. Steckle, 1939. "A note on long enduring emotional responses in the rat." *J. Psychol.*, **8**: 125.

Olds, J., and P. Milner, 1954. "Positive reinforcement produced by electrical stimulation of septal area and other regions of rat brain." *J. comp. physiol. Psychol.*, **47**: 419.

Osbourn, M., and E. B. Sigg, 1960, "Effects of Imipramine on the peripheral autonomic system." *Arch. int. Pharmacodyn.*, **129**: 273.

Otis, L. S., 1964. "Dissociation and recovery of a response learned under the influence of chlorpromazine or saline." *Science*, **143**: 1347.

Overton, D. A., 1966. "State-dependent learning produced by depressant and atropinelike drugs." *Psychopharmacologia*, **10**: 6.

Pavlov, I. P., 1937. *Conditioned Reflexes.* London: Oxford University Press.

———, 1905. "Über die Unvollkommenheit der gegenwartigen physiologischen Analyse der Arzneimittelwirkung," in *Readings in Pharmacology*, eds. B. Holmstedt and G. Liljestrand. New York: The Macmillan Company.

Pickens, R., 1965. "Conditioning of locomotor effects of d-amphetamine." Unpublished doctoral dissertation, University of Mississippi.

————, and T. Thompson, 1967. "Cocaine-reinforced behavior in rats: effects of reinforcement magnitude and fixed-ratio size." (in press).

————, and ————, 1966. "Self-administration of amphetamine and cocaine by rats." *Reports from the Research Labs., Dept. of Psychiatry, Univ. of Minnesota,* No. PR–66–4, September.

Ray, O. S., 1963. "The effects of tranquilizers on positively and negatively motivated behavior in rats." *Psychopharmacologia,* 4: 326.

Razran, G., 1955. "Conditioning and perception." *Psychol. Rev.* **62:** 83.

————, 1961. "The observable unconscious and the inferable conscious in current Soviet psychophysiology: Interoceptive conditioning, semantic conditioning, and the orienting reflex." *Psychol. Rev.,* **68:** 81.

Reynolds, G. S., A. C. Catania, and B. F. Skinner, 1963. "Conditioned and uncondi-tioned aggression in pigeons." *J. exp. anal. Behav.,* 1: 73.

Riker, W. F., 1958. "Cholinergic drugs" in *Pharmacology in Medicine,* ed. V. A. Drill. New York: McGraw-Hill Book Company.

Salzman, N. P., and B. B. Brodie, 1956. "Physiological disposition and fate of chlor-promazine and a method for its estimation in biological material." *J. Pharmacol. and exp. Therap.,* **118:** 46.

————, N. C. Moran, and ————, 1955. "Identification and pharmacological properties of a major metabolite of chlorpromazine." *Nature,* **176:** 1122.

Schaefer, H. H., 1963. "Interspecies comparison of response elements" in *Progress Report, The American Foundation for Creative Research.* Palo Alto, Calif. October.

————, 1960. "Operant learning of systems limitations." *Psychol. Rep.,* 6: 51.

Schoenfeld, W. N., W. W. Cumming, and E. Hearst, 1956. "On the classification of reinforcement schedules." *Proc. Nat. Acad. Sci.,* **42:** 563.

Schuster, C. R., 1962. "The discriminative control of operant behavior by intero-ceptive stimulation." Doctoral dissertation, Univ. of Maryland.

————, and J. V. Brady, 1964. "Zhurnal vysshey Nervnoy Deyatel' nosti im. I. P. Pavlova." *Pavlov J. Higher Nervous Activity,* **448,** May–June.

————, and U. Estrada, 1966. "Effect of morphine on food and visually reinforced behavior in the monkey." (unpublished).

————, and T. Thompson, 1962. "Self-administration of morphine in physically dependent Rhesus monkeys." *Lab. Psychopharmacol. Tech. Rept.* No. 62–29 Univ. of Maryland, July.

————, and J. H. Woods, 1966. "Conditioned reinforcing effects of stimuli asso-ciated with morphine reinforcement." (unpublished).

———— and ————, 1967. "Morphine as a reinforcer for operant behavior. The effect of dosage per injection." (personal communication).

————, and J. Zimmerman, 1961. "Timing behavior during prolonged treatment with d-amphetamine." *J. exp. anal. Behav.,* 4: 327.

Screven, C. G., 1954. "The effects of interference on response strength." *J. comp. physiol. Psychol.,* **47:** 140.

Shapiro, M. M., 1960. "Respondent salivary conditioning during operant lever pressing in dogs." *Science,* 132: 619.

————, 1961. "Salivary conditioning in dogs during fixed-interval reinforcement contingent upon lever pressing." *J. exp. anal. Behav.,* **41:** 361.

Sheffield, F. D., and T. B. Roby, 1950. "Reward value of a non-nutritive sweet taste" *J. comp. physiol. Psychol.,* **43:** 471.

Sherrington, Sir Charles, 1906. *The Integrative Action of the Nervous System.* New Haven, Conn.: Yale University Press.

Shideman, F. E., 1958. "Sedatives and hypnotics II: barbiturates." *Pharmacology in Medicine,* ed. V. A. Drill. New York: The Macmillan Company.

Sidman, M., 1962. "An adjusting avoidance schedule." *J. exp. anal. Behav.,* **5**: 271.

———, 1956. "Drug-behavior interaction." *Ann. N.Y. Acad. Sci.,* **65**: 282.

———, 1960. *Tactics of Scientific Research.* New York: Basic Books, Inc., Publishers.

———, 1955. "Technique for assessing the effects of drugs on timing behavior." *Science,* **122**: 925.

———, R. J. Herrnstein, and D. G. Conrad, 1957. "Maintenance of avoidance behavior by unavoidable shocks." *J. comp. physiol. Psychol.,* **50**: 553.

Singh, S. D., S. N. Manocha, and Satinder, 1966. "The interaction of drug effects with drive level and habit strength." *Psychopharmacologia,* **9**: 205.

Skinner, B. F., 1938. *Behavior of Organisms.* New York: Appleton-Century-Crofts.

———, 1954. "A critique of psychoanalytic concepts and theories." *Scient. Monthly,* November.

———, 1962. "Operandum." *J. exp. anal. Behav.,* **5**: 224.

———, 1948, "'Superstition' in the pigeon." *J. exper. Psychol.,* **38**: 168.

Smith, M. P., and P. J. Capretta, 1956. "Effects of drive level and experience on the reward value of saccharine solutions." *J. comp. physiol. Psychol.,* **49**: 553.

Stewart, J., 1962. "Differential responses based on the physiological consequences of pharmacological agents." *Psychopharmacologia,* **3**: 132.

Sulser, F., J. Watts, and B. B. Brodie, 1962. "On the mechanism of antidepressant action of imipraminelike drugs." *Ann. N.Y. Acad. Sci.,* **96**: 279.

Tatum, A. L., and M. H. Seevers, 1931. "Theories of drug addiction." *Physiol. Rev.,* **11**: 107.

———, ———, and K. H. Collins, 1929. "Morphine addiction and its physiological interpretation based on experimental evidences." *J. Pharmacol. and exp. Therap.,* **36**: 447.

Tedeschi, R. E., D. H. Tedeschi, A. Mucha, L. Cook, P. A. Mattis, and E. J. Fellows, 1959. "Effects of various centrally acting drugs on fighting behavior of mice." *J. Pharmacol. and exp. Therap.,* **125**: 28.

Terrace, H. S., 1963. "Errorless discrimination learning in the pigeon: effects of chlorpromazine and imipramine." *Science,* **140**: 318.

Terry, C. E., and M. Pellens, 1928. *The Opium Problem.* New York: Commission on Drug Addiction.

Thompson, T., 1961. "Effect of chlorpromazine on 'aggressive' responding in the rat." *J. comp. physiol. Psychol.,* **54**: 398.

———, 1962. "The effect of two phenothiazines and a barbiturate on extinction-induced rate increase of a free operant." *J. comp. physiol. Psychol.,* **55**: 714.

———, 1965. "The effects of tolerance on morphine self-administration in the monkey." (unpublished).

———, 1966. "Operant and classically conditioned aggressive behavior in Siamese fighting fish." *Am. Zool.,* **6**: 629.

———, 1964. "Visual reinforcement in fighting cocks." *J. exp. anal. Behav.,* **7**: 45.

———, 1963. "Visual reinforcement in Siamese fighting fish." *Science,* **141**: 55.

————, and W. Bloom, 1966. "Aggressive behavior and extinction-induced response-rate increase." *Psychonom. Sci.*, **5**: 335.

————, and P. Lilja, 1964. "Behavioral toxicity of DDT." *Psy. Tech. Reports* #PR–64–3. Dept. of Psychiatry, Univ. of Minn.

————, and C. R. Schuster, 1964. "Morphine self-administration, food-reinforced and avoidance behaviors in Rhesus monkeys." *Psychopharmacologia*, **5**: 87. Berlin-Göttingen-Heidelberg: Springer-Verlag.

————, and T. Sturm, 1965. "Classical conditioning of aggressive display in Siamese fighting fish." *J. exp. anal. Behav.*, **8**: 397.

————, and ————, 1965. "Visual reinforcer color, and operant behavior in Siamese fighting fish." *J. exp. anal. Behav.*, **8**: 341.

Thorpe, W. H., 1956. *Learning and Instinct in Animals.* Cambridge, Mass: Harvard University Press.

Thudichum, W. L., 1884. *A Treatise on the Chemical Constitution of the Brain.* London: Baillière, Tindall & Cox.

Tinbergen, N., 1951. *The Study of Instinct.* Oxford, Eng.: Clarendon Press.

Tormey, J., and L. Lasagna, 1960. "Relation of thyroid function to acute and chronic effects of amphetamine in the rat." *J. Pharmacol. and exp. Therap.*, **128**: 201.

Torres, A. A., 1961. "Anxiety versus escape conditioning and tranquilizing action." *J. comp. physiol. Psychol.*, **54**: 349.

Trendelenberg, U., 1963. "Supersensitivity and subsensitivity to sympathomimetic amines." *Pharmacol. Rev.*, **15**: 225.

Ulrich, R. E., and N. H. Azrin, 1962. "Reflexive fighting in response to aversive stimulation." *J. exp. anal. Behav.*, **5**: 511.

————, P. C. Wolff, and ————, 1964. "Shock as an elicitor of intra- or interspecies fighting behavior." *Animal Behavior*, **12**: 14.

Van Sommers, P., 1962. "Oxygen-motivated behavior in the goldfish, *Carassius auratus.*" *Science*, **137**: 678.

Vernon, W., and R. Ulrich, 1966. "Classically conditioned aggressive behavior in rats." *Science*, **152**: 668.

Verplanck, W. S., 1957. "A glossary of some terms used in the objective science of Behavior." *Psychol. Rev.*, **64**: Supplement.

Villarreal, J., C. R. Schuster, and E. Domino, 1966. "Methyl-atropine antagonism of arecoline-effects on food-reinforced responding in rats." (unpublished).

Walaszek, E. J., and L. G. Abood, 1956. "Effect of tranquilizing drugs on fighting response of Siamese fighting fish." *Science*, **124**: 440.

Waller, M. B., and P. F. Waller, 1962. "Effects of chlorpromazine on the appetitive and aversive components of multiple schedule." *J. exp. anal. Behav.*, **5**: 259.

Weeks, J. R., 1962. "Experimental morphine addiction: method for automatic intravenous injections in unrestrained rats." *Science*, **138**: 143.

Weiss, B., and V. G. Laties, 1964. "Analgesic effects in monkeys of morphine, nalorphine, and a benzomorphan narcotic antagonist." *J. Pharmacol. and exp. Therap.*, **143**: 169.

————, and ————, 1938. "Behavioral thermoregulation." *Science*, **133**: 1338.

————, and ————, 1964. "Drug effects on the temporal patterning of behavior." *Fed. Proc.*, **23**: 801.

————, and ————, 1958. "Fractional escape and avoidance on a titration schedule." *Science,* **128:** 1575.

————, ————, and F. L. Blanton, 1961. "Amphetamine toxicity in rats and mice subjected to stress." *J. Pharmacol. and exp. Therap.,* **132:** 366.

Weitzman, E. D., and G. S. Ross, 1962. "A behavioral method for the study of pain perception in the monkey." *Neurology,* **12:** 264.

————, ————, W. Hodos, and R. Galambos, 1961. "Behavioral method for study of pain in the monkey." *Science,* **133:** 37.

Wells, J. A., 1958. "Historical background and general principles of drug action," in *Pharmacology in Medicine,* ed. V. A. Drill. New York: McGraw-Hill Book Company.

Werdegar, D., D. G. Johnson, and J. U. Mason, 1964. "A technique for continous measurement of arterial blood pressure in unanesthetized monkeys." *J. appl. Physiol,* **19:** 519.

Wikler, A., 1953. *Opiate Addiction.* Springfield, Ill.: Charles C. Thomas, Publisher.

World Health Organization, 1950. *Technical Report Series,* **21:** 6.

Wright, H. N., and M. Montag, 1949. *A textbook of Pharmacology and Therapeutics.* Philadelphia, Pa.: W. B. Saunders Company.

Yanagita, T., G. Deneau, and M. H. Seevers, 1963. "Methods for studying psychogenic dependence to opiates in the monkey." Minutes of the Committee on Drug Addiction and Narcotics. National Academy of Sciences and National Research Council, Appendix 16.

Yen, C. Y., R. L. Stanger, and N. Millman, 1958. "Ataractic suppression of isolation-induced aggressive behavior." *Arch. int. Pharmacodyn.,* **123:** 179.

Zimmerman, J., and C. R. Schuster, 1962. "Spaced responding in multiple DRL schedules." *J. exp. anal. Behav.,* **5:** 497.

Zbinden, G., 1963. "Experimental and clinical aspects of drug toxicity," in *Advances in Pharmacology,* eds, S. Garattine and P. A. Shore. New York: Academic Press Inc.

Index